INTEGRATED ALGEBRA AND TRIGONOMETRY

ROBERT C. FISHER

ALLEN D. ZIEBUR

The Ohio State University

Integrated

Algebra and

Trigonometry

PRENTICE-HALL, INC.,
Englewood Cliffs, New Jersey

Prentice-Hall Mathematics Series
Dr. Albert A. Bennett, Editor

L.C. Cat. No. 58-6892

Current printing (last digit):

21   20   19   18   17   16   15   14   13   12

Printed in the United States of America
46901–**C**

The typographical design is by Walter Behnke

PREFACE

This book is designed to present certain topics in algebra and trigonometry in a form that will make them most useful for a later study of analytic geometry and calculus. We have tried to present the basic ideas in such a way that they can be grasped easily by the student. In our attempt to achieve this goal, we have passed over some of the fine details that constitute mathematical rigor, but we don't think the student will have to "unlearn" anything he reads here.

The first chapter is intended to serve as a review of elementary topics (adding fractions, factoring, and so forth), but these review topics are interwoven with new topics (inequalities) so that the good student will not become bored.   The systematic introduction of new ideas begins in Chapter Two with the study of functions.   This study forms the basis of the unifying aspect of the whole book—the concept of a function.   Logarithmic and exponential functions are discussed in Chapter Three in such a way that lengthy numerical work with logarithms can almost be avoided, if the instructor wishes.   In Chapter Four, the trigonometric functions are considered initially as functions on the real numbers, and the presentation has been arranged in such a manner that it should neither bore the student who has already studied trigonometry nor overwhelm the student who is meeting the subject for the first time.   The treatment of complex numbers in Chapter Five takes advantage of the fact that trigonometry has already been discussed, and provides a basis for the theory of equations that is covered in Chapter Six.   In Chapter Seven, systems of linear equations are solved using simple matrix manipulations before the concept of a determinant is introduced.   The binomial theorem is treated in the work with permutations and combinations in Chapter Eight so that the binomial coefficients are encountered in a natural and logical way.   The summation notation is introduced in this chapter and the discussion of probability includes a discussion of the binomial distribution.   The presentation of the material concerning sequences in Chapter Nine has been arranged so that it can be taught either with or without the concept of mathematical induction that is presented there.   The book ends with a discussion of inverse functions, with particular emphasis on the inverse trigonometric functions. We hope that the constant reiteration of the concept and notation of functions throughout this book will leave its mark on the student by the time he appears in the calculus classroom.

Most classes contain students of varying mathematical backgrounds and ability.   We have attempted to take this variation into account by arranging our sections so that the most basic and elementary material comes first.   Occasionally the last few paragraphs of a section may treat more difficult ideas—ones which the more able student might like to develop but which are not essential to the continuity of the book.   Every student should attempt to work all the Review Problems and the more able students will profit by tackling some of the Miscellaneous Problems at the end of each chapter.

We are indebted to a number of people for encouragement, advice, and just plain work. Through the cooperation of the administration of The Ohio State University and Chairman R. G. Helsel of the Mathematics Department, a mimeographed edition was prepared. A. A. Bennett and A. E. Taylor read this edition and offered a number of suggestions. Our colleagues at Ohio State—J. F. Leetch, L. H. Miller, C. F. Purtz, and J. M. Shapiro—taught from the mimeographed edition and gave us the benefit of their experience. Mrs. Janet Austin, Mrs. Dolores Donnelly, and Mrs. Ann Tanner provided hours of secretarial assistance. Mrs. Leone Fisher typed the manuscript, Mrs. Nancy Ziebur helped with the illustrations, and both of them were instrumental in keeping our morale high. Our editor, W. E. Mangas, not only served as a capable third author, but saw to it that the innumerable deadlines were met.

R. C. F.
A. D. Z.

CONTENTS

Possibly

THREE

FOUR

INTEGRATED ALGEBRA AND TRIGONOMETRY

CHAPTER ONE

THE SYSTEM OF
REAL NUMBERS

Much of the world of mathematics is a world of numbers. In order to use numbers efficiently, we must know the rules that govern their usage. In this first chapter, we shall discuss some of the important properties of real numbers, review the basic rules of algebra, and learn some new skills that are fundamental to later work in mathematics. It is not our purpose in this chapter to go into a precise, detailed explanation of the development of the real number system. Your familiarity with real numbers and your ability to use them should carry you over any gaps in the presentation.

1   NUMBER SYSTEMS.   THE INTEGERS

The system of real numbers can be considered as an extension of certain other number systems.   As we take up these various systems of numbers, we shall emphasize three points.   First, we must be able to identify the numbers of each of the systems.   Second, since the systems with which we are concerned form a chain leading up to the system of real numbers (and beyond, in Chapter Five), we shall want to be able to tell how a given system is related to a preceding one.   Third, we must consider how the various mathematical operations such as addition and multiplication are performed.

The simplest system of numbers consists of the **positive integers**—namely, the numbers 1, 2, 3, 4, and so on.   You already know how to add and multiply positive integers, of course.   There are, however, certain fundamental rules that are well worth noting explicitly.   If the letters a, b, and c represent any positive integers, then the following laws of arithmetic are true.

1-1 $(a + b) + c = a + (b + c)$.   Associative law of addition.

EXAMPLE: $(3 + 4) + 5 = 3 + (4 + 5)$.

1-2 $(ab)c = a(bc)$.   Associative law of multiplication.

EXAMPLE: $(3 \cdot 4) \cdot 5 = 3 \cdot (4 \cdot 5)$.

1-3 $a + b = b + a$.   Commutative law of addition.

EXAMPLE: $3 + 4 = 4 + 3$.

1-4 $ab = ba$.   Commutative law of multiplication.

EXAMPLE: $3 \cdot 4 = 4 \cdot 3$.

1-5 $a(b + c) = ab + ac$.   Distributive law.

EXAMPLE: $3(4 + 5) = 3 \cdot 4 + 3 \cdot 5$.

Note that Rule 1-4 may be used to rewrite Rule 1-5 in the form

1-6 $(b + c)a = ba + ca$.

The operations of subtraction and division are defined in terms of the operations of addition and multiplication.   The number d that satisfies the equation $a = b + d$ is called the **difference** $a - b$. The number q is the **quotient** a/b if $a = bq$. Observe that for any two positive integers a and b there is always a third, c, such that $a + b = c$; but there is not necessarily a positive integer d, such that $a - b = d$. The expression $3 - 5$, for example, cannot represent a positive integer, since the equation $3 = 5 + d$ is satisfied for no positive integer d. We can skirt this difficulty by introducing the **negative integers** and the number **zero** to form, together with the positive integers, the set of all **integers**, . . . -3, -2, -1, 0, 1, 2, 3, 4, ... Extending the system of positive integers to the system of integers still leaves us with a number system in which division is not always possible. This situation is remedied by a further extension we shall discuss in the next section.

Clearly the positive integers are part of the system of all integers, so our next problem is to define the arithmetic operations on the latter system. These operations are "man-made," not "God-given"; there is no law of nature which says that $(-1)(-1)$ *is* 1. For reasons of consistency, we *choose* the number 1 to represent the value of the product $(-1)(-1)$. According to the ordinary rules of arithmetic (which we assume you know), all integers obey the same fundamental laws that apply to the positive integers (1-1 to 1-6). It can be shown that the rules of arithmetic for integers are the only ones that preserve the associative, commutative, and distributive laws.

The distributive laws 1-5 and 1-6 are used extensively in the familiar process called factoring. An algebraic expression is in **factored form** if it is written as a product. To **expand** a product means to write it as an algebraic sum. The following examples illustrate how the various laws are used in factoring.

EXAMPLE 1-1. Factor: $x(y + z) + u(y + z)$.

Solution. If we use Formula 1-6 with $a = y + z$, $b = x$, and $c = u$, we obtain

$$x(y + z) + u(y + z) = (x + u)(y + z).$$

EXAMPLE 1-2. Factor: $x^2 - y^2$.

Solution.
$$x^2 - y^2 = x^2 - xy + xy - y^2 = x^2 - xy + yx - y^2$$
$$= x(x - y) + y(x - y) = (x + y)(x - y).$$

In this example we used Formulas 1-4, 1-5, and 1-6.

Although we have not mentioned it explicitly up to now, the distributive law is also used in "combining like terms." For example,

$$2x + 3x = (2 + 3)x = 5x.$$

The following examples illustrate how the distributive law and other laws are used in the expanding process.

EXAMPLE 1-3.   Expand: $(x + 5)(x - 4)$.

Solution.
$$(x + 5)(x - 4) = (x + 5)x + (x + 5)(-4)$$
$$= x^2 + 5x - 4x - 20 = x^2 + x - 20.$$

EXAMPLE 1-4.   Expand: $(x - y)(x^2 + xy + y^2)$.

Solution.
$$(x - y)(x^2 + xy + y^2) = x(x^2 + xy + y^2) - y(x^2 + xy + y^2)$$
$$= x^3 + x^2y + xy^2 - yx^2 - xy^2 - y^3$$
$$= x^3 - y^3.$$

Note that this last result tells us how to write $x^3 - y^3$ in factored form.

It is sometimes easier to expand an expression if we recognize it as the factored form of a known expression.

EXAMPLE 1-5.   Expand: $(x + 2y)(x - 2y)(x^2 + 4y^2)$.

Solution.
$$(x + 2y)(x - 2y)(x^2 + 4y^2) = (x^2 - 4y^2)(x^2 + 4y^2)$$
$$= x^4 - 16y^4.$$

Problems 1

1. Calculate the following numbers:
   (a) $4 + (-5) - (2 - 3)(5 - 7)$
   (b) $-[1 - 2(7 - 8)][3 - (4 + 1)]$
   (c) $72^2 - 28^2$

2. Simplify:
  (a) $-2(x-1)-[2x-(x-1)]$
  (b) $3x+2[x-(2x+y)]$
  (c) $-[2x-3(x-2)]$

3. Expand:
  (a) $(x+y)(x^2-xy+y^2)$ (d) $(.1x+.2y)^2$
  (b) $(x-1)(x-2)(x+2)$ (e) $(2x+3y)(3x-2y)$
  (c) $(x-2y)^3$ (f) $(x-y+z)(x-y-z)$

4. Factor:
  (a) x^3+y^3 (g) x^6-64
  (b) $2x^3-8xy^2$ (h) $4x^2-12xy+9y^2$
  (c) $8x^3-\dfrac{27}{y^3}$ (i) $4x^2-4xy+y^2-9z^2$
                        (j) $x^4+2x^3-8x-16$
  (d) $24a^2+14ab-20b^2$ (k) $2z^2x+6z^2y-6x^2z-18xyz$
  (e) $.01x^2-9$
  (f) $\dfrac{x^4}{16}-81y^4$

5. Let x denote a positive integer. For what values of x are the following expressions positive integers? Integers?
  (a) $2x+3-3x$
  (b) $\dfrac{4+2x-2-3x}{2}$ (c) $\dfrac{(x^2-1)}{4}$

2   THE RATIONAL NUMBERS

Given any two integers a and b we can always subtract b from a; that is, we can always find an integer d such that $a = b + d$. But we cannot always divide a by b if the only numbers we use are integers; that is, we cannot always find an integer q such that $a = bq$. For example, there is no integer q that satisfies the equation $5 = 3q$. In this section we will consider an extension of the system of integers, the system of **rational numbers,** in which the operation of division fails in only one case. The presence of the integer 0 creates this special difficulty and we will dispose of it first.

"Division by zero" illustrates the fact that the arithmetic operations are *defined*, and that the definitions are chosen so as to be consistent with previously accepted ones. Let a be any number except 0. What number q should we choose so that $a/0 = q$? From our definition of division in Section 1, the number q should be such that $a = q \cdot 0$. But no matter what number we select for q, this last equation cannot be valid, because $q \cdot 0 = 0$ for every number we choose for q; and we have assumed specifically that $a \neq 0$ (a is not equal to zero). Since we cannot assign any number to the symbol $a/0$ that will be consistent with the method of assigning numbers to other quotients, we simply do not define the symbol $a/0$. A somewhat different problem confronts us in the case of the quotient $0/0$. A number q that would suitably represent this quotient would be one for which $0 = 0 \cdot q$. But this last equation is true for any number q, and there is no particular reason to prefer one number over any other. Again we avoid the difficulty by leaving the symbol $0/0$ undefined. When we say that *the symbols $a/0$ and $0/0$ are meaningless*, we merely mean that *we have assigned no meaning to them*.

Although we always reject division by zero, we will now consider the rational number system in which division by numbers other than zero is always possible. A **rational number** has the form a/b, where a and b are integers and b is not 0. Thus $\frac{2}{3}$ and $\frac{-11}{7}$ are rational numbers. The word "rational" refers to the fact that these numbers are written as the *ratio* of integers. If we agree that the rational number $a/1$ is the "same" as the integer a, then we can consider the system of integers as part of the system of rational numbers.

The definitions of the arithmetical operations that involve the rational numbers are, as usual, motivated by the desire to preserve the fundamental laws we mentioned in Section 1. Though we assume that you have a working knowledge of the arithmetic of fractions, we have supplied the following list of some of the rules that govern the operations with rational numbers. You may assume that the letters represent integers, but the rules are equally valid for other numbers. In no case, of course, may a denominator be zero.

2-1
$$\frac{a}{1} = a.$$

2-2
$$\frac{a}{b} = \frac{c}{d} \text{ if, and only if, } ad = cb.$$

2-3
$$\frac{a}{c} + \frac{b}{c} = \frac{a+b}{c}.$$

2-4
$$\frac{a}{b} \cdot \frac{c}{d} = \frac{ac}{bd}.$$

The first rule is merely the convention that establishes the integers as a part of the system of rational numbers. Equations 2-2, 2-3, and 2-4 are the definitions of equality, addition, and multiplication of rational numbers. The rule for division is

2-5
$$\frac{a}{b} \div \frac{c}{d} = \frac{ad}{bc}.$$

This rule is established by showing that $a/b = (ad/bc)(c/d)$.

The "cancellation" rule is

2-6
$$\frac{ca}{cb} = \frac{a}{b}.$$

This rule stems directly from the definition of equality.

The use of the rules governing mathematical operations with rational numbers is illustrated by the following examples.

EXAMPLE 2-1. Simplify: $\dfrac{x^2 - y^2}{x + y}$.

Solution.

$$\frac{x^2 - y^2}{x + y} = \frac{(x + y)(x - y)}{x + y} = x - y.$$

Note how Rules 2-6 and 2-1 are used in this solution.

EXAMPLE 2-2. Simplify: $\dfrac{x + \dfrac{1}{y}}{x - \dfrac{1}{y}}$.

Solution.

$$\frac{x + \dfrac{1}{y}}{x - \dfrac{1}{y}} = \frac{y\left(x + \dfrac{1}{y}\right)}{y\left(x - \dfrac{1}{y}\right)} = \frac{yx + 1}{yx - 1}.$$

EXAMPLE 2-3. Combine: $\dfrac{2x}{x^2 - 4} + \dfrac{3}{x^2 - 5x + 6}$.

Solution.

$$\frac{2x}{x^2 - 4} + \frac{3}{x^2 - 5x + 6} = \frac{2x}{(x - 2)(x + 2)} + \frac{3}{(x - 2)(x - 3)}$$

$$= \frac{2x(x - 3) + 3(x + 2)}{(x - 2)(x + 2)(x - 3)}$$

$$= \frac{2x^2 - 3x + 6}{(x - 2)(x + 2)(x - 3)}.$$

EXAMPLE 2-4.   Combine: $\dfrac{3x}{x^2 - 4} - \dfrac{4}{2 - x}$.

Solution.

$$\frac{3x}{x^2 - 4} - \frac{4}{2 - x} = \frac{3x}{(x - 2)(x + 2)} + \frac{4}{x - 2}$$

$$= \frac{3x + 4(x + 2)}{(x - 2)(x + 2)}$$

$$= \frac{7x + 8}{(x - 2)(x + 2)}.$$

EXAMPLE 2-5.   Divide: $1 \div \dfrac{x + y}{x^2}$.

Solution.

$$1 \div \frac{x + y}{x^2} = \left(\frac{1}{1}\right) \cdot \frac{x^2}{x + y} = \frac{x^2}{x + y}.$$

You should regard any legitimate "canceling" to simplify fractions as an application of Rule 2-6.   You will avoid a very common error if you will note that *there is no rule which states that $(a + c)/(b + c)$ is the same as $(a + 1)/(b + 1)$.*

If $a \neq 0$, the number $1/a$ is called the **reciprocal of a**.   For example, the reciprocal of $(x + y)/x^2$ is $x^2/(x + y)$.

Problems 2

1. Explain why each of the following numbers is rational.
    (a) 17   (c) $4 + \frac{2}{3}$ (e) .3333 . . .
    (b) 0.17   (d) $\frac{2}{7} - \frac{1}{4}$

2. Reduce the fraction $\frac{126}{66}$ to "lowest terms."   Which of the rules given in this section did you use?

3. Use the rules contained in this section to prove that
$$\frac{a}{b} = \frac{-a}{-b} \quad \text{and that} \quad \frac{a}{-b} = \frac{-a}{b}.$$

4. Simplify the following:

    (a) $\dfrac{ax + ay - bx - by}{az - bz - aw + bw}$

    (b) $\dfrac{x - \dfrac{1}{x}}{x - \dfrac{1}{x^2}}$

    (c) $\dfrac{\dfrac{a}{b} + \dfrac{a}{c}}{ab + ac}$

    (d) $\dfrac{2 - \frac{1}{4}}{\frac{3}{5} + 1}$

    (e) $\dfrac{3x - 9y}{x^2 - 4xy + 3y^2}$

    (f) $1 - \dfrac{1}{2 - \frac{1}{3}}$

    (g) $1 - \dfrac{1}{1 - \dfrac{1}{x}}$

5. Find the reciprocal of each of the following and simplify:

(a) $x + y$

(b) $\dfrac{1}{x} + y$

(c) $\dfrac{1}{x} + \dfrac{1}{y}$

(d) $\dfrac{x - \dfrac{1}{y}}{y - \dfrac{1}{x}}$

(e) $\dfrac{1}{\frac{1}{2} + \frac{1}{4}}$

6. Perform the indicated operations and simplify:

(a) $\dfrac{x^2 - y^2}{x^3 - y^3} \div \dfrac{x + y}{x}$

(b) $x + y + \dfrac{x^2}{x - y}$

(c) $\dfrac{2}{12x^2 - 3} + \dfrac{3}{2x - 4x^2}$

(d) $\dfrac{2x + 3}{3x^2 + x - 2} - \dfrac{3x - 4}{2x^2 - 3x - 5}$

(e) $\dfrac{2x - 1}{4 - x} + \dfrac{x + 2}{3x - 12}$

(f) $\dfrac{z}{x + y} - \left(\dfrac{z}{x} + \dfrac{z}{y} \right)$

(g) $\dfrac{x + y}{z} - \left(\dfrac{x}{z} + \dfrac{y}{z} \right)$

7. Is there any value of x for which $(x^2 - 1)/(x - 1)$ is not equal to $x + 1$?

8. If $a \neq 0$, then $a/0$ is not defined. Does $0/a$ represent a number?

9. Suppose $a \neq 0$. Show that the reciprocal of the reciprocal of a is a.

3   THE NUMBER SCALE.   THE REAL NUMBERS

The rational numbers, together with the operations of addition and multiplication, form a system in which the inverse operations of subtraction and division by non-zero numbers are always possible. From the point of view of mathematical applications this system still lacks certain desirable properties, however, and we must extend it further. Extending the rational numbers to the system of real numbers is much more difficult to describe than were our earlier extensions. Despite the fact that this section is based on intuitive geometrical arguments, there is a solid logical basis for the system of real numbers.

The **number scale** provides us with a convenient geometrical representation of our number system. In constructing the scale, two points are chosen on a horizontal line; one point is labeled 0 and the other is labeled 1. The point labeled 0 is termed the **origin,** and the point labeled 1 is called the **unit point.** The unit point is usually placed to the right of the origin. If we consider the distance between the origin and the unit point as the unit of distance, then it is easy to locate the point that represents any given integer. The point two units to the right of the origin corresponds to the number 2, while the point two units to the left of the origin represents the number −2 (see Fig. 3-1). We can find points that correspond

Figure 3-1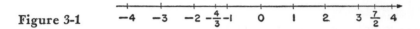

to other rational numbers just as easily. For example, to find the point that corresponds to −$\frac{4}{3}$, we divide the segment from −1 to −2 into thirds. The first division point to the left of −1 then corresponds to the rational number −$\frac{4}{3}$. Logically, a number and its corresponding point on the number scale should be distinguished as two different things. The number associated with a point is called the **coordinate** of the point. In practice, however, it is customary to refer to the "point" 5, and so on.

An **infinite decimal** is associated with every point on the number scale. A single example will illustrate how this association is accomplished. Let's consider the point P in Fig. 3-2. This point

Figure 3-2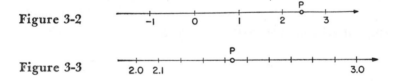

Figure 3-3

lies between the points 2 and 3. Figure 3-3 is an enlarged view of part of the number scale and shows the interval between the points 2 and 3 divided into ten equal parts by the points 2.1, 2.2, . . . , 2.9. The point P lies between the points 2.4 and 2.5. Figure 3-4 is a

Figure 3-4

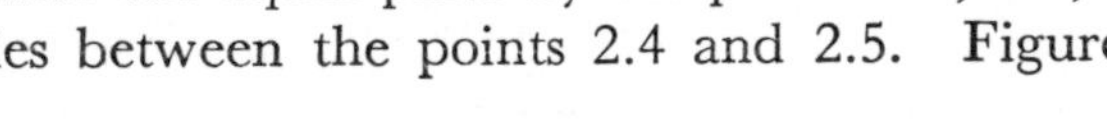

magnified picture of the part of the number scale between the points 2.4 and 2.5 and shows that the point P is between the points 2.41 and 2.42. The decimal expansion associated with P is, to two places, 2.41. Theoretically, we could continue this process indefinitely, if we agree that any subinterval on the number scale, no matter how small, can be subdivided into ten equal parts. The infinite decimal expansion corresponding to the point P is thus generated. If, at any stage of this process, we see that P is on a division point, then all further digits in the expansion are chosen to be zero. For example, the infinite decimal expansion associated with the point $\frac{3}{4}$ would be .75000 . . . . The example we have just described shows how a given point determines an infinite decimal. The converse is also true; any infinite decimal determines a unique point on the number scale.

Each point on the number scale is the graphical representation of a **real number**, and *to every real number there corresponds a point on the scale.* Since an infinite decimal is associated with every point on the number scale, we see that every real number is numerically represented by an infinite decimal. The rules of arithmetic that apply to real numbers are such that all the laws previously listed remain valid.

The rational numbers form part of the system of real numbers. They are represented by points on the number scale, and it is easy to find the decimal expansion of a given rational number by dividing its numerator by its denominator. There are some real numbers, however, that are not rational numbers. These numbers are called **irrational numbers.** As an example of such a number, consider the point Q whose distance from the origin is the length of the diagonal of a unit square (see Fig. 3-5). According to the Pythagorean

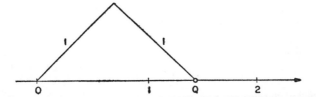

Figure 3-5

Theorem, this point should represent a number r such that $r^2 = 1^2 + 1^2 = 2$. But before we go on to prove that this number r cannot be a rational number, we must consider the following point about factoring integers.

If n is an integer, then we can write it as the product of a unique set of prime numbers (a **prime number** has no factors other than 1 and itself). Thus $n = p_1 \cdot p_2 \ldots p_k$, where the p's are prime numbers that are not necessarily all different. Then $n^2 = p_1 p_1 p_2 p_2 \ldots p_k p_k$. For example, $140 = 2 \cdot 2 \cdot 5 \cdot 7$ and $140^2 = 2 \cdot 2 \cdot 2 \cdot 2 \cdot 5 \cdot 5 \cdot 7 \cdot 7$.

Clearly, every prime number appearing in the factorization of n^2 appears an even number of times.

Now, we will assume that the number r we were speaking about is rational; that is, that there are integers a and b such that $r = a/b$. Then $a^2/b^2 = 2$, or $a^2 = 2b^2$. But it will now be shown that this assumption must be rejected because it contradicts our preceding remarks about factoring integers. In the factorization of a^2, the prime number 2 either appears an even number of times or not at all, and the same is true in the factorization of b^2. Therefore, the left-hand side of the equation $a^2 = 2b^2$ contains an even number of 2's, if any at all, while the right-hand side contains an odd number of 2's. But this situation is impossible, and hence there is no rational number whose square is 2. The point Q represents the real number $\sqrt{2}$, and the preceding argument shows that $\sqrt{2}$ *is an irrational number.*

The following diagram will perhaps make it easier for you to picture the hierarchy of number systems we have developed thus far.

Real numbers

$1, \frac{1}{2}, -2, \sqrt{2}, \ldots$

Rational numbers   *Irrational numbers*

$1, \frac{1}{2}, -2, \ldots$ $\sqrt{2}, \ldots$

Integers

$0, 1, -2, \ldots$

Positive integers

$1, 2, \ldots$

Problems 3

1. On the number scale, what is the number represented by the following points?
    (a) $\frac{1}{3}$ of the way from 2 to 3
    (b) $\frac{1}{5}$ of the way from -5 to -7
    (c) midway between a and b

2. Explain how to construct geometrically the point $\frac{5}{6}$ without using a ruler divided into sixths.

3. Calculate graphically as many decimal places as you can for the infinite decimal expansion of $\sqrt{2}$.

4. By simply dividing, show that the infinite decimal expansions associated with the rational numbers $\frac{1}{7}$ and $\frac{23}{5}$ are "repeating." By a "repeating

decimal expansion" we mean one in which, after a certain point, the digits keep recurring in successive "blocks."   An example is the number 23.46731731731 . . . where we assume that the "block" 731 is repeated indefinitely.

5. If $a = .141414$ . . . (repeating), then $100a = 14.141414$ . . . .   Therefore,
$$100a - a = 14.141414 \ldots - .141414 \ldots$$
or $99a = 14.$
Thus, $a = \frac{14}{99}$.   Use a similar argument to write $b = .142142$ . . . and $c = 2.9999$ . . . as fractions.   (It is a fact that all rational numbers have repeating decimal expansions, and all repeating decimals represent rational numbers.)

6. Is the sum of two rational numbers necessarily rational?   Is the sum of two irrational numbers necessarily irrational?   What about the sum of a rational number and an irrational number?

7. Answer Problem 6 but replace the word "sum" with the word "product."

8. Is there a smallest positive integer?   Is there a smallest positive rational number?

9. Show that the point P whose distance from the origin is the length of the diagonal of a rectangle whose sides are 1 and 2 does not represent a rational number.

10. Are the following numbers rational or irrational?

(a) $\dfrac{3 - \sqrt{2}}{2}$ (b) $\dfrac{1}{\sqrt{2}}$ (c) $\sqrt{3} + \sqrt{2}$

11. Is it possible to tell by physical measurement whether the length of a rod is a rational or an irrational number?

4   THE ORDER RELATION

Any real number is either positive, or zero, or negative, and the sum and product of any two positive numbers are positive.   On the basis of these facts, we can construct an order relation among the real numbers.

DEFINITION 4-1.   *If a and b are two real numbers, and if $a - b$ is a positive number, then a is greater than b (in symbols $a > b$) and b is less than a ($b < a$).   The symbols $>$ and $<$ are called* **inequality signs.**

According to this definition the statement "a is positive" can be written as $a > 0$.   Referring to the number scale, with the usual

convention that the positive direction is to the right, the statement
$a < b$ means that the point a is to the left of the point b. Note that
$-5 < -3$ because $-3 - (-5)$ is positive, and we can verify this
fact by checking these points on the number scale. The notation
$a < b < c$ means that $a < b$ *and* $b < c$, and the number b is said
to be *between* a and c. Thus to say that 4 is between 2 and 7 means
that $2 < 4 < 7$.

The order relation has the following fundamental properties.

4-1   For any two numbers a and b, one and only one of the following three relations is true:
$$a < b, \text{ or } a = b, \text{ or } a > b \text{ (Trichotomy)}.$$

4-2   If $a < b$ and $b < c$, then $a < c$ (Transitivity).

4-3   If $a < b$, then $a + c < b + c$ for any number c, positive,
negative, or zero.

4-4   If $c > 0$ and $a < b$, then $ac < bc$.

4-5   If $c < 0$ and $a < b$, then $ac > bc$.

We will now prove one of these properties. The proofs of the
others are left for the problems.

Proof of Property 4-2. If $a < b$ and $b < c$, then there are positive numbers p and q such that $b - a = p$ and $c - b = q$. Now
$c - a = c - b + b - a = p + q$. Since p and q are positive, so is
$p + q$. Hence $c - a$ is positive, which according to Definition 4-1
means that $c > a$.

Rules 4-4 and 4-5 state that when we "multiply both sides" of an
inequality, it makes a difference whether the multiplier is positive
or negative. As an example, consider the relation $3 < 4$. According to the rules, $(2)(3) < (2)(4)$ and $(-2)(3) > (-2)(4)$, which are,
of course, correct statements.

The following examples show how the properties of the order
relation may be used to derive new relations.

EXAMPLE 4-1.   If $0 < a < 1$, show that $a^2 < a$.

Solution. The relation $0 < a < 1$ means that $a > 0$ *and* $a < 1$. Since
a is positive, Property 4-4 states that we may multiply both sides of the
inequality $a < 1$ by a to get $a^2 < a$.

EXAMPLE 4-2.   If $1 < a$, show that $a < a^2$.

Solution.   Since $a > 1$ and $1 > 0$, a is positive (Property 4-2).   Hence by multiplying both sides of the inequality $1 < a$ by a, and using Property 4-4, we get the desired result.

To "solve" the inequality $3x + 2 < 2x - 3$ means to find out what we can say about the number x if $3x + 2 < 2x - 3$.   Example 4-3 illustrates how the properties of inequalities are used in such solutions.

EXAMPLE 4-3.   Solve the inequality $3x + 2 < 2x - 3$.

Solution.   We first assume that x is a number that satisfies the desired inequality.   By applying Property 4-3, the quantity $2x$ may be subtracted from both sides of the inequality to get $x + 2 < -3$.   Now subtract 2 from both sides of this last inequality to get $x < -5$.   Hence if there is a number x for which $3x + 2 < 2x - 3$, then $x < -5$.

This last sentence does *not* say that any number x that satisfies the second inequality satisfies the first.   As a matter of fact, every such x does satisfy the first inequality, but to *prove* it the preceding steps must be taken in the reverse order.   First, assume that $x < -5$, and then add $2x + 2$ to both sides to obtain the inequality $3x + 2 < 2x - 3$.

EXAMPLE 4-4.   What can you conclude about the number x if $x^2 - x - 2 < 0$?

Solution.   Since $x^2 - x - 2 = (x - 2)(x + 1)$, then $x^2 - x - 2 < 0$ only if the numbers $(x - 2)$ and $(x + 1)$ have opposite signs.   We must examine two cases.

Case I.   Both $x - 2 > 0$ and $x + 1 < 0$, which implies that $x > 2$ *and* $x < -1$.   There is no such number.

Case II.   Both $x - 2 < 0$ and $x + 1 > 0$, which implies that $x < 2$ and $x > -1$, so $-1 < x < 2$.

Because Cases I and II exhaust all possibilities that $(x - 2)$ and $(x + 1)$ have opposite signs, we have completely solved the problem. A number x such that $x^2 - x - 2 < 0$ must lie between -1 and 2. This example is represented schematically in Fig. 4-1.

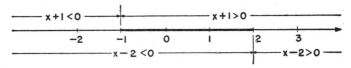

Figure 4-1

Problems 4

1. Prove Property 4-3.

2. Prove Property 4-4.

3. Prove Property 4-5.

4. Prove: If $0 < a < b$, then $a^2 < b^2$. Is the converse true?

5. Which of the following are true?

   (a) $-3 > -1$

   (b) $(-4)(-2) > 8$

   (c) $-[1 - (3 - 4)] < 0$

   (d) $\frac{27}{57} > \frac{62}{119}$

   (e) $\frac{-4}{3} < -1.3$

   (f) $\sqrt{7} < 2.646$

   (g) $\frac{(1 + \sqrt{2})}{3} > \frac{4}{5}$

   (h) $\frac{22}{7} > \pi$

6. Solve the following inequalities:

   (a) $1 - \frac{x}{3} < 0$

   (b) $2x > \frac{x - 4}{2}$

   (c) $\frac{x}{3} - 2 + \frac{5x - 1}{2} > 0$

   (d) $\frac{x}{4} - 7 > \frac{x - 4}{7}$

   (e) $x^3 - x^2 > 0$

   (f) $(x + 1)(x - 2) < (x + 1)^2$

   (g) $\frac{x - 1}{x - 4} > 0$

   (h) $x^4 + 2x^2 + 1 < 0$

   (i) $\frac{1 - x}{x + 4} < 0$

   (j) $x^2 - 6x > 7$

7. Prove: If $0 < x < 1$, then $x^3 < x$.

8. Discuss the following solution:
   Solve: $6 - 3x < 2 - x$.
   Solution. Factoring yields $3(2 - x) < 2 - x$. Dividing both sides by $(2 - x)$ gives $3 < 1$. Since this result is never true, there are no numbers x for which $6 - 3x < 2 - x$.

9. Find rational numbers x and y such that:
   (a) $x < \pi < y$ and $y - x < \frac{1}{100}$
   (b) $x < \sqrt{3} < y$ and $y - x < .1$
   (c) $x < \sqrt{40} < y$ and $y - x < 1$

10. If a/b and c/d are rational numbers with b and d positive, show that $a/b < c/d$, if and only if, $ad < bc$.

11. The total resistance R of an electrical circuit that contains two resistances R_1 and R_2 in parallel is given by the equation

$$\frac{1}{R} = \frac{1}{R_1} + \frac{1}{R_2}.$$

If one resistance, say R_1, is 50 ohms, what are the allowable values for R_2 if the total resistance R is to be between 5 and 10 ohms?

12. The altitude h (in feet) of a certain rocket t sec after firing is given by the equation

$$h = 800t - 16t^2.$$

Find the time interval during which the rocket is above 9600 ft.

5   ADDITIONAL REMARKS ON INEQUALITIES

The notation $a \leq b$ or $b \geq a$ means that a is a number that is either less than b or equal to b; that is, a is a number *not greater than b*. For example, $4 \leq 6$ and $6 \leq 6$, since neither 4 nor 6 is greater than 6. The properties of $<$ stated in Section 4 may also be extended to the $\leq$ relation.

5-1   If $a \leq b$ and $b \leq c$, then $a \leq c$.

5-2   If $a \leq b$, then $a + c \leq b + c$ for any number c.

5-3   If $c \geq 0$ and $a \leq b$, then $ac \leq bc$.

5-4   If $c \leq 0$ and $a \leq b$, then $ac \geq bc$.

In addition to these rules, we list some examples of others that involve various possible combinations of the $<$ and $\leq$ relations.

5-5   If $a \leq b$ and $b < c$, then $a < c$.

5-6   If $c > 0$ and $a \leq b$, then $ca \leq cb$.

5-7   If $c < 0$ and $a \leq b$, then $ca \geq cb$.

EXAMPLE 5-1.   Show that the sum of the squares of two numbers is not less than twice the product of the two numbers.

Solution.   In symbols the question reads, "Show that $a^2 + b^2 \geq 2ab$ for any two numbers a and b." First, we reduce the inequality to a simpler one, which we can easily verify.

$a^2 + b^2 \geq 2ab,$

$a^2 - 2ab + b^2 \geq 0$ (by applying Property 5-2),

$(a - b)^2 \geq 0$ (by factoring).

This argument does not *prove* the inequality, of course, since the chain of reasoning started with the statement to be proved. We prove the inequality by reversing these steps. Since the square of any real number is not negative, the inequality $(a - b)^2 \geq 0$ is surely true for any pair of numbers a and b. Hence $a^2 - 2ab + b^2 \geq 0$. Now add $2ab$ to both sides of this last inequality to obtain the desired one, $a^2 + b^2 \geq 2ab$. Note that equality holds if, and only if, $a = b$.

EXAMPLE 5-2.   Solve the inequality $(x + 1)/(2x - 3) \geq 1$.

Solution. The first step in the solution would appear to be to multiply both sides of the inequality by $2x - 3$. This we will do, but cautiously, for we cannot tell in advance whether the denominator is positive or negative. Thus, we don't know which multiplication rule to use, Formula 5-6 or Formula 5-7. We must consider two cases: the case in which $2x - 3 > 0$, and the case in which $2x - 3 < 0$.

Case I. $2x - 3 > 0$. The only numbers we are considering in this case are those for which $x > \frac{3}{2}$. Since $2x - 3$ is positive, we may multiply both sides of the original inequality by $2x - 3$ and use Formula 5-6 to obtain the inequality $x + 1 \geq 2x - 3$. This relation reduces to the inequality $x \leq 4$. Now we have two conditions: $x > \frac{3}{2}$, and $x \leq 4$. The numbers that satisfy both conditions are given by the inequalities $\frac{3}{2} < x \leq 4$.

Case II. $2x - 3 < 0$. We now consider the numbers for which $x < \frac{3}{2}$. If we multiply both sides of the original inequality by $2x - 3$ and use Formula 5-7, we get the inequality $x + 1 \leq 2x - 3$. This relation reduces to the inequality $x \geq 4$. We have shown that *if* there is a number $x < \frac{3}{2}$ that satisfies the inequality $(x + 1)/(2x - 3) \geq 1$, then it also must satisfy the inequality $x \geq 4$. Clearly there is *no* number that is both less than $\frac{3}{2}$ *and* equal to or greater than 4. Thus there is no number less than $\frac{3}{2}$ that satisfies the original inequality.

Since Cases I and II exhaust all the possibilities for solving the given inequality, we can sum up the results as follows. If x satisfies the inequality $(x + 1)/(2x - 3) \geq 1$, then x must be greater than $\frac{3}{2}$ and less than or equal to 4; that is, $\frac{3}{2} < x \leq 4$.

Frequently we must deal with rational numbers that are approximations of other numbers. The accuracy with which we can measure any physical quantity is always limited to some extent by inadequacies in the instruments we use, or by human factors. Consequently, scientific measurements are usually expressed in some such form as, "The ratio of the mass of a proton to the mass of an electron is 1838 ± 1." This sentence means that the stated ratio is a number r that satisfies the inequalities $1837 \leq r \leq 1839$. Another instance of this type of approximation is the statement that $\sqrt{2} = 1.414$ or $\pi = 3.14$. We already know that $\sqrt{2}$ is not a rational number (and neither is π), so these equalities are not strictly correct. We write them, of course, but only with the understanding that the equation $\sqrt{2} = 1.414$ means that

$$1.4135 \leq \sqrt{2} \leq 1.4145.$$

Now consider the following calculation:

$$\pi\sqrt{2} = (3.14)(1.414) = 4.43996.$$

You should recognize immediately that the given answer to this problem is not as accurate as it seems. To find out just how accurate it is, we use the rules dealing with inequalities. We have

$$1.4135 \leq \sqrt{2} \leq 1.4145 \text{ and } 3.135 \leq \pi \leq 3.145.$$

Therefore,

$$(1.4135)(3.135) \leq (1.4135)\pi$$

$$\leq \sqrt{2}\,\pi \leq \sqrt{2}(3.145) \leq (1.4145)(3.145).$$

If we multiply out the products on the extreme ends of these inequalities, the result, correct to two decimal places, is

$$4.43 \leq \sqrt{2}\,\pi \leq 4.45.$$

Problems 5

1. For what numbers x are the following inequalities true?
   (a) $x^2 \leq 0$
   (b) $x^2 + 1 \leq 2x$
   (c) $x - 1 \leq 2(x - 1)$
   (d) $2x - 1 \leq 2(x + 1)$
   (e) $x \geq 2x$
   (f) $\frac{1}{x} \leq \frac{2}{3}$
   (g) $\frac{x-1}{x+1} \leq 2$
   (h) $x^2 - 5x + 6 \leq 0$
   (i) $\dfrac{\frac{1}{x} + \frac{1}{4}}{\frac{1}{x} - \frac{1}{4}} \leq 1$
   (j) $\frac{x^2 - 4}{3x} \geq 1$

2. Prove that the sum of a positive number and its reciprocal is never less than 2.

3. The dimensions of a table are approximately 3.817 ft by 7.06 ft. What can you say about its perimeter? its area?

4. Using the approximate values $\sqrt{2} = 1.4$ and $\sqrt{3} = 1.7$, calculate $\sqrt{6}$ and determine how accurate the calculation is.

5. The current in a certain stream is 3 mph.   If a man has a motor boat that goes 5 mph in still water, how far can he travel and still return within 2 hr?

6. The current in a certain stream is 3 mph.   A man takes his motor boat to a point 16 miles downstream and back in less than 4 hr.   How fast can the boat travel in still water?

7. Show that if x and y are two numbers such that $x + y = 10$, then $xy \leq 25$.

8. Show that if $xy = 16$, where x and y are positive, then $x + y \geq 8$.

6   ABSOLUTE VALUE

The graphical representation of the system of real numbers as points on the number scale enables us to look at these numbers from a geometrical point of view.   As a result, the geometrical concept of *distance* is introduced into our number system.   Let x be a number that is represented by a point on the scale.   Then the number of units between this point and the origin is called the **absolute value of** x and is denoted by the symbol $|x|$.   Thus $|2| = 2$, $|-3| = 3$, $|\pi| = \pi$, and so on.   The absolute value of a number gives only its distance from the origin, not its direction.   Given $|x| = 5$, for example, we know that x is either the number 5 or the number -5 since both these numbers, and no others, are 5 units from the origin.

We can also formulate a definition of absolute value that does not rely on geometrical notions.   In every case, this definition gives the same result as the geometrical definition.

DEFINITION 6-1.   *For any real number a*

$$|a| = a \ \textit{if} \ a \geq 0, \ \textit{and} \ |a| = -a \ \textit{if} \ a < 0.$$

From this definition we see that $|2| = 2$, since $2 > 0$, while $|-3| = -(-3) = 3$, since $-3 < 0$.   These examples illustrate the fact that *the absolute value of a number is never negative*.

The concept of absolute value is already familiar to you even if the name is not.   For example, the rule for multiplying two real numbers reads, "Multiply the absolute values of the numbers and then multiply this result by 1 or -1, depending on whether the numbers have like or opposite signs." Thus,

$$(2)(-3) = (-1)(|2| \cdot |-3|) = (-1)(2 \cdot 3) = -6.$$

The following facts about absolute value are important. The letters represent real numbers.

6-1 $|-a| = |a|.$

6-2 $|a| > 0$ if $a \neq 0$ and $|0| = 0.$

6-3 $|ab| = |a| \, |b|.$

6-4 $\left|\dfrac{a}{b}\right| = \dfrac{|a|}{|b|}.$

6-5 $|a|^2 = a^2.$

Property 6-1 simply states that the points a and $-a$ are at equal distances from the origin; Property 6-2 states that the number 0 is the only number at the origin; all others are at some positive distance from it. Properties 6-3 and 6-4 stem from the definitions of multiplication and division. For example, the product ab is either the number $|a| \, |b|$ or $-|a| \, |b|$. The absolute value of both these numbers is $|a| \, |b|$, and so in either case $|ab| = |a| \, |b|$. If a is a positive number, then $a = |a|$; if a is negative, $a = -|a|$. In either event, $a^2 = |a|^2$, so Property 6-5 is true.

If a and b are any two real numbers, then $(a - b) = -(b - a)$. It therefore follows from Property 6-1 that $|a - b| = |b - a|$. This number is the *distance between a and b*, as a study of these points on the number scale will show. Geometrically interpreted, the equations $|4 - 1| = |1 - 4| = 3$ tell us that the points that represent the numbers 1 and 4 are 3 units apart. Similarly, the points representing the numbers 3 and (-2) are 5 units apart, and the equation expressing this relation is $|3 - (-2)| = |(-2) - 3| = 5$. Since $a + b = a - (-b)$, *the expression* $|a + b|$ *represents the distance between the points a and* $(-b)$.

If x is a number such that $|x - 5| = 2$, then x is 2 units from the number 5 on the number scale and, therefore, either $x = 7$ or $x = 3$. We can get the same result by applying the more formal Definition 6-1. If $|x - 5| = 2$, then either $x - 5 = 2$ or $x - 5 = -2$. In the first case, $x = 7$, and in the second, $x = 3$.

If we interpret the quantity $|a - b|$ as representing the distance between the two numbers a and b, then several useful inequalities follow easily, one of which is

6-6 $$|a - b| \leq |a| + |b|.$$

This inequality states that since a is $|a|$ units from the origin, and b is $|b|$ units from the origin, then a and b cannot be more than $|a| + |b|$ units apart.   Indeed, it is clear that two numbers, each a given distance from 0, will be farthest apart if they are on opposite sides of the origin, so that $|a - b| = |a| + |b|$ only when a and b have opposite signs.

Inequality 6-6 is true for any pair of numbers; hence if a and b are arbitrary real numbers, the inequality holds for the pair a and $-b$.   Thus $|a - (-b)| \leq |a| + |-b|$ or

6-7 $$|a + b| \leq |a| + |b|.$$

Notice that $|a| = |(a - b) + b| \leq |a - b| + |b|$, according to Inequality 6-7.   We can subtract $|b|$ from both sides of this last inequality to obtain

6-8 $$|a| - |b| \leq |a - b|.$$

The same reasoning that allowed us to replace b with $-b$ in Inequality 6-6 to obtain Inequality 6-7 now permits us to substitute $-b$ for b in Inequality 6-8 to obtain

6-9 $$|a| - |b| \leq |a + b|.$$

A good way to convince yourself of the truth of these inequalities is to try to find values of a and b for which they are false.

Problems 6

1. Find the numbers x for which the following equations are true:
  (a) $|x| = 6$
  (b) $|x| = 2.7$
  (c) $|x| = -2$
  (d) $|x| = |-2|$
  (e) $|2x| = 10$

2. Find the numbers x for which the following equations are true:
  (a) $|2x| = 2x$
  (b) $|2x| = 4x$
  (c) $|x - \frac{1}{2}| = \frac{3}{2}$
  (d) $x - 1 = |1 - x|$
  (e) $|x + 1| = |x| + 1$

3. If you know that a point x is 5 units away from 2, what can you say about the distance between x and the origin? The point 10?

4. If $|x - 1| = 4$, what can you say about the following:
    (a) $|x|$ (c) $|x - 4|$
    (b) $|x + 1|$

5. If $|y| \geq x$, does it follow that $|y| \geq |x|$?

6. If $|y| \geq -x$, does it follow that $|y| \geq |x|$?

7. If $|y| \geq x$ and $|y| \geq -x$, does it follow that $|y| \geq |x|$?

8. By interchanging a and b in the Inequality 6-8, show that
$$|a - b| \geq -(|a| - |b|).$$

9. Use Problems 7 and 8 and the Inequality 6-8 to show that
$$||a| - |b|| \leq |a - b|.$$

7   INEQUALITIES INVOLVING ABSOLUTE VALUES

We often use inequalities to locate a point between two extreme limits. We might, for example, say that x is a number such that $3 < x < 5$, to indicate that x lies somewhere in the interval from 3 to 5. Another way of approximately locating a point is to say that it is within a certain distance of a specified "base point." In this case, we can use the concepts of inequality and of absolute value together.

If p is a positive number, then the statement $|x| < p$ means that the point x is less than p units from the origin; that is, x is between $-p$ and p. *The inequalities*

7-1 $$|x| < p \quad \text{and} \quad -p < x < p$$

therefore mean exactly the same thing. Now let a be a real number, and replace x in Inequalities 7-1 with the quantity $(x - a)$. We see then that the inequality $|x - a| < p$ is equivalent to the two inequalities $-p < x - a < p$. If we add a to each term, these last relations become $a - p < x < a + p$. Hence *the inequalities*

7-2 $$|x - a| < p \quad \text{and} \quad a - p < x < a + p$$

mean exactly the same thing.

You should recall from Section 4 that the symbols "$-p < x < p$" are merely a concise way of saying that "The number x is less than p *and* also greater than $-p$." Now the inequality $|x| > p$ means that the distance between x and the origin is *more* than p units. So the number x is either greater than p *or* less than $-p$. This last phrase cannot be expressed wholly in terms of inequality symbols. We must be content to say that the inequality $|x| > p$ is equivalent to the statement, "$x > p$ *or* $x < -p$."

Notice the distinction here between the use of the words "and" and "or." The letter x stands for a real number, and it is perfectly possible for a number to be less than a positive number p and greater than the number $-p$, as is implied by the inequalities $-p < x < p$. On the other hand, there is no number x that is greater than p and also less than $-p$. It is therefore absurd to write $-p > x > p$, for these inequalities mean "$x > p$ *and* $x < -p$." We must say instead "$x > p$ *or* $x < -p$."

It should be clear how the preceding remarks must be modified if the inequality sign is replaced by the $\leq$ sign.

EXAMPLE 7-1. Express the inequality $|x| < 3$ without using absolute values.

Solution. In accordance with Relations 7-1, the desired solution consists of the inequalities $-3 < x < 3$.

EXAMPLE 7-2. Express the inequality $|2x - 1| < 5$ without using absolute values.

Solution. According to Relations 7-2, the given inequality is equivalent to the two inequalities $-4 < 2x < 6$. Divide each term of these inequalities by 2 to obtain the inequalities $-2 < x < 3$.

If x is a number such that $|x - m| < p$, then x must lie in the interval between the points $m - p$ and $m + p$, and conversely. Observe that the point m is the *midpoint* of this interval and that the length of the interval is $2p$. Thus the equivalence of the inequalities $m - p < x < m + p$ and $|x - m| < p$ is simply a symbolic expression of the geometrically obvious fact that a point lies in a certain interval on the number scale if, and only if, it is less than half the length of the interval from the midpoint.

Now let a and b, where $a < b$, be two points on the number scale. The distance between them is $|b - a|$ units. Since $b - a > 0$, $|b - a| = b - a$; this quantity therefore is the length of the interval. Let m denote the midpoint of the interval between a and b. Then the distance from a to m is the same as the distance from m to b, so $m - a = b - m$. Upon solving the last equation for m, we see that $m = (a + b)/2$. It then follows from the last sentence of the preceding paragraph that *the inequalities*

7-3
$$a < x < b \quad \text{and} \quad \left| x - \frac{(a + b)}{2} \right| < \frac{(b - a)}{2}$$

mean exactly the same thing.

EXAMPLE 7-3. Replace the inequality $1 < x < 3$ by a single inequality involving an absolute value.

Solution. We may use Inequalities 7-3 with $a = 1$ and $b = 3$ to see that the inequalities $1 < x < 3$ and $|x - 2| < 1$ mean the same thing.

Problems 7

1. Express the following inequalities without using absolute value signs:
   (a) $|3x| < 2$
   (b) $\left| \frac{x}{3} \right| < 2$
   (c) $|x - 1| < 3$
   (d) $|2x - 7| \leq 5$
   (e) $|x - \frac{1}{2}| \leq \frac{2}{3}$
   (f) $\left| \frac{2x^2 - x}{x} \right| \leq 4$

2. Express the following inequalities without using absolute value signs:
   (a) $|2x| > 3$
   (b) $|\frac{1}{2}x| > 3$
   (c) $|x - 1| > 8$
   (d) $|4x - 5| \geq 2$
   (c) $|x - \frac{1}{2}| \geq \frac{3}{2}$

3. What can you say about the number x in each of the following?
   (a) $|x - 1| \leq |x| + 1$
   (b) $|x - 1| \leq |x| - 1$
   (c) $|x - 3| \leq |x - 2|$
   (d) $|x - 1| \leq 0$
   (e) $|x| > |x - 1|$

4. Indicate those numbers x on the number scale that would satisfy the following inequalities:
   (a) $|x - 3| < 2$
   (b) $|3x - 4| < 5$
   (c) $|x + 1| \leq 2$
   (d) $|x - 2| > \frac{3}{2}$
   (e) $|2x - 7| \geq 1$

5. Replace each of the following inequalities with a single inequality involving an absolute value:
   (a) $1 < x < 3$
   (b) $-2 \leq x \leq 4$
   (c) $1 < 2x + 1 < 6$
   (d) $3 < 1 - 2x < 5$
   (e) $-3 < 2x - 1 < \frac{1}{2}$

8 EXPONENTS

You are accustomed to using positive integral exponents to denote products of a number of identical factors.   A brief review of the rules that govern the operations with these exponents will set the stage for an extension of the exponent notation to the other integers and fractions.

DEFINITION 8-1.   *If a is any number, and n is a positive integer, then*

$$a^n = a \cdot a \cdot \ldots \cdot a \ (n \ factors).$$

The equation $5^3 = 5 \cdot 5 \cdot 5$ is a numerical example of Definition 8-1; here, $a = 5$ and $n = 3$.

The following laws of exponents stem from this definition.   We assume that m and n are positive integers, and a and b can be any numbers (with the obvious restriction that no denominator may be 0).

8-1 $\qquad\qquad\qquad a^m a^n = a^{m+n}.$

8-2 $\qquad\qquad\qquad (a^m)^n = a^{mn}.$

8-3 $\qquad\qquad\qquad (ab)^n = a^n b^n.$

8-4 $\qquad\qquad\qquad \left(\dfrac{a}{b}\right)^n = \dfrac{a^n}{b^n}.$

8-5 $\qquad\qquad \dfrac{a^n}{a^m} = \begin{cases} a^{n-m} \text{ if } n > m. \\ \dfrac{1}{a^{m-n}} \text{ if } n < m. \\ 1 \text{ if } n = m. \end{cases}$

The example $a^3 \cdot a^4 = (a \cdot a \cdot a)(a \cdot a \cdot a \cdot a) = a^7 = a^{3+4}$ illustrates Rule 8-1.   It will be easy for you to verify these rules to your satisfaction.

Definition 8-1 applies only if n is a positive integer.   The symbols 7^0, 3^{-2}, and $5^{1/2}$ are, in terms of this definition, meaningless.   They will acquire meaning only as the result of new definitions, which we will now proceed to formulate.   These definitions are chosen to preserve Rules 8-1 to 8-5.   It can be shown that they are the only ones that allow us to continue to use these rules when dealing with exponents that are not necessarily positive integers.

DEFINITION 8-2. *If $a \neq 0$, then $a^0 = 1$.*

No meaning is assigned to the symbol 0^0. Thus $\pi^0 = 1$, $(-1)^0 = 1$, and so on.

At first glance, this definition may seem somewhat arbitrary. Let us show first that Rule 8-1 is still valid. Let a be a non-zero number and n be a positive integer or 0, and let $m = 0$. The rule then reads $a^{0+n} = a^0 \cdot a^n$. Since $0 + n = n$, and $a^0 = 1$ (Definition 8-2), this last equation is true. Hence Rule 8-1 is valid if either (or both) of the integers m and n is 0. Now we will show that Definition 8-2 is the *only* definition of the symbol a^0 that preserves Rule 8-1. Suppose that a is a number different from 0 and that a value has been assigned to the symbol a^0. Let $m = 0$ and $n = 1$ in Rule 8-1. If this rule still applies, then $a^{0+1} = a^0 \cdot a^1$; that is, $a = a^0 \cdot a$. Since $a \neq 0$, we can divide by it to get $a^0 = 1$. Therefore, if we insist on preserving Rule 8-1, the only value that we can assign to the symbol a^0 is 1. As a matter of fact, we can also show that Definition 8-2 does not violate Rules 8-2 to 8-5.

The way we define negative exponents is also motivated by Rule 8-1. Suppose $a \neq 0$ and n is a positive integer. We wish to assign a value to the symbol a^{-n} so that we may still use Rule 8-1. According to that rule, we should have $a^n \cdot a^{-n} = a^{n+(-n)} = a^0 = 1$; hence $a^n \cdot a^{-n} = 1$, which suggests the following definition.

DEFINITION 8-3. *If $a \neq 0$, then $a^{-n} = 1/a^n$.*

For example,

$$5^{-2} = \left(\frac{1}{5}\right)^2, \quad \left(\frac{1}{2}\right)^{-3} = \frac{1}{(\frac{1}{2})^3} = 8.$$

Once we have decided on the definition, we must still check to see whether or not the rules of exponents are true. We find that they are. Indeed, we can simplify Rule 8-5 by removing the restrictions on m and n to read

8-6 $$\frac{a^n}{a^m} = a^{n-m} \text{ for any integers } m \text{ and } n.$$

For example,

$$\frac{a^5}{a^7} = a^{5-7} = a^{-2} = \frac{1}{a^2} \quad \text{and} \quad \frac{a^{-5}}{a^{-7}} = a^{-5-(-7)} = a^2.$$

The statement $(a/b)^{-n} = (b/a)^n$ is an **identity** in the sense that it is true whenever the letters are replaced by numbers for which the expressions involved have meaning.   We must verify the statement by using arguments that do not depend on a particular choice of a, b, and n:

$$\left(\frac{a}{b}\right)^{-n} = \frac{1}{(a/b)^n} \qquad \text{(Definition 8-3)}$$

$$= \frac{1}{(a^n/b^n)} \qquad \text{(Rule 8-4)}$$

$$= \frac{b^n}{a^n} \qquad \text{(division of fractions)}.$$

We assume that neither a nor b is 0, for then the expressions are meaningless.   But otherwise, the result is true.

Suppose now that we are asked to show that two expressions, for example $(x^{-1} + y^{-1})$ and $(x + y)^{-1}$ are not identically equal.   This problem is intrinsically easier than the preceding one, in which we were asked to demonstrate equality for all possible substitutions (with certain obvious exceptions).   Here we must deny such equality. Equality cannot *always* hold if there is at *least one* situation in which it does not apply.   Hence it is sufficient to find numbers for which the given expressions have meaning but are not equal.   If we let $x = 1$ and $y = 2$ in the expressions $(x^{-1} + y^{-1})$ and $(x + y)^{-1}$, then the first expression becomes $1 + \frac{1}{2} = \frac{3}{2}$, and the second becomes $\frac{1}{3}$. Since these two numbers are not equal, we can conclude that the expressions $(x^{-1} + y^{-1})$ and $(x + y)^{-1}$ do not always represent the same number.

The following examples illustrate the use of exponents.

EXAMPLE 8-1.   Simplify the quotient $\dfrac{(x^{-2}y^4)^3}{(xy)^{-3}}$.

Solution.

$$\frac{(x^{-2}y^4)^3}{(xy)^{-3}} = \frac{x^{-6}y^{12}}{x^{-3}y^{-3}} = x^{-3}y^{15}.$$

EXAMPLE 8-2.   Simplify the quotient $\dfrac{2x^0}{(2x)^0}$.

Solution.

$$\frac{2x^0}{(2x)^0} = \frac{2 \cdot 1}{1} = 2.$$

Note that the exponent in the numerator applies only to the letter x.

EXAMPLE 8-3.　Simplify the expression $xy(x^{-1} + y^{-1})$.

Solution.

$$xy(x^{-1} + y^{-1}) = xyx^{-1} + xyy^{-1} = y + x.$$

EXAMPLE 8-4.　Simplify the expression $(3^{-1} + 2^{-1})^{-2}$.

Solution.

$$(3^{-1} + 2^{-1})^{-2} = (\tfrac{1}{3} + \tfrac{1}{2})^{-2} = (\tfrac{5}{6})^{-2} = (\tfrac{6}{5})^2 = \tfrac{36}{25}.$$

EXAMPLE 8-5.　Simplify the expression $(x + y^{-1})^{-1}$.

Solution.

$$(x + y^{-1})^{-1} = \left(x + \frac{1}{y}\right)^{-1} = \left(\frac{xy + 1}{y}\right)^{-1} = \frac{y}{xy + 1}.$$

Problems 8

1. Simplify the following expressions:

(a) -3^{-2}

(b) $(-3)^{-2}$

(c) $\dfrac{-3}{4^{-1}}$

(d) $(a^{-2})^{-3}$

(e) $\left(\dfrac{2}{3}\right)^2 \left(\dfrac{x}{y}\right)^0$

(f) $(x^2y)^0(xy^2)^3$

(g) $(x^{-1}y^{-3})(x^2y^3)$

(h) $(a^{-2}b^3c)^2(ab^2c^3)^{-3}$

(i) $\dfrac{2xy^{-4}}{3x^{-1}y}$

(j) $\dfrac{(2x^{-1})^3}{x^3}$

(k) $[(x^{-2})^3]^{-1}$

(l) $\left[\dfrac{u^{-2}v^3}{u^{-4}v^{-1}}\right]^{-2}$

2. Reduce each of the following expressions to the simplest form not involving zero or negative exponents.

(a) $2^{-2} + 3^{-1}$

(b) $a^{-1} + b^{-1}$

(c) $(x^0 + x)^{-1}$

(d) $(x + x^{-1})^2$

(e) $(x^2 - y^2)(x - y)^{-1}$

(f) $x^2 + y^{-2}$

(g) $\dfrac{4^{-1} + 3^{-2}}{2}$

(h) $x^2y^3(x^{-1} + y^{-2})$

(i) $\dfrac{x^{-1} + x^{-2}}{x}$

(j) $\dfrac{x}{x^{-1} + x^{-2}}$

3. Write an expression that involves no positive exponents and is equivalent to each of the following.

(a) $x^2 - y^2$

(b) $\dfrac{x^2}{y^3}$

(c) $x^2 + \dfrac{1}{y^3}$

(d) $(x + 1)^2$

(e) $\left(\dfrac{3}{x}\right)^2$

(f) $\left(\dfrac{a^2}{3}\right)^{-2}$

4. Prove that the following expressions are not identical.

(a) xy^{-3} and $(xy)^{-3}$

(b) $1 + x^{-1}$ and $\dfrac{1}{1 + x}$

(c) $\dfrac{1}{1 + x^{-1}}$ and $1 + x$

(d) $\dfrac{1}{x^{-1} + y^{-1}}$ and $x + y$

5. For what numbers x are the following inequalities true?

(a) $|x - 1| < 3^{-1}$

(b) $2x - 4^{-2} < 2^{-1}x + 1$

(c) $|x|^{-1} < 2^{-1}$

(d) $|x|^{-1} > 3^{-2}$

(e) $(x - 1)^0 \leq x - 2$

9 RADICALS AND RATIONAL EXPONENTS

Following the pattern of the previous section, we now seek to assign a value to the symbol $a^{1/n}$, where a is a given number and n is a positive integer, in such a way that the laws of exponents are preserved. If such a choice can be made, then according to Rule 8-2 we should have

$$(a^{1/n})^n = a^{(1/n)n} = a^1 = a.$$

We should therefore like $a^{1/n}$ to represent a number r that satisfies the equation $r^n = a$. Some discussion of this last equation is necessary before we can proceed with the consideration of rational exponents.

DEFINITION 9-1. *If n is a positive integer and $r^n = a$, then r is an **nth root of a**.*

For example, 3 is a 4th root of 81, since $3^4 = 81$, and -2 is a 5th root of -32, since $(-2)^5 = -32$. There may be no (real) nth roots of a given number, or there may be more than one. Both 2 and -2, for example, are square roots of 4, since $2^2 = 4$ and $(-2)^2 = 4$. We won't discuss exactly how many nth roots a number has and how to describe them until Chapter five, but we will take on faith the following fundamental property of the real number system. *If a is a positive real number and n is a positive integer, then there exists exactly one positive real nth root of a. If a is a negative real number and n is an odd positive integer, then there exists exactly one negative real nth root of a.* Each of these nth roots, whether a is positive or negative, is designated by the symbol $\sqrt[n]{a}$, and is called the **principal nth root of a.**

The symbol $\sqrt[n]{a}$ is called a **radical,** and the number a is called the **radicand.**   Note one fact.   If n is even and a is positive, there are always two real numbers (one positive and one negative) that satisfy the equation $r^n = a$.   Only the *positive* number is called the *principal nth root* and is designated by the symbol $\sqrt[n]{a}$.   Thus $\sqrt{4} = 2$, not -2, and not ± 2.   In particular, the radical $\sqrt{x^2}$ is not the number x if x is negative.   Hence you must write $\sqrt{x^2} = |x|$ unless you are sure that x is not negative.   For example, $\sqrt{(-3)^2} = |-3| = 3$, not -3.   If a is positive, the negative nth root of a is designated by $-\sqrt[n]{a}$.

No even power of a real number can be negative.   Thus if a is a negative real number and n is an even integer, there is no real nth root of a.   For example, there is no real number whose square is -1. We simply do not define the symbol $\sqrt[n]{a}$ as a real number if a is negative and n is even, so the symbol $\sqrt{-1}$ has no meaning here.   It is possible to enlarge the number system beyond the real numbers to include numbers whose even powers are negative, but for the moment we will not consider such numbers.

We are now ready to define fractional exponents.   Recalling from our earlier discussion that $a^{1/n}$ must be a number r such that $r^n = a$ if Rule 8-2 is to remain true, we make the following definition.

DEFINITION 9-2.   *If n is a positive integer, and if $\sqrt[n]{a}$ exists, then*

$$a^{1/n} = \sqrt[n]{a}.$$

Thus $32^{1/5} = \sqrt[5]{32} = 2$, $(-8)^{1/3} = \sqrt[3]{-8} = -2$, but $(-4)^{1/2}$ is undefined.

The definition of the symbol $a^{m/n}$ also stems from our wish to preserve Rule 8-2.   It is clearly desirable to have $a^{m/n} = (a^{1/n})^m = (\sqrt[n]{a})^m$.   Also we can demonstrate without too much trouble that

$(\sqrt[n]{a})^m = \sqrt[n]{a^m}$ whenever $\sqrt[n]{a}$ exists. We therefore formulate the following definition.

DEFINITION 9-3. *If m and n are both integers with $n > 0$, and if $\sqrt[n]{a}$ exists,* then

$$a^{m/n} = (\sqrt[n]{a})^m = \sqrt[n]{a^m}.$$

The above definition preserves Rules 8-1 to 8-5 in the sense that they apply when all terms involved have meaning. The following example illustrates what may happen when the rules are improperly applied.

EXAMPLE 9-1. According to Rule 8-1,

$$(-2)^{1/2}(-2)^{1/2} = (-2)^{1/2+1/2} = (-2)^1 = -2.$$

According to Rule 8-3 and Definition 9-2,

$$(-2)^{1/2}(-2)^{1/2} = [(-2)(-2)]^{1/2} = 4^{1/2} = 2.$$

But $2 \neq -2$; what is wrong?

Solution. We simply cannot apply the rules to undefined symbols such as $(-2)^{1/2}$.

The following examples illustrate the use of the rules of exponents with fractional exponents.

EXAMPLE 9-2. Simplify the quotient $\sqrt{x}/\sqrt[4]{x}$. Write the result in exponential notation.

Solution. Here, since we are dealing with even roots, we tacitly assume that x is positive. If we use the exponent form and the rules of exponents, we have

$$\frac{\sqrt{x}}{\sqrt[4]{x}} = \frac{x^{1/2}}{x^{1/4}} = x^{1/2-1/4} = x^{1/4}.$$

EXAMPLE 9-3. Simplify the radical $\sqrt{\sqrt[3]{x^4}}$. Write the result in radical form.

Solution.

$$\sqrt{\sqrt[3]{x^4}} = (x^{4/3})^{1/2} = x^{2/3} = \sqrt[3]{x^2}.$$

It is sometimes convenient to wri_e quotients containing radicals in such a way that no radical appears in the denominator; for example,

$$\frac{1}{\sqrt{2}} = \frac{1}{\sqrt{2}} \cdot \frac{\sqrt{2}}{\sqrt{2}} = \frac{\sqrt{2}}{2}.$$

The following examples illustrate methods used to **rationalize denominators.**

EXAMPLE 9-4.   Rationalize the denominator in the quotient $1/\sqrt[5]{x^2}$.

Solution.

$$\frac{1}{\sqrt[5]{x^2}} = \frac{1}{x^{2/5}} = \frac{1}{x^{2/5}} \cdot \frac{x^{3/5}}{x^{3/5}} = \frac{x^{3/5}}{x} = \frac{\sqrt[5]{x^3}}{x}.$$

EXAMPLE 9-5.   Express the product $1/\sqrt[3]{x^2} \cdot 1/\sqrt[4]{x}$ in simplest radical form, rationalizing the denominator.

Solution.

$$\frac{1}{\sqrt[3]{x^2}} \cdot \frac{1}{\sqrt[4]{x}} = \frac{1}{x^{2/3}} \cdot \frac{1}{x^{1/4}} = \frac{1}{x^{11/12}} = \frac{1 \cdot x^{1/12}}{x^{11/12} \cdot x^{1/12}} = \frac{x^{1/12}}{x} = \frac{\sqrt[12]{x}}{x}.$$

EXAMPLE 9-6.   Rationalize the denominator in the quotient $1/(\sqrt{x} - \sqrt{y})$.

Solution.   The trick here is to multiply both the numerator and the denominator by $\sqrt{x} + \sqrt{y}$, for then

$$\frac{1}{\sqrt{x} - \sqrt{y}} \cdot \frac{\sqrt{x} + \sqrt{y}}{\sqrt{x} + \sqrt{y}} = \frac{\sqrt{x} + \sqrt{y}}{x - y}.$$

Problems 9

1. Find the numerical value of the following:
   (a) $8^{2/3}$
   (b) $25^{3/2}$
   (c) $-81^{3/4}$
   (d) $64^{-5/6}$
   (e) $27^{4/3}$
   (f) $49^{-3/2}$
   (g) $(-64)^{5/3}$
   (h) $(1024)^{.3}$

2. Use the laws of exponents to prove the following laws of radicals.

    (a) $\sqrt[n]{ab} = \sqrt[n]{a}\,\sqrt[n]{b}$

    (b) $\sqrt[n]{\sqrt[m]{a}} = \sqrt[nm]{a}$

    (c) $\sqrt[km]{a^{kn}} = \sqrt[m]{a^{n}}$

3. Write in radical form without negative exponents, rationalizing denominators.

    (a) $(x^{1/3})^{-3/4}$

    (b) $x^{1/6} \div x^{-2/3}$

    (c) $(x^2 + 2xy + y^2)^{1/2}$

    (d) $x^{1/4}y^{-1/4}$

    (e) $\dfrac{1}{x^{1/2} + y}$

    (f) $\dfrac{x}{2^{1/2} - 3^{1/2}}$

4. Write in fractional exponent form with no denominators.

    (a) $\sqrt[3]{\dfrac{x}{y}}$

    (b) $\sqrt[3]{3}$

    (c) $\sqrt[4]{x^2}\,\sqrt[3]{xy^{-1}}$

    (d) $\sqrt[3]{x}\,\sqrt[5]{x^2}$

    (e) $\sqrt[3]{-x^{-1}}$

    (f) $\dfrac{1}{\sqrt{x} - \sqrt{y}}$

    (g) $\sqrt{x^{-1}}\,\sqrt[4]{x^3}$

    (h) $\sqrt{a\sqrt{a}\sqrt{a}}$

Review Problems, Chapter One

You should be able to answer the following questions without referring back to the text.

1. List all the integers that satisfy the following inequalities.

    (a) $-1 < n < 5$ (b) $3 \le n \le 6$

2. Write the following expressions in factored form.

    (a) $2x^2 - 8$ (b) $3x^2 - 15x + 18$ (c) $64x^6 - 1$

3. If $ab = ac$, does it follow that $b = c$?

4. Give an example of a rational number r such that $3 < r < 4$.

5. Criticize the statement, "The square root of 2 is 1.414."

6. Is there a number x such that $3 > x > 5$? Explain.

7. What can you say about the relative position of the points a and b on the number scale if $a < b$? If $|a - b| < 1$? If $|a| < |b|$?

8. Find the numbers x for which the following inequalities are true.

    (a) $|2x - 3| < 7$ (b) $|x - 3| > \frac{1}{2}$

9. Replace the inequalities $1 < x < 4$ by a single inequality involving an absolute value.

10. Is the inequality $|x| \ge x$ true for any number x? Explain.

11. Can you find integers a and b such that $1/a + 1/b = 2/(a + b)$?

12. What was the motivating factor in the definition of a^{-n} by the formula $a^{-n} = 1/a^n$?

13. Does $(a^{-1} + b^{-1})^{-1}$ always equal $a + b$?

14. Which is larger, $3x^0$ or $(3x)^0$?

15. Does $\sqrt{x^2}$ always equal x?   Explain.

16. Does $9^{1/2}$ equal 3, or -3, or ± 3?

17. Simplify the following expressions:

(a) $\dfrac{1}{\sqrt[3]{xy^2}}$

(b) $\dfrac{x^{1/2}y^2}{x^{-1}y^{1/4}}$

Miscellaneous Problems, Chapter One

These exercises are designed to test your ability to apply your knowledge of numbers to somewhat more difficult problems.

1. Suppose that a, b, c, and d are numbers such that $a < b$ and $c < d$. Which of the following statements are true, which false, and which may be either true or false depending on the values of a, b, c, and d?

(a) $a - b < d - c$

(b) $b - c < a - d$

(c) $a - c < b - d$

(d) $a - b < c - d$

(e) $b - c < d - a$

(f) $a - c < d - b$

2. Show that $x^2 + xy + y^2 \geq 0$ for all real numbers x and y.
[*Hint:* Look at the quotient $(x^3 - y^3)/(x - y)$.]

3. The integers $x = 0$ and $y = 0$ satisfy the equation $xy = x + y$.   Are there any other pairs of integers that satisfy this equation?

4. If a and b are positive numbers, show that $\sqrt{a + b} < \sqrt{a} + \sqrt{b}$.

5. Show that $\left|\dfrac{1}{x} - 2\right| < 1$ if, and only if, $\left|\dfrac{2}{3} - x\right| < \dfrac{1}{3}$.

6. Suppose that $0 < a < b$ and that $c \geq 0$.   Show that $\dfrac{a}{b} \leq \dfrac{a + c}{b + c}$.

7. To install certain piping would cost $1000 for labor plus the amount spent for materials.   Suppose that copper pipe would cost $1200, while iron pipe would cost $400.   If the copper pipe would last more than twice as long as the iron, which installation would be cheaper on a cost-per-year basis?   Assuming that other factors are equal, what can you say about the price of the iron pipe if the cost-per-year is the same for the two kinds of pipe?

8. To construct a certain building of stone would cost more than $1\frac{1}{2}$ times as much as to build it with brick, while wood would be less than $\frac{3}{4}$ the cost of brick.   What can you say about the relative cost of wood and stone?

9. The relationship between the Fahrenheit and centigrade temperature scales is given by the formula $F = \frac{9}{5}C + 32$, where F represents the Fahrenheit temperature and C is the centigrade temperature.   If the temperature of a body is $(50 \pm .1)°$ Fahrenheit, what is its temperature in degrees centigrade?

10. A man is $\frac{1}{4}$ of the way across a railroad trestle when he sees a train that is 1 trestle length behind him approaching the trestle.   Which way should he run?

11. Rationalize the denominator: $1/(5 - \sqrt[3]{2})$.

12. Find *all* pairs of integers (x,y) such that $x^2 + 2x + y^2 = 4$.

FUNCTIONS

Scientists in almost every field have long been concerned with the establishment of quantitative relationships. Engineers use formulas which tell them *how many* inches certain beams bend when subjected to a certain *number* of pounds of load; geneticists ask for the *number* of mutations associated with a *measured* dose of radiation; chemists are interested in the relation between the *rate* of a chemical reaction and the *quantity* of each reacting substance.

The law of a falling body is a quantitative relationship. If a body is released from rest in a vacuum, then one second after its release it will be 16 feet below its starting point, two seconds after its release, 64 feet, and so on. If we know *how many* seconds the body has fallen, the formula $s = 16t^2$ tells us *how many* feet it has fallen. You are surely familiar with many other examples of quantitative relationships.

In this chapter we shall concentrate on the essential features of quantitative relationships. Basically, the idea involves *two sets of numbers*, each representing measurements of a certain physical quantity. *To each number in one set there corresponds a number in the other.* In the example of the falling body, the numbers in one set would represent durations of fall, and the numbers in the other set would represent distances. Then to 1 (second) there corresponds 16 (feet), and so forth. In mathematics, we strip away any physical meaning that may be attached to the numbers and simply discuss correspondences between sets of numbers.

One of the main purposes of this chapter is to introduce you to the definitions and terminology of the mathematical relationships known as *functions*. Although some of the concepts may seem rather abstract, they are motivated by distinctly practical problems such as the expression of the law of a falling body. Since the topics covered in this chapter will be cropping up again and again throughout your entire study of mathematics, your later work will be easier if you master these topics as early as possible.

10 DEFINITIONS AND TERMINOLOGY

Suppose we have two sets of numbers. In order to distinguish between them, we shall call one the "first set" and the other the "second set." Suppose, also, that with each number in the "first set" there is associated a number in the "second set." These *three* things, the two sets of numbers and the correspondence between the numbers in the two sets, comprise a **function.** It is easy to construct examples of functions. For instance, there is the function in which

   (i) the first set consists of the positive integers 1, 2, 3, and 4,
   (ii) the second set is made up of the integers 4, 5, and 6,
   (iii) the correspondence between the numbers in these two sets is given by the following table.

Number in the first set:	1	2	3	4
Corresponding number in the second set: 5	4	4	6

Functions are usually denoted by letters, such as f, g, F, G, and ϕ. The set of numbers that we have referred to as the "first set" is called the **domain** of the function, and the "second set" is called the **range** of the function. Every number in the range corresponds to some number in the domain. The domain of the function of the example above is the set $\{1,2,3,4\}$, and its range is the set $\{4,5,6\}$.

The heart of a function is the correspondence between the numbers of the domain and those of the range. *With each number x of the domain there is associated a number y of the range.* In the example above, this association was defined by means of a table, but it also can be established in other ways. For the functions that you will encounter most often, the correspondence between x and y will be given by an equation. For example, f may represent the function whose domain is the set of all real numbers, whose range is the set of all non-negative real numbers, and whose rule of correspondence is given by the equation $y = x^4$. Thus to the number $x = 2$ there corresponds the number $y = 2^4 = 16$; and to the number -3 there corresponds the number 81, and so on.

If x represents a number in the domain of a function f, then the corresponding number in the range is often denoted by the symbol $f(x)$ rather than by the letter y. The symbol $f(x)$ is read "f of x" or "f at x." If f is the function described in the preceding paragraph, we can now write $f(-3) = 81$, which means the same thing as the phrase "in the function f, the number that corresponds to -3 is 81." For a given function f we shall use either a letter such as y or the symbol $f(x)$ to denote the number in the range that corresponds to the number x in the domain.

> EXAMPLE 10-1. Let f be the function whose domain is the set of all real numbers, whose range is the set of all numbers greater than or equal to 2, and whose rule of correspondence is given by the equation $y = x^2 + 2$. Find $f(0), f(-1)$, and $f(2)$.
>
> *Solution.* By definition, $f(0), f(-1)$, and $f(2)$ are the numbers corresponding to $0, -1$, and 2. Hence $f(0) = 0^2 + 2 = 2$, $f(-1) = (-1)^2 + 2 = 3$, and $f(2) = 2^2 + 2 = 6$.

The rule of correspondence of the function f of Example 10-1 is given by the equation $f(x) = x^2 + 2$. To find the number in the range associated with any particular number in the domain, we merely replace the letter x wherever it appears in the equation

$f(x) = x^2 + 2$ by the given number. We followed this procedure in the solution of Example 10-1. Suppose, for instance, that a, $|a|$, and $(2 + h)$ represent numbers in the domain of f. Then the corresponding numbers in the range are $f(a) = a^2 + 2$, $f(|a|) = |a|^2 + 2 = a^2 + 2$, and $f(2 + h) = (2 + h)^2 + 2 = 6 + 4h + h^2$. It is sometimes helpful to think of the correspondence in this case as being defined by the equation $f(\ ) = (\ )^2 + 2$, where any symbol representing a number in the domain of f may be inserted in both parentheses.

Although the domain and range are essential parts of a function, they are frequently not mentioned explicitly, especially when the correspondence between these sets is given by an equation. For example, G may be the function whose domain is the set of all positive numbers and whose rule of correspondence is given by the equation $G(x) = 3x^2 + 7$ (or $y = 3x^2 + 7$). It follows that the range of G is the set of numbers greater than 7, for each of these numbers, and no others, can be obtained from the expression $3x^2 + 7$ by replacing x with a positive number. Similarly, the domain is often not listed if it consists of all the numbers for which the formula has meaning. For example, we may say that the function g is defined by the equation $g(x) = \sqrt{1 - x^2}$ (or $y = \sqrt{1 - x^2}$). This equation simply gives the rule of correspondence between the numbers of the domain and range. For this function g we are to assume that the domain consists of those numbers x for which the expression $1 - x^2$ is not negative; hence the domain consists of those numbers x that satisfy the inequalities $-1 \leq x \leq 1$. The range then consists of those numbers y that satisfy the inequalities $0 \leq y \leq 1$.

EXAMPLE 10-2. The equation $f(x) = 2x + 4\sqrt{x} + 2$ determines a function f. What can you say about the domain and range of f?

Solution. The domain of f is the set of numbers that are greater than or equal to zero; the formula does not apply to negative numbers. If $x \geq 0$, then $2x \geq 0$ and $4\sqrt{x} \geq 0$. The expression $2x + 4\sqrt{x} + 2$ can therefore not be less than 2. It follows that the range of f must consist of numbers greater than or equal to 2.

We have given a somewhat restrictive definition of a function in this section. In some other useful functions, the domain and range contain mathematical entities other than numbers. Later we shall encounter a range that consists of points and a domain that consists of angles. But for the moment we will concentrate solely on our present definition.

Problems 10

1. Each of the statements below determines a function. In each case, designate the function by a letter, determine its domain and range, and find a formula giving its rule of correspondence.
   - (a) To each positive integer n let there correspond the next largest integer.
   - (b) To each integer n let there correspond the sum of n and the previous integer.
   - (c) To each integer n let there correspond the difference between n and the previous integer.

2. Each of the following equations determines a function. In each case, determine the domain of the function if the domain consists of all real numbers to which the formula is applicable.
   - (a) $f(x) = \sqrt{\dfrac{1}{x}}$
   - (b) $y = \sqrt{(x-1)^2}$
   - (c) $F(x) = \sqrt{x^2 + x - 2}$
   - (d) $F(x) = \dfrac{x-1}{x+1}$
   - (e) $s = \sqrt{\dfrac{t}{t-1}}$
   - (f) $\phi(y) = \dfrac{|y|}{y}$

3. Determine the range of f if the domain consists of the integers $\{1,2,3\}$ and the rule of correspondence is as follows:
   - (a) $f(x) = 3x - 1$
   - (b) $f(x) = (1 + x)^{-1}$
   - (c) $f(x) = |2 - x|$
   - (d) $f(x) = \left(1 + \dfrac{x}{2}\right)^{1/2}$
   - (e) $f(x) = \dfrac{|x|}{x}$
   - (f) $f(x) = \sqrt[4]{(x-1)^2}$

4. If $F(x) = 3x - 1$, evaluate each of the following:
   - (a) $F(2)$
   - (b) $3F(2)$
   - (c) $F(\sqrt{y})$
   - (d) $F(y^2)$
   - (e) $F(|a|)$
   - (f) $F(x + 1)$
   - (g) $F(x + 1) - F(x)$
   - (h) $F(3x)$
   - (i) $\dfrac{F(3y)}{3}$
   - (j) $\sqrt{F(z) + 1}$

5. If $f(x) = x^2$, evaluate each of the following:

(a) $f(3 - 2)$

(b) $f(3) - f(2)$

(c) $3f(2)$

(d) $f(a + 1)$

(e) $f(a + h)$

(f) $f(a + h) - f(a)$

(g) $\dfrac{f(a + h) - f(a)}{h}$

(h) $f(t^2)$

(i) $f(\sqrt{y})$

(j) $\sqrt{f(z)}$

11   EXAMPLES OF FUNCTIONS

To help you become familiar with the concept and terminology of functions, we shall devote this section to a number of illustrations.

Illustration 11-1.   The **identity function** I assigns to every real number the number itself.   In other words, $I(x) = x$.   Both the domain and range of the function I consist of the set of all real numbers.

Illustration 11-2.   The **absolute value function** is defined by the equation $y = |x|$.   Its domain is the set of all real numbers, and its range is the set of all non-negative real numbers.   The table below gives a few examples of the correspondence between numbers in the domain and range.

x	1	$-\frac{1}{2}$	π	0
$y = |x|$	1	$\frac{1}{2}$	π	0

Illustration 11-3.   The symbol $[x]$ denotes the greatest integer n such that $n \le x$.   Thus $[\pi] = 3$, $[\sqrt{2}] = 1$, $[3] = 3$, $[-3] = -3$, and $[-\frac{1}{2}] = -1$.   We may define a function f, the **greatest integer function,** by the equation $f(x) = [x]$.   The domain of this function is the set of all real numbers, and its range is the set of all integers. Almost every time you state your age you are using the greatest integer function.   You say you are 18, for example, when you are actually $18\frac{1}{4}$, and $18 = [18\frac{1}{4}]$.   When a dealer prices a certain item at \$4.95 he hopes you will read the tag as $[4.95] = 4$ dollars.   If x is a given real number, then $[x]$ can be determined graphically by locating x on the number scale and choosing the first integer at or to the left of this point.

Illustration 11-4. When an iron rod 1 inch in cross section and 10 inches long is subjected to a tension of x pounds it will stretch, say, s inches. Hooke's Law of Elasticity states that the relation between the numbers x and s is given by the equation $s = \dfrac{x}{3 \cdot 10^6}$. Thus a force of 30 pounds will stretch the rod 10^{-5} inches. Note that the mathematical function determined by this last equation makes sense for any real value of x; that is, its domain is the set of all real numbers. The engineer knows, though, that this function represents the behavior of the rod only for certain values of x. It certainly will not apply, for instance, if the force is so great that the rod breaks. Thus, for practical purposes, specifying the domain of a function may be important.

Illustration 11-5. Let us assume that the materials used in making a cylindrical tin can cost .012¢ per square inch for the sides and .021¢ per square inch for the top or bottom. Suppose we want to make a can with a capacity of 54π cubic inches. But the volume alone won't completely determine the dimensions of the can; it may be tall and thin, or short and squat. We may select any positive number r and make the radius of the base of the can r inches. Since the volume is already fixed, the choice of r determines the height of the can, and hence the dimensions of the can are completely determined. The cost of the can depends on its dimensions, so we see that the cost of the can depends on our choice of the base radius r. Let us denote the cost, in cents, of a can of base radius r inches by c and find a formula that expresses c in terms of r.

Clearly, $c =$ (area of sides) $\times$ .012 + (area of ends) $\times$ .021. If the can is h inches high and has a base radius of r inches, then the area of the sides is $2\pi r h$ square inches and the area of the top (or bottom) is πr^2 square inches. Therefore

11-1 $$c = (2\pi r h)(.012) + (2\pi r^2)(.021).$$

We have now expressed the cost of the can in terms of the dimensions r and h, but we wanted to express c in terms of r alone. We therefore write a formula for h in terms of r. Since the volume of the can is 54π cubic inches, $\pi r^2 h = 54\pi$ and hence $h = 54/r^2$. Now replace h in Equation 11-1 by $54/r^2$ to obtain the equation

11-2 $$c = \left(\frac{108\pi}{r}\right)(.012) + (2\pi r^2)(.021).$$

From this equation, we can calculate the cost of the can if the base radius is 1 inch, 2 inches, 3 inches, or 4 inches, as 4.21 cents, 2.57 cents, 2.54 cents, and 3.13 cents. A question often asked in a course in calculus is, "For what value of r is c least?" That is, "What are the dimensions of the cheapest can?" In the present case, the answer would be a radius of 2.49 inches. The cost of such a can is 2.45 cents.

Illustration 11-6. Consider the function f whose domain is the set of positive integers and whose rule of correspondence is, "To each positive integer n let correspond the digit in the nth decimal place of the infinite decimal representation of the number π." Since $\pi = 3.14159\ldots$, we have $f(1) = 1$, $f(2) = 4$, $f(3) = 1$, $f(4) = 5$, $f(5) = 9$, and so on. The rule of correspondence is easy to state, but there is no simple algebraic formula that defines the function for all positive integers n.

Problems 11

1. Let f be the function defined by the equation $f(x) = |x| + x$. Find the following numbers:
   (a) $f(2)$
   (b) $f(-2)$
   (c) $f(\frac{3}{2})$
   (d) $f(-\frac{3}{2})$
   (e) $f(\sqrt{2})$
   (f) $2f(-1)$

2. Let f be the absolute value function $(f(x) = |x|)$. Which of the following statements are true for all numbers in the domain of f?
   (a) $f(x^2) = [f(x)]^2$
   (b) $f(x + y) = f(x) + f(y)$
   (c) $f(|x|) = |f(x)|$
   (d) $f(2x) = 2f(x)$

3. If f denotes the identity function, which of the statements in Problem 2 are true?

4. If f denotes the greatest integer function, which of the statements in Problem 2 are true?

5. A rectangular area of 3000 sq ft is to be fenced on three sides with fencing costing 30¢ per ft, and on the fourth side with fencing costing 50¢ per ft. If x denotes the length of the fourth side and C denotes the corresponding cost of the fence in cents, express C in terms of x. What is the domain of the resulting function?

6. A ship is steaming due north at 12 mph. At midnight a lighthouse is sighted at a distance of 3 miles directly west of the ship. If the distance between the ship and the lighthouse t hours later is d miles, find a formula that expresses d in terms of t.

7. An airplane leaves an airport at noon flying due north at 200 mph. At 1 P.M. another plane leaves the airport and flies due east at 250 mph. If the distance in miles between the two planes t hr after noon is denoted by d, find a formula that expresses d in terms of t.

8. A snowball is melting at a rate that decreases its radius 1 in. per hr. If the ball has a radius of 25 in. at a certain time, find a formula for its volume, V cu in., t min later. $\left(\text{The volume of a sphere is } \dfrac{4\pi r^3}{3}.\right)$ What is the domain of the associated function?

9. An open box is to be made from a rectangular piece of tin 10 in. long and 8 in. wide by cutting pieces x in. square from each corner and bending up the sides. Express the volume, V cu in., of the box in terms of x. What is the domain of the associated function?

10. An open box with a square base is to be made of wood costing 4¢ per sq ft for the sides and 5¢ per sq ft for the bottom. The volume of the box is to be 10 cu ft. If the bottom of the box is to be x ft by x ft, express the cost, C cents, in terms of x.

12 CARTESIAN COORDINATES AND THE DISTANCE FORMULA

In Section 3, we discussed the manner in which real numbers are associated with points on a line. In this section, we will consider the same procedure in two dimensions.

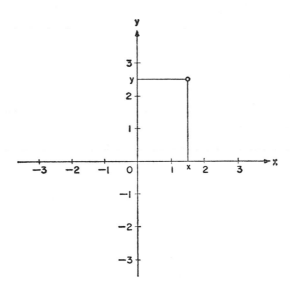

Figure 12-1

Let us begin by drawing two number lines meeting at right angles at their origins with the positive direction upward on one line and to the right on the other (see Fig. 12-1). These number lines are called **coordinate axes.** The horizontal line is the **x-axis,** and the vertical line is the **y-axis.** Let P be any point of the plane and construct lines through P that are perpendicular to the axes. If x is the number represented by the foot of the perpendicular to the x-axis and y is the corresponding number on the y-axis, then the pair of numbers (x,y) is associated with P. Conversely, let (x,y) be any

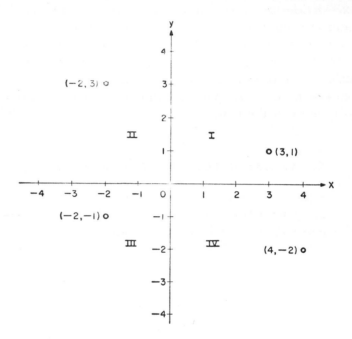

Figure 12-2

pair of numbers. Then construct a line perpendicular to the x-axis at the point x, and construct a line perpendicular to the y-axis at the point y. The intersection of these two lines will determine exactly one point P to be associated with the pair of numbers (x,y). In summary, with each point in the plane is associated a pair of numbers (x,y) and with each pair of numbers is associated a point P in the plane. The numbers x and y are the **coordinates** of P.

We have just described a **cartesian coordinate system** (named after the seventeenth-century French philosopher and mathematician, René Descartes). We have established a correspondence between a geometric system (points) and an algebraic system (pairs of numbers). This correspondence makes it possible to solve certain geometric problems algebraically and certain algebraic problems by means of geometry.   We sometimes ignore the logical distinction between a point and its coordinates, and no confusion will arise if we speak of the "point" (x,y).

The points $(3,1)$, $(-2,3)$, $(-2,-1)$, and $(4,-2)$ are shown in Fig. 12-2.   Note carefully that the *first* number of the number pair (a,b) is the *x*-coordinate, and the *second* is the *y*-coordinate.   The two axes divide the plane into four regions or **quadrants**.   These quadrants are numbered I, II, III, and IV, as shown in Fig. 12-2.   For example, the point $(-2,3)$ is in the second quadrant.

We have seen that the distance between the points on the number scale that represent the two real numbers a and b is given by the expression $|a - b|$.   We can also calculate the distance between two points in the plane.

EXAMPLE 12-1.   The point P_1 has coordinates $(-2,-1)$ and the point P_2 has coordinates $(2,2)$.   Find the distance $\overline{P_1P_2}$ between these points.

Solution.   The points P_1 and P_2 are plotted in Fig. 12-3.   Let P_3 be the point whose coordinates are $(2,-1)$.   It is apparent that the points P_1, P_2, and P_3 are the vertices of a right triangle, with right angle at P_3.   Since the points P_2 and P_3 lie on the same vertical line, you can easily see that the distance between them is 3 units.   Similarly,

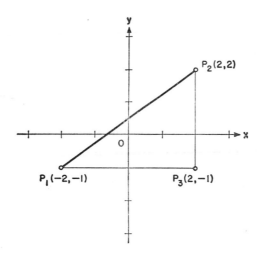

Figure 12-3

the distance $\overline{P_1P_3} = 4$.   Now according to the Pythagorean Theorem,

$$\overline{P_1P_2}^2 = \overline{P_1P_3}^2 + \overline{P_3P_2}^2 = 16 + 9 = 25.$$

It follows that $\overline{P_1P_2} = 5$.

The concept of distance between two points is so important that we shall develop a formula for it.   The arguments we use are the same as the ones we applied to Example 12-1.   Before deriving the general distance formula, we first consider a special case.

If two points Q_1 and Q_2 have the same x-coordinate, then the distance $\overline{Q_1Q_2}$ is the absolute value of the difference of the y-coordinates of these points. In symbols, if Q_1 is the point (x_0, y_1) and Q_2 is the point (x_0, y_2), then $\overline{Q_1Q_2} = |y_2 - y_1|$.   To verify this fact, we note that the statement that two points have the same x-coordinate means that the line passing through the two points is parallel to the y-axis (examine the points P_2 and P_3 in Fig. 12-3).   It follows that the distance between the points (x_0, y_1) and (x_0, y_2) is the same as the distance between the points y_1 and y_2 on the number scale used for the y-axis.   We have already seen that this distance is $|y_2 - y_1|$.

You should be able to convince yourself that *when two points have the same y-coordinate, the distance between them is the absolute value of the difference of the x-coordinates of the points* (examine the points P_1 and P_3 in Fig. 12-3).

With the aid of the results we have collected from these special cases, we can now derive the general distance formula.

THEOREM 12-1.   *Let P_1 and P_2 with coordinates (x_1, y_1) and (x_2, y_2) be any two points in the plane.   Then the distance $\overline{P_1P_2}$ is given by the formula*

12-1 $$\overline{P_1P_2} = \sqrt{(x_2 - x_1)^2 + (y_2 - y_1)^2}.$$

Proof.   As in Example 12-1, the auxiliary point P_3 with coordinates (x_2, y_1) is introduced (see Fig. 12-4) in such a way that the points P_1, P_2, and P_3 form a right triangle with right angle at P_3.   The lengths of the legs of this triangle are the distances $\overline{P_1P_3}$ and $\overline{P_2P_3}$, while the length of the hypotenuse, $\overline{P_1P_2}$, is the distance we wish to find.   Again, according to the Pythagorean Theorem,

12-2 $$\overline{P_1P_2}^2 = \overline{P_1P_3}^2 + \overline{P_2P_3}^2.$$

Now the points P_1 and P_3 have the same y-coordinate, so we have $\overline{P_1P_3} = |x_2 - x_1|$, and hence

$$\overline{P_1P_3}^2 = |x_2 - x_1|^2 = (x_2 - x_1)^2.$$

Similarly,

$$\overline{P_2P_3}^2 = |y_2 - y_1|^2 = (y_2 - y_1)^2.$$

We can therefore write Equation 12-2 as

$$\overline{P_1P_2}^2 = (x_2 - x_1)^2 + (y_2 - y_1)^2,$$

which is equivalent to Equation 12-1.

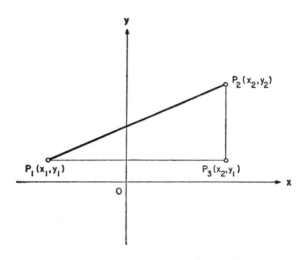

Figure 12-4

You will use the distance formula so often that you should memorize it.

EXAMPLE 12-2.   Find the distance between the points $(-3,2)$ and $(2,-3)$.

Solution.   You should realize that it makes no difference which point is designated P_1.   If the first point is labeled P_2 and the second P_1, the distance formula yields

$$\overline{P_1P_2} = \sqrt{(-3 - 2)^2 + (2 + 3)^2} = 5\sqrt{2}.$$

EXAMPLE 12-3.   Find the distance of the point (x, y) from the origin.

Solution.   Let P_1 be the point $(0,0)$ and P_2 be the point (x,y) and apply the distance formula.   The distance turns out to be

$$\sqrt{(x-0)^2 + (y-0)^2} = \sqrt{x^2 + y^2}.$$

An important property of distance is that, if P_1, P_2, and P_3 are any three points, then

12-3 $$\overline{P_1P_3} \leq \overline{P_1P_2} + \overline{P_2P_3},$$

and the equality sign holds if, and only if, the three points are collinear; that is, if they lie in a straight line.   This property of distance is called the **triangular inequality** for reasons that will be obvious

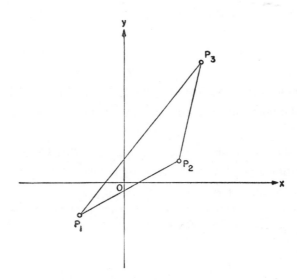

Figure 12-5

to you from a glance at Fig. 12-5.   The truth of this property becomes apparent if we consider the geometry of the situation, but we can prove it by using Formula 12-1 and considerable algebraic manipulation.

Problems 12

1. Sketch the following pairs of points in a cartesian coordinate system and find the distance between them.

   (a) $(1,2)$ and $(3,7)$

   (b) $(2,1)$ and $(-2,6)$

   (c) $(1,1)$ and $(-3,-2)$

   (d) $(-\frac{3}{2},\frac{1}{2})$ and $(0,0)$

   (e) $(-\sqrt{2},2)$ and $(\sqrt{5},5)$

2. Find the distance between the following points.

    (a) $(a + b, a - b)$ and $(b - a, b + a)$

    (b) $(0,0)$ and $(\sqrt{a + b}, \sqrt{a - b})$

    (c) $(a^{1/2}, b^{1/2})$ and $(-a^{1/2}, -b^{1/2})$

3. Use the distance formula to determine if the triangle whose vertices are $(1,1)$, $(3,2)$, and $(2,12)$ is a right triangle.

4. Show that the triangles with the following points as vertices are isosceles triangles.

    (a) $(3,-6)$, $(8,-2)$, $(-1,-1)$

    (b) $(3,1)$, $(4,3)$, $(6,2)$

5. Two vertices of a square are $(-3,2)$ and $(-3,-5)$. Find two sets of other possible vertices.

6. Without using the distance formula, find the point midway between the points $(-7,-1)$ and $(3,-1)$.

7. Find the area of the triangle whose vertices are the points $(-1,2)$, $(3,2)$ and $(-4,6)$.

8. The point $(x,2)$ is 5 units from the point $(2,6)$. Find the number x.

9. Find the point on the x-axis that is equidistant from the points $(0,-2)$ and $(6,4)$.

10. Prove that the point $(\sqrt{2},2)$ lies on the circle whose center is at the origin and which passes through the point $(-1,\sqrt{5})$.

11. Use the distance formula to determine whether or not the points listed are collinear. Sketch the points to check your answer.

    (a) $(4,-3)$, $(-5,4)$, and $(0,0)$

    (b) $(2,-3)$, $(-4,2)$, and $(-1,\frac{1}{3})$

    (c) $(3,2)$, $(-\frac{4}{3},\frac{5}{9})$, and $(6,3)$

12. Draw a cartesian coordinate system and shade the region(s) in which the point (x,y) can be found if the following is known.

    (a) $x > 0$ and $y < 0$ (e) $-1 \leq x < 0$ and $y \geq 0$

    (b) $x > 0$ or $y < 0$ (f) $-1 \leq x < 0$ or $y \geq 0$

    (c) $0 < x < 2$ and $2 < y < 3$ (g) $|x| \geq 2$ and $|y| \geq 1$

    (d) $0 < x < 2$ or $2 < y < 3$ (h) $|x| \geq 2$ or $|y| \geq 1$

13   GRAPHS OF FUNCTIONS

A coordinate system allows us to construct geometric representations of functions. With each number in the domain of a function there is associated a number in the range. This pair of numbers can be represented as a point in the plane.   For example, let f be the function determined by the equation $f(x) = x^2 - 1$.   This equation associates with the number 2 the number $f(2) = 3$.   Then the pair of numbers (2,3) may be plotted as a point in the cartesian plane. If this same procedure is followed for every number in the domain of f, the resulting collection of points forms the *graph* of the function f.

DEFINITION 13-1.   *The **graph** of a function f consists of all points $(x, f(x))$, where x is in the domain of f and $f(x)$ is the corresponding number in the range.*

EXAMPLE 13-1.   What is the graph of the function f whose domain is the set of integers {1,2,3,4}, whose range is the set of integers {4,5,6}, and whose rule of correspondence is stated by the equations $f(1) = 5$, $f(2) = 4, f(3) = 4$, and $f(4) = 6$?

Solution.   Since the domain consists of only four numbers, this function is easy to graph.   There are only four points of the form $(x, f(x))$, and they are (1,5), (2,4), (3,4), and (4,6).   These four points comprise the graph of f, which is shown in Fig. 13-1.

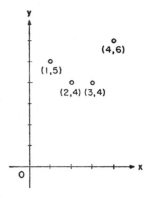

Figure 13-1

In many cases the domain of a function does not consist of merely a finite number of points, as was the case in Example 13-1.   For example, the function f determined by the equation $f(x) = x^2$ has for its domain the set of all real numbers. For each number of the domain there is a number in the range, and hence a point of the graph of f.   The graph of f therefore consists of an infinite number of points, and when a graph consists of an infinite number of points it is clearly impossible to plot them individually.   We take what appears to be a representative sample of the points on the graph and plot them.   We obtain the remaining points of the graph by joining those already plotted.

EXAMPLE 13-2.   Sketch the graph of the function f determined by the equation $f(x) = x^2$.

Solution. If $x = 2$, then $f(2) = 4$. Thus the point $(2,4)$ is on the graph of f. We can obtain a number of other points on the graph in the same way. The table for Fig. 13-2 gives the calculated points from which the graph of f shown in Fig. 13-2 is sketched.

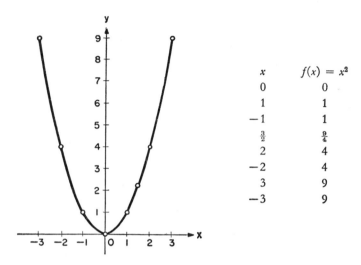

x	$f(x) = x^2$
0	0
1	1
-1	1
$\frac{3}{2}$	$\frac{9}{4}$
2	4
-2	4
3	9
-3	9

Figure 13-2

EXAMPLE 13-3. Sketch the graph of the function determined by the equation $f(x) = [x]$.

Solution. First, we make up a table showing a few points of the graph of this function, and then we plot these points. It is then an easy matter to convince yourself that Fig. 13-3 really does represent the graph of the greatest integer function.

In each of the examples given in this section, we have considered a graph as a picture of a given function. Many times it is useful to reverse the situation and use a graph to define a function. In order to construct the graph in Fig. 13-4, several measurements of the vapor pressure of helium at very low temperatures were taken and the appropriate points were plotted and joined by a curve. The pressure is measured in centimeters of mercury and the temperature in degrees on the absolute temperature scale. In addition to the measured values shown in the table, you can now use the graph to find vapor pressures corresponding to other temperatures.

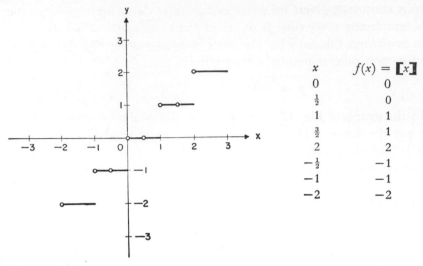

x	$f(x) = [\![x]\!]$
0	0
$\frac{1}{2}$	0
1	1
$\frac{3}{2}$	1
2	2
$-\frac{1}{2}$	-1
-1	-1
-2	-2

Figure 13-3

Once we obtain an experimental curve such as the one shown in Fig. 13-4, we often try to "fit a formula to it." We try to express the relation between the quantities in terms of an equation. This equation determines a function and the graph of this function should be the same, or very nearly the same, as the experimentally determined graph. A correctly chosen formula can help in determining values between and beyond measured ones. It is not at all difficult to find any number of functions determined by equations whose

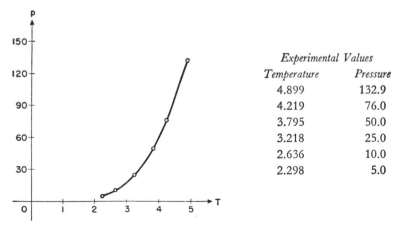

Experimental Values

Temperature	*Pressure*
4.899	132.9
4.219	76.0
3.795	50.0
3.218	25.0
2.636	10.0
2.298	5.0

Figure 13-4

graphs contain a given set of experimentally determined points; the problem facing a scientist is to select the right one. The physicists who presented the data for the table accompanying Fig. 13-4 chose the function determined by the equation

$$p = T^{2.208} \cdot 10^{1.217 - 3.024/T}.$$

In the graph of Fig. 13-4, the units of distance along the two axes are not the same. This difference was almost unavoidable in this case. Unless otherwise mentioned, however, the units of distance along the two axes will be the same throughout this book.

Problems 13

1. Graph the functions in the first problem of Problems 10 for positive integers n such that $1 \le n \le 5$.

2. Plot seven points of the graphs of the functions defined by the following equations and sketch what appears to be the graph.
   (a) $f(x) = x$ (d) $g(x) = |x|$
   (b) $f(x) = -3$ (e) $h(x) = 1 - x^2$
   (c) $F(x) = -3x + 1$ (f) $\phi(x) = 1/x$

3. Plot the graphs of the functions f and g determined by the equations $f(x) = -\frac{1}{2}(x - 1)$ and $g(x) = -x - 1$, using the same coordinate axes. From your figure, locate a point that lies on both the graph of f and the graph of g. Check your answer algebraically.

4. Plot five points of the graph of the function f if $f(x) = \sqrt{4 - x^2}$. Show that these points all lie on a semicircle with a radius of two units and with its center at the origin. Show that any point of the graph of f lies on this semicircle.

5. Let f be the function defined by the equation $f(x) = \sqrt{x}$ for values of x that satisfy the inequalities $0 \le x \le 4$. Graph this function as well as you can and try to determine the following numbers from your graph.
   (a) $\sqrt{1.5}$ (c) $2^{1/4}$
   (b) $\sqrt{\pi}$ (d) $\sqrt{5}/2$

6. If g is the function defined by the equation $g(x) = 2x^2 + 1$, what is the distance between the points on the graph of g that correspond to the values $x = 1$ and $x = 2$?

7. How are the graphs of the functions f, g, and h related if $f(x) = x^2$, $g(x) = x^2 + 3$, and $h(x) = x^2 - 2$?

8. Let h be the function defined by the equation $h(x) = x^2 + 2x - 1$. To construct the graph of h, draw the graphs of the two functions f and g that are defined by the equations $f(x) = x^2$ and $g(x) = 2x - 1$, and note that $h(x) = f(x) + g(x)$.

9. Let the function f be defined by the equation $f(x) = \sqrt{x^2 + 1}$. If the point (a,b) is on the graph of f, which of the following points are on the graph of f?

    (a) (b,a) (b) $(-a,b)$ (c) $(-a,-b)$

10. When a certain rocket has a velocity of v fps, it encounters an air pressure of p lb. For a certain fixed air density, it is found experimentally that $p = 6$ when $v = 100$, $p = 13$ when $v = 200$, $p = 23$ when $v = 300$, and $p = 38$ when $v = 400$. Sketch a graph of the associated function and estimate the value of p when $v = 350$.

14   GRAPHS OF EQUATIONS

We have used either the letter y or the symbol $f(x)$ to denote the number in the range of a function f that corresponds to the number x in the domain of f. The fact that y and $f(x)$ represent the same number is expressed by the equation $y = f(x)$. A point (a,b) is on the graph of the function f if and only if $b = f(a)$, that is, if and only if the equals sign is valid when x is replaced by a and y by b in the equation $y = f(x)$. The graph of the equation $y = f(x)$ consists of all points whose coordinates have this property. Clearly the graph of the equation $y = f(x)$ and the graph of the function f are identical. Later you will encounter graphs of equations that are not of the form $y = f(x)$. For example, the graph of the equation $x^2 + y^2 = 1$ consists of all points, such as $(1,0)$, $(-\sqrt{2}/2, \sqrt{2}/2)$, and so on, whose coordinates satisfy the given equation.

EXAMPLE 14-1. Let f be the function defined by the equation $f(x) = x^2 - 3x + 2$. Are the points $(1,0)$ and $(2,3)$ on the graph of the equation $y = f(x)$?

Solution. The equation $y = f(x)$ is $y = x^2 - 3x + 2$. The point $(1,0)$ is on the graph of this equation since $0 = 1 - 3 + 2$, while the point $(2,3)$ is not on the graph since $3 \neq 4 - 6 + 2$.

EXAMPLE 14-2. Graph the equation $y = |x| + x$.

Solution. We construct the table for Fig. 14-1 by choosing various values for x and calculating the corresponding values of y. Thus if $x = -1$, then $y = |-1| + (-1) = 0$, and so forth. We plot and join the resulting points to construct the graph shown.

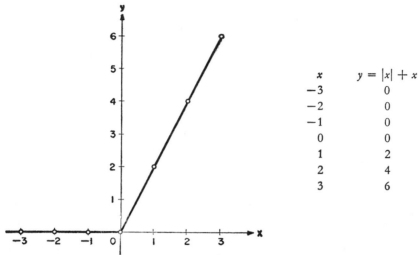

x	$y = |x| + x$
-3	0
-2	0
-1	0
0	0
1	2
2	4
3	6

Figure 14-1

A function consists of two sets of numbers (the domain and the range) and a rule of correspondence that associates a number of the range with each given number of the domain. It is convenient to have this correspondence determined by a simple formula that applies to all numbers in the domain of the function. There is no reason why a correspondence should be given by a *single* formula, however. We merely need a set of rules that assigns a number of the range to each number of the domain.

EXAMPLE 14-3. Let f be the function whose domain is the set of all real numbers and for which the correspondence is determined by the following set of rules:

(i)　　　　　　　If $x < 0$, then $f(x) = -2x$

(ii)　　　　　　If $x \geq 0$, then $f(x) = 3x$.

Find $f(3)$ and $f(-1)$ and sketch the graph of f.

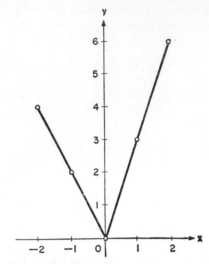

x	f(x)
−2	4
−1	2
0	0
1	3
2	6

Figure 14-2

Solution. The rule of correspondence for this function f is perfectly definite. It associates a number of the range of f with each number of the domain of f. When a number is chosen from the domain we merely have to notice whether it is a positive or a negative number and choose the appropriate expression for $f(x)$. Thus $f(3) = 3 \cdot 3 = 9$, and $f(-1) = (-2) \cdot (-1) = 2$. The graph is shown in Fig. 14-2.

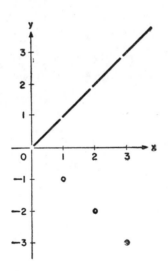

Figure 14-3

EXAMPLE 14-4. Let f be the function whose domain is the set of all positive numbers and for which the correspondence is determined by the following rules:

(i) $f(x) = x$ if x is not an integer and

(ii) $f(x) = -x$ if x is an integer.

Find $f(\frac{1}{2})$, $f(\pi)$, and $f(3)$ and sketch the graph of the equation $y = f(x)$.

Solution. To find $f(\frac{1}{2})$ and $f(\pi)$, we use Rule (i) since $\frac{1}{2}$ and π are not integers. Therefore $f(\frac{1}{2}) = \frac{1}{2}$ and $f(\pi) = \pi$. Since 3 is an integer, we use Rule (ii) and obtain $f(3) = -3$. The domain was specified as the set of *positive* numbers and therefore symbols such as $f(0)$ and $f(-\pi)$ have no meaning here. Figure 14-3 shows the graph of the equation $y = f(x)$.

Problems 14

1. Determine which of the following points lie on the graph of the equation $y = \sqrt{1 + x}$:

   $(3,2)$, $(8,-3)$, $(1,2)$, $(9,4)$.

2. Determine which of the following points lie on the graph of the equation $y = x^{3/2} - x$:

   $(1,0)$, $(-1,0)$, $(4,4)$, $(9,17)$.

3. Determine which of the following points lie on the graph of the equation $y = (x^{-1} + x)^{-1}$:

   $(1,1)$, $(2,\frac{5}{2})$, $(\frac{1}{2},\frac{2}{5})$, $(-1,\frac{1}{2})$.

4. Determine which of the following points lie on the graph of the equation

$$y = \left[\frac{2x^0}{x^2 + x^{1/2}} \right]^{-1/2} :$$

   $(4,3)$, $(-4,2\sqrt{2})$, $\left(2, 2 + \dfrac{1}{\sqrt[4]{2}}\right)$, $\left(\dfrac{1}{3}, \sqrt{\dfrac{1 + 3\sqrt{3}}{6}}\right)$.

5. Graph the following equations:
   (a) $y = |x| - x$ (d) $y = 2[x]$
   (b) $y = |2 - x|$ (e) $y = [2x]$
   (c) $y = 2 - |x|$ (f) $y = x - [x]$

6. Construct the graph of the equation $y = f(x)$ if $f(x)$ is given by:
   (a) $f(x) = x|x|$ (c) If $x < 0, f(x) = [2x]$
   (b) If $x < 0, f(x) = |x| + x$ If $x \geq 0, f(x) = 2[x]$
        If $x \geq 0, f(x) = |x| - x$ (d) $f(x) = |[x]|$

7. Compare the graphs of the equations $y = f(x)$ and $y = -f(x)$.

8. If the point (a,b) is on the graph of the equation $y = 3/x$, determine which of the following points are on the graph:

   (b,a), $(-a,b)$, $(-a,-b)$, $(a,-b)$, $(-b,-a)$.

9. If the point $(a,3)$ is on the graph of the equation $y = |x - 1| + 2$, what can you say about the number a?

10. Graph the equation $y = \sqrt{4 - x^2}$ and then use this graph to find the graph of the following equations.
    (a) $y = \frac{1}{2}\sqrt{4 - x^2}$ (c) $y = -\sqrt{4 - x^2}$
    (b) $y = 2\sqrt{4 - x^2}$

11. How are the graphs of the equations $y = f(x)$ and $y = |f(x)|$ related?

12. A resistor of 4 ohms is connected across the terminals of a 12 v battery. The number of amp I that will flow when the internal resistance of the battery is r ohms is given by the equation $I = 12/(4 + r)$. Graph this equation for numbers r that satisfy the inequalities $0 \le r \le 5$.

15   DIRECT VARIATION

Among the simplest types of functions are those determined by equations of the form $y = mx$, where m is a given number. Many applications of such functions are found in science: distance = rate × time (constant rate), work = force × distance (constant force), force = mass × acceleration (constant mass), energy = mass × c^2 (c^2 is a constant), and many others.

DEFINITION 15-1.   *To say that* **y is directly proportional to x** *or that* **y varies directly as x** *means that there is a number m such that y = mx for all numbers x.   The number m is called the* **constant of proportionality.**

> EXAMPLE 15-1.   Express y in terms of x if y is directly proportional to x and if $y = 2$ when $x = 3$.

> *Solution.*   We are told that y is directly proportional to x and therefore, from Definition 15-1, we know that $y = mx$, so the problem is to find the number m. If we substitute 3 for x and 2 for y in the equation $y = mx$, we find that $2 = 3m$, and hence $m = \frac{2}{3}$. It follows that the equation defining y is $y = \frac{2}{3}x$.

If f is a given function, we cannot assume that $f(2x)$ and $2f(x)$ are the same number for every number x. Nor is it generally true that $f(2 + 3)$ and $f(2) + f(3)$ are the same. We will now prove that both these statements are true for a function f that is defined by an equation of the form $f(x) = mx$.

THEOREM 15-1.   *If m is a given number and the function f is defined by the equation y = mx, then f(ax) = af(x) for any two numbers a and x.*

Proof.   Since $f(x) = mx$ we have

$$f(ax) = m(ax) = a(mx) = af(x).$$

Theorem 15-1 states that if $f(x) = mx$, then $f(ax) = af(x)$ for any two numbers a and x. Conversely, if f is a function such that $f(ax) = af(x)$, then we can show that f is defined by an equation of the form $f(x) = mx$ (indeed $m = f(1)$). If $y = mx$, then doubling, tripling, or halving x, doubles, triples, or halves y.

THEOREM 15-2. *If m is a given number and the function f is defined by the equation $f(x) = mx$, then $f(x_1 + x_2) = f(x_1) + f(x_2)$ for any two numbers x_1 and x_2.*

Proof. Since $f(x) = mx$ we have

$$f(x_1 + x_2) = m(x_1 + x_2) = mx_1 + mx_2 = f(x_1) + f(x_2).$$

No other function you are likely to encounter has the property described in Theorem 15-2.

Just because y increases when x increases does not mean that y is necessarily directly proportional to x. You may easily convince yourself that if $y = x^3 + x$, then y increases when x does; but y is not directly proportional to x. Nevertheless when a scientist knows only that two quantities are so related that one increases when the other does, he is likely to guess that one is directly proportional to the other because direct variation is such a simple relationship. He then tests the accuracy of his guess by performing experiments. For example, we can stretch a steel rod by subjecting it to a pulling force. By increasing the force, we can increase the stretch. It is then natural to guess that the amount of stretch is proportional to the pulling force, and experiments show that this guess is, for practical purposes, correct. (See Illustration 11-4.)

EXAMPLE 15-2. The velocity of a body falling from rest is directly proportional to the time it falls. If a body attains a speed of 48 feet per second after falling $1\frac{1}{2}$ seconds, how fast will it be falling 2 seconds later?

Solution. If the body reaches a velocity of v feet per second at the end of t seconds, then, by the assumption of direct proportionality, $v = mt$. Since $v = 48$ when $t = \frac{3}{2}$, we have $48 = 3m/2$ and hence $m = 32$. Therefore $v = 32t$ and from this equation we find $v = 112$ feet per second when $t = \frac{7}{2}$.

The terminology of direct variation is also associated with the function determined by the equation $y = mx^2$. In this case, *y is directly proportional to x^2, or y varies directly as x^2*. A common example of this type of variation is found in area formulas. The area A of a circle, for instance, is directly proportional to the square of its radius r. Thus $A = mr^2$. If we measure the radius in certain units (inches, yards, and so forth) and the area in square units of the same type (square inches, square yards, and the like), then the constant of proportionality is, of course, π. We also use the language of variation if y is a multiple of powers of x other than 1 or 2. For example, *y is directly proportional to $x^{1/2}$ or to the square root of x if $y = mx^{1/2}$*.

Problems 15

1. The point (2,3) is on the graph of the equation $y = f(x)$ and y is directly proportional to x. Find the formula for $f(x)$.

2. Let y be directly proportional to x, and let $y = f(x)$.
   (a) Show that $f(x_1)/f(x_2) = x_1/x_2$ for any two numbers x_1 and x_2 $(x_2 \neq 0)$.
   (b) Does $f(1/a) = 1/f(a)$?
   (c) Does $f(ab) = f(a)f(b)$?
   (d) Does $f(a + 1) = f(a) + 1$?
   (e) Does $f(x^2) = [f(x)]^2$?
   (f) Find the quotient $\dfrac{f(a + h) - f(a)}{h}$.

3. An automobile travels 115 miles in 2 hr and 40 min. Assuming constant velocity:
   (a) How far will it go in 3 hr?
   (b) How long will it take to make a trip of 200 miles?

4. If an automobile travels 1 mile at 30 mph and 1 mile at 40 mph, what is its average velocity?

5. If y varies directly as x^2 and $y = f(x)$, does $f(ax) = af(x)$?

6. The surface area of a sphere is directly proportional to the square of the radius. If a sphere of radius 3 in. has a surface area of 36π sq in., deduce the formula for the surface area of a sphere.

7. The amount of money a worker earns is directly proportional to the number of hours he works. What does the constant of proportionality represent in this case? If a man earns $96 in a 40 hr work week, how long would he have to work to earn $200?

8. A body on the surface of the earth is acted on by a gravitational force that is directly proportional to its mass. If a mass of 1 g encounters a force of 980 dynes, what is the formula relating gravitational force and mass?

9. The number of gallons of gasoline used by an automobile traveling at constant speed is directly proportional to the number of miles traveled, while the number of miles traveled is in turn directly proportional to the number of hours of driving. Can you conclude that the number of gallons of gasoline used is directly proportional to the time driven?

10. If u is directly proportional to x and v is directly proportional to x, what can you say about:

  (a) uv?　　　　　(b) u/v?　　　　　(c) $u + v$?

11. The total pressure exerted by the wind on the wall of a house is directly proportional to the square of the velocity of the wind. The pressure is 250 lb when the velocity of the wind is 10 mph. What will be the pressure on the wall when the wind velocity is 40 mph?

12. Kepler's third law states that the time it takes a planet to revolve about the sun varies directly as the $\frac{3}{2}$ power of the maximum radius of its orbit. Using 93 million miles as the maximum radius of the Earth's orbit and 142 million miles as the maximum radius of Mars' orbit, how many days does it take Mars to make one revolution about the sun?

16　LINEAR FUNCTIONS

A function defined by an equation $y = mx + b$, where m and b are given numbers, is called a **linear function.** In the last section, we considered functions defined by equations of the form $y = mx$, which are simply linear functions for which $b = 0$. Linear functions are so named because the graph of a linear function is a straight line. The proof of this assertion may be easier to follow if we first consider an example.

EXAMPLE 16-1. Suppose the function f is defined by the equation $y = 2x - 3$. Choose any three points on the graph of f and show that they lie on a line.

Solution. We were asked to choose *any* three points, so let us arbitrarily set $x = 0$, $x = 1$, and $x = 2$ to find the three points $P_1\,(0, -3)$,

$P_2\,(1,-1)$, and $P_3(2,1)$ on the graph of f (see Fig. 16-1). The points will lie on a line if the distance $\overline{P_1P_3}$ is equal to the sum of the distances $\overline{P_1P_2}$ and $\overline{P_2P_3}$. (The shortest path between 2 points is a straight line; see Inequality 12-3.)   Now

$$\overline{P_1P_3} = \sqrt{2^2 + 4^2} = \sqrt{20} = 2\sqrt{5},$$
$$\overline{P_1P_2} = \sqrt{1^2 + 2^2} = \sqrt{5},$$
$$\overline{P_2P_3} = \sqrt{1^2 + 2^2} = \sqrt{5},$$
$$\text{and therefore } \overline{P_1P_3} = \overline{P_1P_2} + \overline{P_2P_3}.$$

We shall now apply the same argument to the general linear function.

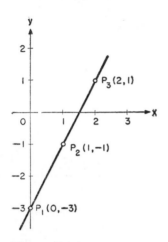

Figure 16-1

THEOREM 16-1.   *The graph of a linear function f is a straight line.*

Proof.   Since f is a linear function, it is defined by an equation of the form $y = mx + b$. We have to show that any three points on the graph of f lie on a line, so suppose that x_1, x_2, and x_3 are three numbers such that $x_1 < x_2 < x_3$ and consider the corresponding three points on the graph of f. These three points are $P_1(x_1, mx_1 + b)$, $P_2(x_2, mx_2 + b)$, and $P_3(x_3, mx_3 + b)$ (see Fig. 16-2). These points lie on a straight line if the distance $\overline{P_1P_3}$ is equal to the

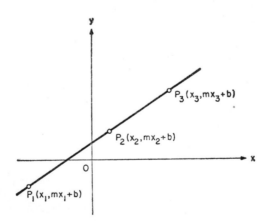

Figure 16-2

sum of the distances $\overline{P_1P_2}$ and $\overline{P_2P_3}$. Now

$$
\begin{aligned}
\overline{P_1P_3} &= \sqrt{(x_3 - x_1)^2 + [(mx_3 + b) - (mx_1 + b)]^2} \\
&= \sqrt{(x_3 - x_1)^2 + m^2(x_3 - x_1)^2} \\
&= \sqrt{(x_3 - x_1)^2(1 + m^2)} \\
&= \sqrt{(x_3 - x_1)^2}\, \sqrt{1 + m^2}.
\end{aligned}
$$

Since $x_3 > x_1$, $x_3 - x_1$ is positive, and hence $\sqrt{(x_3 - x_1)^2} = x_3 - x_1$. We therefore have

$$
\overline{P_1P_3} = (x_3 - x_1)\, \sqrt{1 + m^2}.
$$

In exactly the same way we could calculate

$$
\overline{P_1P_2} = (x_2 - x_1)\, \sqrt{1 + m^2}, \text{ and}
$$

$$
\overline{P_2P_3} = (x_3 - x_2)\, \sqrt{1 + m^2}.
$$

We can therefore write

$$
\begin{aligned}
\overline{P_1P_2} + \overline{P_2P_3} &= (x_2 - x_1)\, \sqrt{1 + m^2} + (x_3 - x_2)\, \sqrt{1 + m^2} \\
&= [(x_2 - x_1) + (x_3 - x_2)]\, \sqrt{1 + m^2} \\
&= (x_3 - x_1)\, \sqrt{1 + m^2} = \overline{P_1P_3},
\end{aligned}
$$

and the theorem is proved.

EXAMPLE 16-2.   Sketch the graph of the equation $y = 3x - 5$.

Solution.   The graph in question is a straight line and therefore it is only necessary to find two points on the graph in order to draw it. Two points are (2,1) and (1,−2), and the graph is shown in Fig. 16-3.

EXAMPLE 16-3.   What can be said about a linear function f if $f(3) = f(1) + f(2)$?

Solution.   Since f is a *linear function*, it must be defined by an equation of the form $y = mx + b$. Therefore $f(3) = 3m + b$, $f(1) = m + b$, and $f(2) = 2m + b$. The equation $f(3) = f(1) + f(2)$ is valid only if $3m + b = (m + b) + (2m + b)$; that is, if $3m + b = 3m + 2b$. But this equation means that $b = 2b$, and hence $b = 0$. Therefore the function f is defined by an equation of the form $y = mx$.

EXAMPLE 16-4. If the temperature of a body is C degrees centigrade and if the corresponding Fahrenheit temperature is denoted by F, then the relation between these numbers is a linear one. Find it.

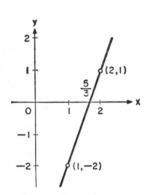

Figure 16-3

Solution. Since we are given that the relation is *linear*, we know that $F = mC + b$, so our problem is to determine the numbers m and b. Now $F = 32$ when $C = 0$, and $F = 212$ when $C = 100$; and therefore $32 = b$ and $212 = 100m + b$. Thus $212 = 100m + 32$ and we see that $m = \frac{9}{5}$. The formula connecting these two units of temperature measurement is therefore $F = \frac{9}{5} C + 32$.

The numbers (if any) in the domain of a function f that satisfy the equation $f(x) = 0$ are called the **zeros of the function.** To find the zeros of the linear function defined by the equation $f(x) = mx + b$ we must solve the equation $mx + b = 0$, so such equations are called **linear equations.** A linear function for which $m \neq 0$ has only one zero, $x = -b/m$. From the geometric viewpoint, a zero of a function is the x-coordinate of a point at which the graph of the function meets the x-axis.

EXAMPLE 16-5. Find the zeros of the function f defined by the equation $f(x) = 3x - 5$.

Solution. The solution of the equation $f(x) = 3x - 5 = 0$ is $x = \frac{5}{3}$ and this number is the only zero of f (see the graph of f in Fig. 16-3).

Problems 16

1. The graph of a linear function f contains the points $(1,1)$ and $(2,4)$. What is the formula for $f(x)$?

2. What can we say about a linear function f if we know that:
    (a) $2f(x) = f(2x)$ for every number x?
    (b) $f(x + 1) = f(x) + 1$ for every number x?
    (c) $f(2x + 1) = 2f(x) + 1$ for every number x?
    (d) $f(3) = 2$?
    (e) $f(3) = 2$ and $f(-1) = 1$?
    (f) $f(2) = -4$ and $f(-1) = -f(2)$?

3. Let f be a linear function.
    (a) Is the function g defined by $g(t) = f(6t + 1)$ linear?
    (b) Find $\dfrac{f(x + h) - f(x)}{h}$, $h \neq 0$.

4. Graph the function f if:
    (a) $f(x) = -2x + 3$ (c) $f(x) = .01x + .2$
    (b) $f(x) = 1 - 5x$

5. Find the zeros of f.
    (a) $f(x) = 1 - 4x$ (c) $f(x) = 2(x - 1) + 5$
    (b) $f(x) = 6x + \frac{1}{2}$ (d) $3f(x) - 17 = 2x - 4$

6. Two linear functions, f and g, are determined by the equations $f(x) = 2x + 3$ and $g(x) = \frac{1}{2}(x + 3)$. Find the point at which their graphs intersect.

7. A projectile fired straight upward attains a velocity of v fps after t sec of flight, and the relation between the numbers v and t is a linear one. If the projectile is fired at a velocity of 100 fps and reaches a velocity of 36 fps after 2 sec of flight, find the formula for v in terms of t. At what time does the projectile reach its highest point?

8. If the temperature h ft above the surface of the earth is $T°$, then for practical purposes the associated function can be assumed to be linear. Suppose the temperature on the surface of the earth is 70° and the temperature at 3000 ft is 61°. What is the temperature at 6000 ft?

9. Graph the two equations $y = 2x + 3$ and $y = 2x - 2$. Can you convince yourself that the resulting two lines are parallel?

10. If the total accumulation (principal + interest) of an investment of $50 at $5\frac{1}{2}\%$ simple interest at the end of t years is A dollars, then the associated function is linear. Find a formula for A and determine how long it will take to double the investment.

11. If the quantity of heat in calories required to change 1 g of solid ice at 0° centigrade to water at $T°$ centigrade is denoted by Q, then the associated function is linear when $0 \leq T \leq 100$. If $Q = 90$ when $T = 10$, and $Q = 150$ when $T = 70$, what is the quantity of heat required to transform the ice into 0° water?

17   INVERSE VARIATION

In Section 15 we noted that direct variation is a simple relationship which describes many situations in which one quantity increases when another quantity does.   If two quantities are so related that one decreases when the other increases, we might guess that they are connected by a linear relationship $y = mx + b$, where m is a negative number.   For example, if $y = -x + 5$, then y decreases when x increases.

There are many practical situations, however, in which an increase in one quantity leads to a decrease in the other that are not described by a linear relationship.   The centrifugal force on an automobile rounding a curve at a given speed can be expressed in terms of the radius of the curve.   An increase in the radius of the curve produces a decrease in the centrifugal force, but the relationship is not linear. If air in a cylinder is kept at a constant temperature and is compressed by a piston, the air pressure increases as the volume decreases, but again the relationship is not linear.   Both of these examples, and many others, can be described in terms of inverse variation, which we shall now consider in its mathematical context.

DEFINITION 17-1.   *To say that **y is inversely proportional to** x or that **y varies inversely as** x means that there is a number k such that $y = k/x$ for all numbers x (except $x = 0$).*

EXAMPLE 17-1.   Express y in terms of x if y is inversely proportional to x and $y = 2$ when $x = 3$.

Solution.   Since we are told that y is inversely proportional to x, we know from Definition 17-1 that $y = k/x$.   Our problem will be solved when we determine the number k.   If we substitute 3 for x and 2 for y in the equation $y = k/x$, we find $2 = k/3$ and hence $k = 6$.   It follows that the equation defining y is $y = 6/x$.

EXAMPLE 17-2.   The electrical resistance of a wire of given length and material is inversely proportional to its cross-sectional area.   The resistance in a circuit composed of wire that has a cross section of 82 sq mm is 210 ohms.   What would the resistance have been if the wire had a cross section of 70 sq mm?

Solution. **Let** R denote the resistance in ohms corresponding to wire with a cross-sectional area of A sq mm. Then $R = k/A$. Now $R = 210$ when $A = 82$, so $210 = k/82$ and hence $k = 82 \cdot 210$. The equation determining R is therefore $R = 82 \cdot 210/A$. It is now clear that $R = 82 \cdot 210/70 = 246$ when $A = 70$.

EXAMPLE 17-3. Sketch the graph of the equation $y = f(x)$, where $f(x) = 2/x$.

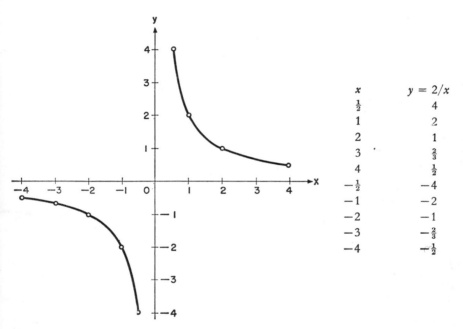

x	$y = 2/x$
$\frac{1}{2}$	4
1	2
2	1
3	$\frac{2}{3}$
4	$\frac{1}{2}$
$-\frac{1}{2}$	-4
-1	-2
-2	-1
-3	$-\frac{2}{3}$
-4	$-\frac{1}{2}$

Figure 17-1

Solution. The graph is shown in Fig. 17-1 and is an example of an *equilateral hyperbola.* Note the appearance of the graph when x is near 0 (x cannot *be* 0, since $\frac{2}{0}$ is not defined). What can you say about $|f(x)|$ when $|x|$ is very large?

The terminology of inverse variation is also applied to functions that are determined by equations of the type $y = k/x^p$. Thus if $y = k/x^2$ we say that y is inversely proportional to the square of x; if $y = k/\sqrt[3]{x}$ we say that y is inversely proportional to the cube root of x, and so on.

EXAMPLE 17-4.   Sketch the graph of the equation $y = 1/x^2$.

Solution.   The graph is shown in Fig. 17-2.

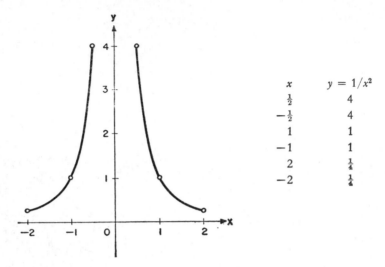

x	$y = 1/x^2$
$\frac{1}{2}$	4
$-\frac{1}{2}$	4
1	1
-1	1
2	$\frac{1}{4}$
-2	$\frac{1}{4}$

Figure 17-2

Problems 17

1. If y is inversely proportional to x and the graph of the equation $y = f(x)$ contains the point $(1,5)$, what is the formula that defines $f(x)$?

2. If y is inversely proportional to x and if $y = f(x)$:
   (a) Show that $f(x_1)/f(x_2) = x_2/x_1$ (assume that neither x_1 nor x_2 is 0).
   (b) Does $f(1/a) = 1/f(a)$?
   (c) Does $f(x_1 + x_2) = f(x_1) + f(x_2)$?

3. If y is inversely proportional to x^3 and if the graph of the equation $y = f(x)$ contains the point $(2,3)$, find the formula for $f(x)$.

4. The current in a certain circuit varies inversely as the resistance in the circuit. If the current is 10 amp when the resistance is 24 ohms, what will the current be when the resistance is increased to 30 ohms? What values of the resistance will insure that the current is less than 1 amp?

5. The force of attraction of two oppositely charged bodies is inversely proportional to the square of the distance between them. If the two bodies are 10 cm apart, the attractive force is 40 dynes. How far apart should the bodies be moved to make the force of attraction 16 dynes? What is the attractive force when they are 1 m apart?

6. The number of oscillations per sec of a pendulum varies inversely as the square root of its length. If a pendulum 8 ft long makes 1 oscillation every 3 sec (that is, $\frac{1}{3}$ oscillation per sec) what length pendulum will make 1 complete oscillation per sec?

7. If y varies inversely as x, show that $1/y$ varies directly as x.

8. If P denotes the amount of work required to bring a unit electrical charge from a great distance to within r cm of a certain charged body, then P is inversely proportional to r. If a certain amount of work is required to bring the charge to within 10 cm of the body, how close could the charge be brought if twice as much work were expended?

9. A light on a lamp post h ft high is placed on top of a wall 6 ft high. A man 6 ft tall stands 4 ft from the base of the wall. Show that the length of his shadow is inversely proportional to h, and calculate h if his shadow is 12 ft long.

Review Problems, Chapter Two

You should be able to answer the following questions without referring back to the text.

1. Let f be a function whose domain is the set of all real numbers. Which of the following statements are surely true?
   (a) $f(3 - 2) = f(3) - f(2)$
   (b) $f(3 - 2) = f(1)$
   (c) $f(\sqrt{2}) = \sqrt{f(2)}$
   (d) $f(|-3|) = f(3)$
   (e) $f(2) \cdot f(3) = f(6)$

2. The graph of a function f is shown in Fig. II-1.
   (a) What is the domain of f?
   (b) What is the range of f?
   (c) Find $f(2)$ and $f(\pi)$
   (d) If $f(x) = 2$, what is x?

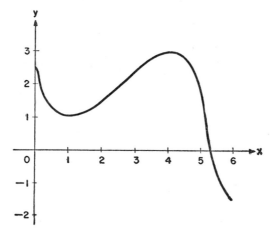

Figure II-1

3. Let x be a number such that $|x| < 1$ and y be a number such that $|y| < 2$. What can you say about the location of the point (x,y)?

4. The graph of a linear function f contains the points $(0,1)$ and $(2,5)$. Find a formula that determines f.

5. The perimeter of a Norman window (rectangle surmounted by a semi-circle) is 240 in. The vertical side of the window is h in. Find a formula that expresses the area A in sq in. in terms of h.

6. Use the graphs of the equations $y = x$ and $y = 1/x$ to sketch the graph of the equation $y = x + (1/x)$.

7. Sketch all points (x,y) for which $y = 3x + 1$ and $|y| < 2$.

8. If u is directly proportional to x and v is inversely proportional to x, what can you say about the product uv.

9. If y is directly proportional to x, is x directly proportional to y? If z is inversely proportional to x, is x inversely proportional to z?

10. What are the zeros of the function defined by the equation $y = |x - 1| - 2$?

11. Define the function F as follows: With the page number of each of the first 10 pages of this book, associate the number of letters in the first complete word in the text on the page. What is the domain of this function? What is its range? Plot its graph.

12. If x is a real number and if P denotes the corresponding point on the graph of the equation $y = x^2$, find an expression for the distance d between the origin and the point P.

13. Denote by $f(i)$ the length in ft of an object that is i in. long. What is the relation between the numbers i and $f(i)$?

Miscellaneous Problems, Chapter Two

These exercises are designed to test your ability to apply your understanding of this chapter to somewhat more difficult problems.

1. What can you say about the location of the point (x,y) if you know that $x < y$?

2. If a number of electrical resistances are connected in parallel, then the reciprocal of the resistance of the entire circuit is the sum of the reciprocals of the individual resistances. If resistances of 5, 10, and x ohms are connected in parallel, find a formula for the resulting resistance R. Sketch a graph of the equation for $x > 0$. What can you say about R if x is a very small number? A very large number?

3. At a temperature of $0°$, the length of an iron bar is L_0 in., and at a temperature of $t°$ its length is L in.   If the ratio of the change in length of the bar to its original length is directly proportional to the temperature t, what is the formula for L?

4. A man is in a boat 6 miles from the nearest point on a straight shore, and he wants to reach a point 12 miles up the shore.   He can row 4 mph and walk 5 mph.   If he rows straight to a point on the shore x miles from the nearest point and then walks the rest of the way to his destination, it will take t hr.   Express t in terms of x.

5. The points $(1,-2)$, $(x,2)$, and $(5,6)$ lie on a line.   Use the distance formula to find x.

6. Graph the equation $y = x + |x - 1| + |x - 2|$.

7. The graphs of two functions f and g are shown in Fig. II-2.   Solve the following equations graphically.
   (a) $g(x) = f(2)$
   (b) $f(x) = g(3)$

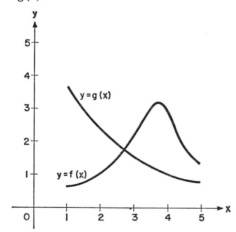

Figure II-2

8. Instead of defining both direct and inverse variation, it would be more economical to say that the statement "y varies as x^p" means that there is a number k such that $y = kx^p$.
   (a) If y varies as x^p and y is directly proportional to x, what is the value of p?
   (b) If y varies as x^p and y is inversely proportional to x, what is the value of p?
   (c) If y varies as x^p and y is inversely proportional to the cube root of x, what is the value of p?
   (d) If y varies as x^p and $p < 0$, then y varies inversely as what?

9. A baseball club sells tickets at $1 apiece if they are purchased in lots of 5 or less. If a person buys 6 tickets, the price per ticket is 95¢, if he buys 7, the price per ticket is 90¢, and so on, the price per ticket being reduced by 5¢ as the number of tickets purchased increases until the price per ticket reaches 75¢. From this point on, all tickets cost 75¢ each. If x tickets cost d dollars, plot the graph showing the relation between x and d.

10. Let $f(x) = |x|$ and $g(x) = [x]$. Find the numbers (if any) for which $f[g(x)] = g[f(x)]$.

EXPONENTIAL AND LOGARITHMIC FUNCTIONS

Under favorable conditions, a single cell of the bacterium *Escherichia coli* will divide into two about once every 20 minutes. If a plate contains 3000 of the organisms at a certain time, we can expect to find $2 \cdot 3000$ organisms if we inspect the plate 20 minutes later, $2 \cdot (2 \cdot 3000) = 3000 \cdot 2^2$ organisms 40 minutes later, $2 \cdot (3000 \cdot 2^2) = 3000 \cdot 2^3$ organisms 60 minutes later, and so on. If t represents the number of 20-minute periods after our initial observation, the equation $N = 3000 \cdot 2^t$ gives the number N of bacteria present at the end of t periods. The number of bacteria at time t is given by the number originally present times a factor, 2^t, in which t appears as an exponent. Equations of the form $N = kb^t$ describe many kinds of growth—dollars invested at compound interest, charges on an electrical condenser, grams of a decaying radioactive substance, and so forth.

The function f that is defined by the equation $f(t) = 2^t$ is called an *exponential function*.   Such functions, and the closely related *logarithmic functions*, form the subject of this chapter.

18   EXPONENTIAL FUNCTIONS AND THEIR GRAPHS

Suppose that a function f is defined by the equation $f(x) = 2^x$. Whenever a function is defined in terms of a formula, we assume that the domain of the function consists of all the numbers to which the formula may be applied.   In the present case, then, the domain of f consists of all the numbers that can be used as exponents of 2. Therefore the domain includes all the rational numbers, for we saw in Chapter One that $f(4) = 2^4 = 16, f(-3) = 2^{-3} = \frac{1}{8}, f(\frac{1}{2}) = 2^{1/2} = \sqrt{2},$ $f(0) = 2^0 = 1, f(1.41) = 2^{1.41} = (\sqrt[100]{2})^{141}$, and so on.   But irrational numbers, such as π and $\sqrt{2}$, are not to be considered in the domain

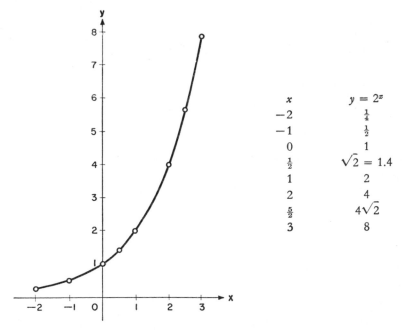

x	$y = 2^x$
-2	$\frac{1}{4}$
-1	$\frac{1}{2}$
0	1
$\frac{1}{2}$	$\sqrt{2} = 1.4$
1	2
2	4
$\frac{5}{2}$	$4\sqrt{2}$
3	8

Figure 18-1

of f until we can reach an agreement about the value of such symbols as 2^π and $2^{\sqrt{2}}$.

A detailed discussion of irrational exponents is wholly out of place here. Instead, we shall be content to state a few of the pertinent facts about such exponents. If b is a positive number and if x is any real number, then a positive real number can be assigned to the symbol b^x in such a way that all the laws of exponents remain valid. In particular, $b^x \cdot b^y = b^{x+y}$, $(b^x)^y = b^{xy}$, and $b^{-x} = 1/b^x$.

To construct the graph of an exponential function (for example, the graph of the equation $y = 2^x$), we make a table of values as usual and plot the points we obtain. If we plot enough points, there will seem to be just one "natural" way we can join them to form a curve. Exponents are defined in such a way as to make this curve the graph of the equation $y = 2^x$. We may use the graph to find the value of a number like $2^{\sqrt{3}}$. We see from Fig. 18-1 that $2^{\sqrt{3}} = 3.3$ (approximately).

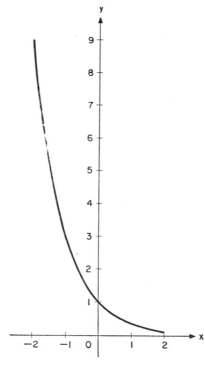

Definition 18-1. *If b is a positive number and f is the function defined by the equation $f(x) = b^x$, then f is called an* **exponential function.** *The number b is called the* **base** *of the exponential function f.*

Figure 18-2

If $b > 1$, the graph of the exponential function with base b looks very much like the graph of Fig. 18-1. Note that for $x < 0$, $b^x < 1$, and for $x > 0$, $b^x > 1$. If $x_1 < x_2$, then $b^{x_1} < b^{x_2}$.

If $b < 1$, the graph of the equation $y = b^x$ will have a different appearance.   A typical example is the case in which $b = \frac{1}{3}$.   The graph of the equation $y = (\frac{1}{3})^x$ is shown in Fig. 18-2.   Let g be the function defined by the equation $g(x) = (\frac{1}{3})^x$.   Then for $x < 0$, $g(x) > 1$; $g(0) = 1$; and for $x > 0$, $g(x) < 1$.   Further, whenever $x_1 < x_2$, then $g(x_1) > g(x_2)$.

Since $(\frac{1}{3})^x = 3^{-x}$, we can also say that the graph of Fig. 18-2 is typical of the graph of an equation of the form $y = b^{-x}$, where $b > 1$.

All exponential functions possess an important property that results from the laws of exponents.

THEOREM 18-1.   *If f is an exponential function, then*

$$f(x_1 + x_2) = f(x_1) \cdot f(x_2)$$

for any two real numbers x_1 and x_2.

Proof.   By hypothesis, $f(x) = b^x$ for some positive number b.   Hence

$$f(x_1 + x_2) = b^{x_1 + x_2} = b^{x_1} \cdot b^{x_2} = f(x_1) \cdot f(x_2).$$

The exponential function is the only function you are likely to encounter that has this property.

EXAMPLE 18-1.   The graph of an exponential function f contains the point (2,9).   What is the base of f?

Solution.   Since f is an exponential function, $f(x) = b^x$, where b is a positive number.   We are given $f(2) = 9$, and hence $b^2 = 9$.   It follows that $b = 3$.

EXAMPLE 18-2.   A certain radioactive salt decays at such a rate that at the end of a year there is only $\frac{500}{501}$ times as much as there was at the beginning of the year.   If there are 50 milligrams of the salt at a certain time, how much will be left t years later?

Solution.   Let $m(t)$ be the number of milligrams at the end of t years.   Then $m(0) = 50$, $m(1) = (\frac{500}{501})50$, $m(2) = (\frac{500}{501})(\frac{500}{501})50 = (\frac{500}{501})^2 50$, and so on.   It is then clear that $m(t) = (\frac{500}{501})^t 50$.   Thus $m(t) = 50b^t$ with $b = \frac{500}{501}$.

Problems 18

1. Why is the base b in Definition 18-1 restricted to *positive* numbers?

2. Discuss the exponential function if the base is 1.

3. From the graph of $y = 2^x$ shown in Fig. 18-1, find approximate values for the following numbers:

    (a) $2^{\sqrt{2}}$ (c) $2^{\pi/2}$ (e) $2^{1.7}$

    (b) $2^{\sqrt{3.5}}$ (d) $2^{7/9}$ (f) $\sqrt[4]{2}$

4. Sketch the graph of the equation $y = 3^x$ and use it to find approximate values for the following numbers:

    (a) $3^{\sqrt{2}}$ (c) 3^{π} (e) $3^{4/5}$

    (b) $3^{\sqrt{3}}$ (d) $3^{.91}$ (f) $\sqrt[4]{3}$

5. Sketch the graph of the equation $y = -2^x$. Describe the graph of $y = -b^x$ in terms of the graph of $y = b^x$.

6. From the graph of $y = 2^x$ (Fig. 18-1), find the approximate values of x when $y = 2$, $y = 5$, $y = .5$. Can you find an x such that $y = -2$?

7. Draw approximate graphs of the following equations.

    (a) $y = \pi^x$ (b) $y = (\sqrt{2})^x$

8. The gas in a balloon is escaping at such a rate that at the end of any min the volume of the balloon is .6 of what it was at the beginning of the min. If the volume of the balloon is 3000 cu ft at 1 P.M., find a formula for the volume of the balloon t min after 1 P.M. What is the volume of the balloon at 1:05 P.M.?

9. Radium A with an at. wt 214 undergoes radioactive decay at such a rate that at the end of any min there is only .8 as much as there was at the beginning of the min. Write a formula giving the amount that is left from N_0 grams after t min of disintegration.

10. The **half life period** of a radioactive substance is the time required for one half of the active material present at any time to decay. Sketch a graph of the function obtained in Problem 9, and find the approximate half life period of Radium A.

19 DEFINITION OF THE LOGARITHM

Figures 18-1 and 18-2 show the two possible forms of the graph of the equation $y = b^x$, where b is a positive number not equal to 1. In either case, a horizontal line through a given point on the positive y-axis will intersect the graph at exactly one point. Hence *if N is a given positive number and b is a given base, there is just one solution to the equation $N = b^x$.* It is the x-coordinate of the point of intersection of the graph with a horizontal line through N. The equation

$N = b^x$ can be solved by inspection for a few special values of b and N; for example, the equation $8 = 2^x$ has the solution $x = 3$. Most exponential equations are not this easy to solve. To find that $x = .3010$ is the solution to the equation $2 = 10^x$, we must use tables, which we shall study later.

The exponent that satisfies the equation $b^x = N$ is called the **logarithm of N to the base b,** and we write $x = \log_b N$. We state this definition more formally as follows.

DEFINITION 19-1.   *The equation $\log_b N = x$ is equivalent to the equation $b^x = N$.*

We always assume that *the base b is a positive number different from 1.* Since $b^x > 0$ for any real number x, the equation $b^x = N$ does not have a solution when $N \leq 0$. Thus, *neither the logarithm of zero nor the logarithm of any negative number is defined.*

EXAMPLE 19-1.   Find $\log_2 8$ and $\log_{10} 2$.

Solution. According to Definition 19-1, we must solve the equations $2^x = 8$ and $10^x = 2$. The solutions to both these equations are found in the first paragraph of this section; and hence $\log_2 8 = 3$, and $\log_{10} 2 = .3010$.

EXAMPLE 19-2.   If $\log_3 N = 2$, find N.

Solution. According to Definition 19-1, the equation $\log_3 N = 2$ is equivalent to the equation $3^2 = N$. Hence $N = 9$.

EXAMPLE 19-3.   Find $\log_9 \left(\frac{1}{27}\right)$.

Solution. The desired number satisfies the equation $9^x = \frac{1}{27}$. Since $9 = 3^2$ and $\frac{1}{27} = 3^{-3}$, this last equation may be written $3^{2x} = 3^{-3}$. Therefore $2x = -3$, so $x = -\frac{3}{2}$.

EXAMPLE 19-4.   Find the base b for which $\log_b 16 = \log_6 36$.

Solution. According to Definition 19-1, the number $\log_6 36$ is the solution to the equation $6^x = 36$, and hence $\log_6 36 = 2$. The given equation is therefore $\log_b 16 = 2$. But this equation is equivalent to the equation $b^2 = 16$, and hence $b = 4$ or $b = -4$. Since only a positive number can be a base, $b = 4$.

Since we have defined the number $\log_b N$ as the solution to the equation $b^x = N$, we can replace x by $\log_b N$ in this equation to obtain

19-1
$$b^{\log_b N} = N.$$

This relation, which is valid for any base b and any positive number N, has many uses, and you should be sure that you understand it.

EXAMPLE 19-5.   If a is a positive number and x is any number, express a and a^x as powers of 10.

Solution.   According to Equation 19-1, we have $a = 10^{\log_{10} a}$, and therefore $a^x = 10^{(\log_{10} a)x}$.

It should not be difficult for you to use the definition of a logarithm to show that the following equation is true for any base b.

19-2
$$\log_b b = 1$$

Problems 19

1. Write the following equations in logarithmic form:
   (a) $3^4 = 81$ (b) $10^0 = 1$ (c) $M^k = 5$

2. Find the number x for which the following equations are true:
   (a) $\log_5 x = 3$ (d) $\log_9 3 = x$
   (b) $\log_8 x = \frac{2}{3}$ (e) $\log_x 16 = 4$
   (c) $\log_5 25 = x$ (f) $\log_x 10 = 3$

3. What can you say about the number x if:
   (a) $\log_b x = 0$ (c) $\log_x x = 1$
   (b) $\log_x 1 = 0$ (d) $x^{\log_x 5} = 5$

4. Use the graph of $y = 2^x$ shown in Fig. 18-1 to estimate the values of the following:
   (a) $\log_2 3$ (b) $\log_2 6$ (c) $\log_2 .75$

5. Why are logarithmic bases never 1?

6. If $\log_b x = 2$, $\log_{1/b} x = $?

7. If $\log_b x = 2$, $\log_b (1/x) = $?

8. Prove that $\log_{1/b} x = \log_b (1/x)$.

9. Solve for x.
  (a) $2^{\log_2 x} = 5$ (c) $5^{\log_5 7} = 7$
  (b) $3^{\log_3 5} = x$ (d) $x^{\log_7 9} = 9$

10. Solve for x.
  (a) $\log_5 5^3 = x$ (c) $\log_5 x^7 = 7$
  (b) $\log_5 5^x = 3$ (d) $\log_x 5^7 = 7$

11. Show that for every real number x, $5^x = 10^{x \log_{10} 5}$.

12. Show that for any base b, $\log_b b^p = p$. (Note that this equation is a generalization of Equation 19-2).

20 FUNDAMENTAL PROPERTIES OF LOGARITHMS

There are two basic relations involving logarithms that can be derived from the laws of exponents. We state them here in the following two theorems.

THEOREM 20-1. *If M and N are positive numbers and b is any base, then,*

20-1 $log_b M \cdot N = log_b M + log_b N.$

Proof. In accordance with Formula 19-1, we have $M = b^{\log_b M}$ and $N = b^{\log_b N}$. Therefore

$$M \cdot N = b^{\log_b M} b^{\log_b N} = b^{(\log_b M + \log_b N)}.$$

This last equation means that the number $x = \log_b M + \log_b N$ satisfies the equation $b^x = M \cdot N$, and hence (Definition 19-1), $\log_b M \cdot N = \log_b M + \log_b N$.

THEOREM 20-2. *If N is a positive number, p is any real number, and b is any base, then*

20-2 $log_b N^p = p \, log_b N.$

Proof. Since $N = b^{\log_b N}$ we have

$$N^p = (b^{\log_b N})^p = b^{p \log_b N}.$$

The number $x = p \log_b N$ therefore satisfies the equation $b^x = N^p$ and so (Definition 19-1) $\log_b N^p = p \log_b N$.

EXAMPLE 20-1. If $\log_b 2 = .69$ and $\log_b 3 = 1.10$, find $\log_b 6$ and $\log_b 8$.

Solution. According to Theorem 20-1,

$$\log_b 6 = \log_b 2 + \log_b 3 = .69 + 1.10 = 1.79.$$

According to Theorem 20-2,

$$\log_b 8 = \log_b 2^3 = 3 \log_b 2 = 3(.69) = 2.07.$$

EXAMPLE 20-2.   Using the information given in Example 20-1, find $\log_b (1/\sqrt{3})$ and $\log_b (\sqrt[3]{16})$.

Solution. According to Theorem 20-2,

$$\log_b \left(\frac{1}{\sqrt{3}}\right) = \log_b 3^{-1/2} = -\frac{1}{2} \log_b 3 = \left(-\frac{1}{2}\right)(1.10) = -.55.$$

According to Theorem 20-2,

$$\log_b (\sqrt[3]{16}) = \log_b 2^{4/3} = (\tfrac{4}{3}) \log_b 2 = (\tfrac{4}{3})(.69) = .92.$$

EXAMPLE 20-3.   Derive the identity $\log_b \left(\dfrac{1}{N}\right) = -\log_b N$.

Solution. According to Theorem 20-2,

$$\log_b \left(\frac{1}{N}\right) = \log_b N^{-1} = (-1) \log_b N = -\log_b N.$$

The following theorem, which stems directly from Theorems 20-1 and 20-2, is frequently useful.

THEOREM 20-3.   *If M and N are positive numbers and b is any base, then*

20-3
$$log_b \frac{M}{N} = log_b M - log_b N.$$

Proof. From Theorems 20-1 and 20-2 we have

$$\log_b \frac{M}{N} = \log_b MN^{-1} = \log_b M + \log_b N^{-1} = \log_b M - \log_b N.$$

The logarithms of numbers to a few particular bases have been tabulated.   A table of logarithms of numbers to the base 10 is provided at the end of this book.   Using just one such table, we can find the logarithm of any positive number to any other base by means of a formula that we shall now derive.

THEOREM 20-4.   *If a and b are two bases and if N is any positive number, then*

20-4
$$log_a N = \frac{log_b N}{log_b a}$$

Proof. We may write $N = a^{log_a N}$. Hence $log_b N = log_b (a^{log_a N})$. According to Theorem 20-2, this last equation may be written $log_b N = (log_a N)(log_b a)$, and this equation is equivalent to Equation 20-4.

EXAMPLE 20-4.   Show that $log_a b = \dfrac{1}{log_b a}$.

Solution. If we let $N = b$, Equation 20-4 becomes

$$log_a b = \frac{log_b b}{log_b a}.$$

But $log_b b$ is 1, so we have the result we wanted.

EXAMPLE 20-5.   If $log_{10} 2 = .3010$ and $log_{10} 3 = .4771$, find $log_3 2$.

Solution. Here we let $2 = N$, $3 = a$, and $10 = b$ in Equation 20-4 to obtain

$$log_3 2 = \frac{log_{10}2}{log_{10}3} = \frac{.3010}{.4771} = .6309.$$

You can avoid some common misunderstandings if you keep clearly in mind the fact that *a logarithm is a number.*   In particular, Equation 20-4 says that the number $log_a N$ is obtained by *dividing* the number $log_b N$ by the number $log_b a$.

The laws of logarithms are frequently used to change the form of an equation that involves logarithms.

EXAMPLE 20-6.   If $\frac{1}{2} log_3 M + 3 log_3 N = 1$, express M in terms of N.

Solution. The given equation can be written as

$$log_3 M + 6 log_3 N = 2.$$

Thus $log_3 M + log_3 N^6 = 2$, or $log_3 MN^6 = 2$.   Hence, from the definition of a logarithm, $MN^6 = 3^2 = 9$, and therefore $M = 9N^{-6}$.

Problems 20

1. Formula 20-1 may be generalized to apply to a product of any number of factors.   Prove that
$$\log_b (x_1 x_2 x_3) = \log_b x_1 + \log_b x_2 + \log_b x_3.$$

2. Given $\log_b 2 = .69$, $\log_b 3 = 1.10$, $\log_b 5 = 1.61$, and $\log_b 7 = 1.95$, find the following numbers:

(a) $\log_b \frac{2}{3}$
(b) $(\log_b 2)/(\log_b 3)$
(c) $\log_b 2^2$
(d) $(\log_b 2)^2$
(e) $\log_b 9$
(f) $\log_b 15$
(g) $\log_b 24$

(h) $\log_b 30$
(i) $\log_b 90$
(j) $\log_b 350$
(k) $\log_b \frac{1}{3}$
(l) $\log_b \sqrt{\frac{2}{3}}$
(m) $\log_b \frac{27}{25}$
(n) $\log_b 70/b$

3. Simplify the following expressions:

(a) $\log_b x^3 - \log_b \sqrt{x}$
(b) $\log_b (x^2 - 1) - \log_b (x - 1)$
(c) $\log_b x - .75 \log_b x + \log_b 3x$
(d) $\log_b (b/\sqrt{x}) - \log_b \sqrt{x/b}$

4. If $\log_b 2 = .69$ and $\log_b x = 1.22$, find the following numbers:

(a) $\log_2 b$
(b) $\log_2 x$

5. If $\log_{10} 5 = .6990$ and $\log_{10} x = .2330$, then what is x?

6. Solve the following equations for x:

(a) $\log_e \frac{18}{5} + \log_e \frac{10}{3} - \log_e \frac{6}{7} = \log_e x$

(b) $2 \log_b x = 2 \log_b (1 - a) + 2 \log_b (1 + a) - \log_b \left(\frac{1}{a} - a\right)^2$

(c) $\log_b x = 2 - a + \log_b \frac{a^2 b^a}{b^2}.$

7. If $\log_e I = -(R/L)t + \log_e I_0$, show that $I = I_0 e^{-(R/L)t}$.

8. If $\log_b y = \frac{1}{2} \log_b x + c$, show that $y = b^c \sqrt{x}$.

9. Given $\log_{10} 2 = .3010$ and $\log_{10} 3 = .4771$, find the logarithms of the numbers 4, 5, 6, 8, and 9.   (*Hint:* $\log_{10} 10 = 1$)

10. If y is directly proportional to x^p, show that the relation between the numbers $\log_b y$ and $\log_b x$ is linear.

21   LOGARITHMIC FUNCTIONS AND THEIR GRAPHS

According to Definition 19-1, the exponential equation $N = b^x$ and the logarithmic equation $x = \log_b N$ are equivalent.   Hence there might seem to be no reason to study both exponents and logarithms since whenever we are dealing with one we are at the same time concerned with the other. But there are some cases in which the exponential form of an equation seems more "natural" and other instances in which the logarithmic form seems more appropriate. If the plates of a charged electrical condenser are connected by a wire with a certain resistance, the condenser will discharge at a rate depending on the resistance in the wire and certain characteristics of the condenser. When calculus is used to compute the charge q on one plate of the condenser t seconds after the circuit is made, the equation that arises "naturally" is $\log_e q - \log_e q_0 = -kt$, where q_0 represents the original charge on the plate, k is a positive number associated with the circuit, and e is a logarithmic base. The exponential form of this equation is $q = q_0 e^{-kt}$, and in this form it is easier to see how q depends on t. To solve a problem such as this one, we must understand both exponential and logarithmic functions and the relation between them.

We saw in Section 18 that some of the properties of an exponential function depend on whether the base is a number greater than 1 or less than 1. The same is true for logarithmic functions. To avoid discussing two cases, we shall assume in the remainder of this chapter that *every logarithmic base is a number greater than 1.* The logarithmic bases that are used most often are greater than 1.

DEFINITION 21-1. *The function f defined by the equation $f(x) = \log_b x$ is a* **logarithmic function with base b.** (*The domain of f is the set of all positive numbers.*)

EXAMPLE 21-1. If f is the logarithmic function with base 4, find $f(4), f(\frac{1}{4})$, and $f(8)$.

Solution. By definition, $f(x) = \log_4 x$ and hence $f(4) = \log_4 4 = 1$, $f(\frac{1}{4}) = \log_4 \frac{1}{4} = -1$, and $f(8) = \log_4 8 = \frac{3}{2}$.

We obtain the graph of the logarithmic function with base b by graphing the equation $y = \log_b x$. Now according to Definition 19-1, the equations

21-1 $y = \log_b x$ and

21-2 $x = b^y$

are equivalent, which will simplify our graphing problem. In Section 18, we saw the graph of a typical equation of the form

21-3 $$y = b^x.$$

We can obtain the equation $x = b^y$ from the equation $y = b^x$ by interchanging x and y and therefore we obtain the graph of Equation 21-2 from the graph of Equation 21-3 merely by relabeling the axes. In the same fashion we can obtain the graph of the equation $x = 2^y$ from the graph of the equation $y = 2^x$, as shown in Fig. 18-1. The result appears in Fig. 21-1. To get the axes in their customary

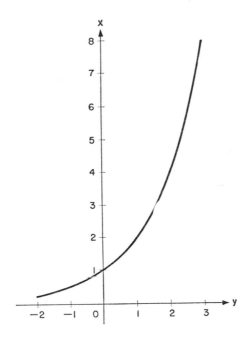

Figure 21-1

position, we must rotate the figure about the origin and then "turn it over." Once we have done this (see Fig. 21-2), we have the graph of the equation $x = 2^y$ and hence the graph of the equivalent equation $y = \log_2 x$.

Although Fig. 21-2 shows the graph of the logarithmic function with the particular base 2, it is representative of the graph of a logarithmic function to any base greater than 1. The graph illustrates a number of the characteristics of such a logarithmic function

   (i) If $x < 1$, then $\log_b x < 0$.
   (ii) If $x > 1$, then $\log_b x > 0$

(iii) If $x_1 < x_2$, then $\log_b x_1 < \log_b x_2$, and conversely. Thus, for example, if b is any base (greater than 1), then $\log_b 3 > \log_b 2$.

(iv) Any line parallel to the x-axis cuts the curve at exactly one point. Thus for a given number y there is just one number x such that $\log_b x = y$ (namely, $x = b^y$). *If, therefore, we know that $\log_b x_1 = \log_b x_2$, then we can conclude that $x_1 = x_2$.*

(v) The curve is very "steep" when x is small, but when x is large the curve, although rising, does so much more slowly.

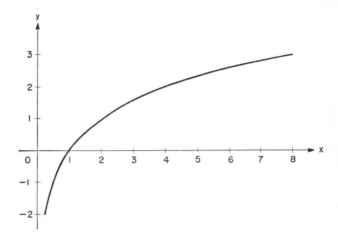

Figure 21-2

For computational purposes the number 10 is used as a logarithmic base, but a certain irrational number is a more suitable base to use in problems that involve calculus. This number is denoted by the letter e (just as we use the letter π to denote an irrational number that arises naturally in certain geometry problems). Fig. 21-3 shows a graph of the equation $y = \log_e x$.

EXAMPLE 21-2. From the graph in Fig. 21-3, find as well as you can (a) $\log_e 1.5$, (b) $\log_e .5$, (c) the number x for which $\log_e x = 1.5$, and (d) the value of e.

Solution. We see from Fig. 21-3 that the answers to (a), (b), and (c) are .4, $-.7$, and 4.5. The number e satisfies the equation $\log_e x = 1$. From the figure, it appears that $e = 2.7$ (actually, to 5 decimal places, **$e = 2.71828$**).

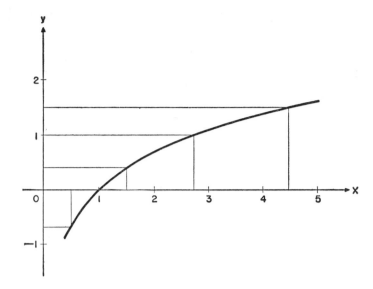

Figure 21-3

Problems 21

1. Use the graph shown in Fig. 21-2 to estimate the following numbers:
   (a) $\log_2 3$ (b) $\log_2 4.5$ (c) $\log_2 \frac{2}{3}$

2. On the same set of axes, sketch the curves $y = \log_2 x$ and $y = \log_3 x$. From the graph, determine whether $\log_3 x$ or $\log_2 x$ is larger in the following cases:
   (a) $x > 1$, (b) $x = 1$, or (c) $x < 1$.

3. Use the curves of Problem 2 to find x if $\log_2 x = \log_3 \frac{1}{2}$.

4. Sketch the graph of the equation $y = b^x$ for some convenient value of b on paper you can see through. Turn the paper over and by using only what you can see through the paper, sketch the graph of the equation $y = \log_b x$.

5. For some convenient value of b, sketch the graphs of the equations $y = b^x$ and $y = \log_b x$ on the same set of axes. Do you notice any symmetry? Can you find a way to fold the paper so that the two graphs coincide?

6. Sketch the graph of the equation $y = e^x$ ($e = 2.718$).

7. Using the rules of logarithms, can you suggest a way to obtain the graph of the equation $y = \log_2 2x$ from the graph of the equation $y = \log_2 x$?

8. Using the rules of logarithms, can you suggest a way to obtain the graph of the equation $y = \log_2 \sqrt{x}$ from the graph of the equation $y = \log_2 x$?

9. If f is the logarithmic function with base 8, find the following numbers:

(a) $f(64)$ (c) $f(4)$

(b) $f(\frac{1}{8})$ (d) $f(\sqrt[3]{2})$

10. If the graph of a logarithmic function contains the point (100,2), what is the base?

11. If f is a logarithmic function and $f(7) = 1$, what is the base?

12. Let f be the logarithmic function defined by $f(x) = \log_e x$. With the aid of Fig. 21-3, solve graphically the equation $2f(x) = 2f(e^2) - 3$.

22 LOGARITHMS TO THE BASE 10

To increase your understanding of the theory of logarithms, we shall make a rather detailed study of the system of logarithms to the base 10. Logarithms to the base 10 are called **common logarithms,** and the subscript denoting the base is often omitted. In this book, **log N means $\log_{10} N$.**

To find the logarithm of a positive number N to the base 10, we must solve the equation $10^x = N$. We can solve the equation easily only for certain values of N; for example, $N = 100 = 10^2$, $N = \frac{1}{10} = 10^{-1}$, and so forth. For other values of N we must use tables. We shall first show that only logarithms of numbers between 1 and 10 need to be tabulated; logarithms of other numbers can be found from the same table.

As a result of the decimal notation we use in writing numbers, to any number N there corresponds a number n, where $1 \leq n < 10$, and an integer c (which may be positive, negative, or zero) such that

22-1 $$N = n \cdot 10^c.$$

For example, if $N = 238$, then $n = 2.38$ and $c = 2$, since $238 = (2.38) \cdot 10^2$. If $N = .00238$, then $n = 2.38$ and $c = -3$, since $.00238 = (2.38) \cdot 10^{-3}$. When we write a number in the form shown in Equation 22-1, we say that it is expressed in **scientific notation.** The number n lists the digits used in writing N and the integer c locates the decimal point. Shifting the decimal point corresponds to changing c by an integral amount.

If we write a number N in scientific notation, as in Equation **22-1,** then

$$\log N = \log n \cdot 10^c = \log n + \log 10^c = \log n + c.$$

We therefore see that *the logarithm to the base* 10 *of any positive number N can be written as the sum of a logarithm of a number between* 1 *and* 10 *and an integer c.*   We can easily find the integer c by writing N in scientific notation and choosing the exponent of 10 that results.   The number log n can be found from Table I on pages 393-394.

Since $1 \leq n < 10$, it follows that $\log 1 \leq \log n < \log 10$, and hence $0 \leq \log n < 1$.   If we write $m = \log n$, we see that

22-2 $$\log N = m + c,$$

where m is a number between 0 and 1 (the positive decimal part of log N), and c is an integer (which may be positive, negative, or zero). The integer c is called the **characteristic** of log N, and the number m is termed its **mantissa.**   For example, the characteristic of log 238 is 2, and the mantissa is log 2.38; the characteristic of log .00238 is -3, and the mantissa is log 2.38.   When log N is written as in Equation 22-2, it is in **standard form.**

Now let us illustrate the use of Table I and Formula 22-2.   According to the table, log 2.38 = .3766, and therefore

22-3 $\log 238 = \log 2.38 + 2 = .3766 + 2 = 2.3766,$ and
$\log .00238 = \log 2.38 - 3 = .3766 - 3 = -2.6234.$

You should note that $.3766 - 3 = -2.6234$ and *not* -3.3766.   It is frequently convenient to leave this number in standard form rather than in the form -2.6234.

EXAMPLE 22-1.   Find x if $10^x = 3$.

Solution.   According to Definition 19-1, we can write the equation as $x = \log 3$.   From Table I we find that $x = .4771$.

EXAMPLE 22-2.   Find x if $10^x = .4$.

Solution.   From Table I we have $x = \log .4 = .6021 - 1 = -.3979$.

The inverse problem—namely, finding the number N whose logarithm is a given number x—is equivalent to finding the number 10^x, since by definition log $N = x$ if, and only if, $N = 10^x$.   The first step in solving this problem is to express the given number x in standard form, $x = \log N = m + c$, where c is an integer and m is a number between 0 and 1; that is, m is a positive decimal.   Then the number N is given by the equation

$$N = 10^{m+c} = 10^m \cdot 10^c = n \cdot 10^c,$$

where we have written $n = 10^m$.   The equation $n = 10^m$ is equivalent to the equation $\log n = m$, and hence n is the number whose logarithm is m.   We find the number n directly from Table I, since $0 \leq m < 1$. Since c is an integer, multiplying n by 10^c amounts to shifting the decimal point.

EXAMPLE 22-3.   If $\log N = .4771$, find N.

Solution.   The number $\log N$ is already in standard form with $c = 0$. From Table I, we find that the number whose logarithm is .4771 is 3. Thus $N = 3$.

EXAMPLE 22-4.   If $\log N = 6.8904$, find N.
Solution.   In standard form, $\log N = .8904 + 6$.   If $\log n = .8904$, we find from Table I that $n = 7.77$.   Thus $N = n \cdot 10^6 = (7.77) \cdot 10^6 = 7,770,000$.

EXAMPLE 22-5.   Find the number $10^{6.8904}$.

Solution.   If $N = 10^{6.8904}$, then $\log N = 6.8904$ by definition, so this problem is the same as the one in Example 22-4.

EXAMPLE 22-6.   Find N if $\log N = -1.6180$.

Solution.   We note first that -1.6180 is not the same as $.6180 - 1$. Instead, $-1.6180 = -.6180 - 1$, and this number is not in standard form, since $-.6180$ is not a number between 0 and 1.   To put this number in standard form we simply add 1 and subtract 1.   The motivation for this procedure is the fact that $-.6180 + 1$ is a positive decimal.   Thus

$$-.6180 - 1 = 1 - .6180 - 1 - 1 = (1 - .6180) - 2 = .3820 - 2.$$

Now we may write

$$\log N = .3820 - 2.$$

From Table I we find that $\log 2.41 = .3820$, so

$$N = (2.41) \cdot 10^{-2} = .0241.$$

Problems 22

1. Evaluate from Table I:
  (a) log 72,900
  (b) log 36.2
  (c) log .0000912
  (d) 1 − log 4.61

2. Solve for x.
  (a) $10^x = 8.91$
  (b) $10^x = 273$
  (c) $10^x = .0171$
  (d) $10^x = \frac{33}{2500}$
  (e) $10^x = 4010$

3. Solve for x:
  (a) $\log x = 5.1903$
  (b) $\log x = 3.9053$
  (c) $\log x = .4014$
  (d) $\log x = 9.49$

4. Compute the following numbers:
  (a) $10^{1.786}$
  (b) $10^{-2.699}$
  (c) $\sqrt[5]{10^4}$

5. Solve the following equations for N:
  (a) $\log N = .6580 - 3$
  (b) $\log N = 2.9309 - 1$
  (c) $\log N = -1.1232$
  (d) $\log N = -4.5317$
  (e) $\log N = \frac{1}{2}(1.6702)$
  (f) $\log N = 1.3145 + 2.3631$
  (g) $\log N = \frac{1}{2} + 3.1160$
  (h) $\log N = \frac{9}{5} - 2.4478$

6. Using Table I, we can evaluate $\log \frac{5}{2}$ in two ways.
  (i) $\log \frac{5}{2} = \log 2.5 = .3979$
  (ii) $\log \frac{5}{2} = \log 5 - \log 2 = .6990 - .3010 = .3980$
  Why do we get two different answers?

7. Use the two procedures indicated in Problem 6 to find the following logarithms and compare your answers.
  (a) $\log \frac{4}{5}$
  (b) $\log \frac{9}{4}$
  (c) $\log \frac{3}{8}$
  (d) $\log \frac{13}{4}$
  (e) $\log \frac{61}{2}$
  (f) $\log \frac{101}{2}$

8. Use Theorem 20-4 and Table I to find the following numbers (see Example 20-5):
  (a) $\log_5 10$
  (b) $\log_5 6$
  (c) $\log_7 2$
  (d) $\log_8 3.07$

9. Use the rules of logarithms and Table I to solve for x.
  (a) $10^x = \sqrt[3]{12.3}$
  (b) $10^x = (1.42)(7.89)$

23   INTERPOLATION

From Table I, we can immediately find the logarithm of 2.34 and the number whose logarithm is .7168.   But the logarithm of 2.347

and the number whose logarithm is .1234 are not listed in Table **I**, and we shall now try to find such non-listed numbers.

The simplest way to find the logarithm of a number N that is not listed in Table I is to use the logarithm of the number that we get by "rounding off" the number N. If N is written in scientific form as $n \cdot 10^e$, then the number of digits in n is called the number of **significant digits** of N. In order to use Table I directly to find $\log n$, we must first round off n to three significant digits by choosing the number nearest n that has three significant digits. For example, instead of $\log 2.347$, we could use $\log 2.35$. When we are in doubt about which number to choose in the rounding off process, we adopt the convention that the rounded number should be even. For example, 1.415 is rounded to 1.42, and 7.465 is rounded to 7.46. If we are given a positive decimal x that is not listed in the body of Table I and are asked to find the number N for which $\log N = x$, we could choose the number whose logarithm is the number in Table I nearest to x. We might say that the solution to the equation $\log N = .1234$ is $N = 1.33$, because $\log 1.32 = .1206$ and $\log 1.33 = .1239$, and .1239 is nearer to .1234 than .1206 is.

A more sophisticated (and more accurate) way to approximate non-listed values is by the method of **linear interpolation.** Although we shall apply this method to the table of logarithms here, we may also use it with other tables. We present the explanation in geometrical terms to increase your understanding of the use of graphs.

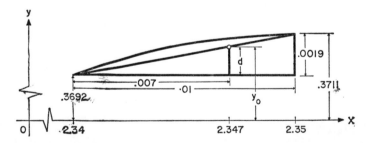

Figure 23-1

Suppose we wish to find $\log 2.347$. In Fig. 23-1, that part of the graph of the equation $y = \log x$ for which $2.34 \leq x \leq 2.35$ is drawn. The number we wish to find, $\log 2.347$, is the y-coordinate of the point on this arc whose x-coordinate is 2.347. The only points on the arc whose coordinates we know (from Table I) are the end points

(2.34, .3692) and (2.35, .3711).   A straight line joining these points closely approximates the arc, and in addition, it is easy to find the y-coordinate of any point on this line whose x-coordinate is known. If y_0 is the y-coordinate of the point on the line whose x-coordinate is 2.347, it appears that y_0 is a good approximation of the desired value of log 2.347, and we shall now calculate this number y_0.   If we let $d = y_0 - \log 2.34 = y_0 - .3692$, we see from the similar triangles in Fig. 23-1, that

$$\frac{d}{.007} = \frac{.0019}{.01}$$

and hence $d = .7(.0019) = .0013$ (to four decimal places).   Then $y_0 = \log 2.34 + d = .3705$, so we write log 2.347 = .3705.   Actually, the curve in Fig. 23-1 is somewhat exaggerated; the logarithmic curve is more nearly a straight line.   Our value of .3705 is really the value of log 2.347 correct to four decimal places.

The inverse procedure is similar.   If we are asked, for example, to find the number x such that $\log x = .1234$, we first note from Table I that log 1.32 = .1206 and log 1.33 = .1239.   Figure 23-2

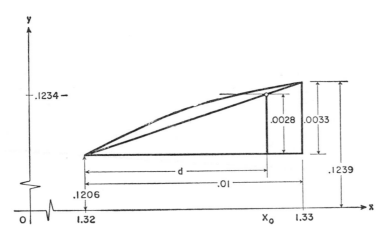

Figure 23-2

shows a graph similar to the one in Fig. 23-1 for those values of x that are involved in this problem.

The number x we want to find is the x-coordinate of the point on the graph whose y-coordinate is .1234, and we can see that the x-coordinate of the point on the line, call it x_0, whose y-coordinate is

.1234, is a fair approximation of the number x. We can find the number x_0 quite easily. For if we let $d = x_0 - 1.32$ and use similar triangles,

$$\frac{d}{.0028} = \frac{.01}{.0033}.$$

Hence $d = (.01)(\frac{28}{33}) = .008$, so $x_0 = 1.320 + d = 1.328$. We therefore say that the solution to the equation $\log x = .1234$ is $x = 1.328$.

In actual practice, we do not construct a graph each time we wish to interpolate. Let a and b be numbers listed in Table I and let n

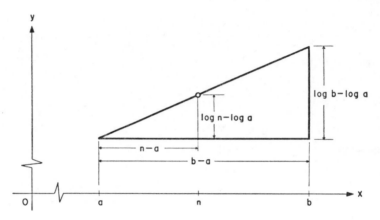

Figure 23-3

be a number that satisfies the inequalities $a < n < b$. If we assume that the graph of the logarithmic function joining known points is a straight line and use similar triangles (see Fig. 23-3), we get the following equation:

23-1
$$\frac{\log n - \log a}{\log b - \log a} = \frac{n - a}{b - a}.$$

With a little practice you should be able to perform mentally most of the calculations involved in linear interpolation.

EXAMPLE 23-1.   Use linear interpolation to find $\log 5.723$.

Solution. If we let $a = 5.72$, $b = 5.73$, and $n = 5.723$, we see immediately that $(n - a)/(b - a) = .3$. Using Table I, we find $\log 5.72 = .7574$, and $\log 5.73 = .7582$, so Equation 23-1 yields
$$\log 5.723 = .7574 + .3(.0008) = .7576 \text{ (approximately)}.$$

EXAMPLE 23-2.   Solve the equation $\log n = .7133$.

Solution. From Table I we find that $\log 5.16 = .7126$ and $\log 5.17$ $= .7135$. Letting $a = 5.16$ and $b = 5.17$, we see immediately that $(\log n - \log a)/(\log b - \log a) = \frac{7}{9}$. It then follows from Equation 23-1 that

$$n = 5.16 + \tfrac{7}{9}(.01) = 5.168 \text{ (approximately)}.$$

Linear interpolation yields the best results when the graph of the function involved *does* approximate a straight line for the values under consideration. If f is the function defined by the equation $f(x) = x^2 - 1$, then the graph of f is not even approximately linear, for $-1 \leq x \leq 1$. If we use linear interpolation here to argue that since 0 is half-way between -1 and 1, then $f(0)$ is half-way between $f(-1) = 0$ and $f(1) = 0$, we would conclude that $f(0) = 0$ when in fact $f(0) = -1$. This simple example shows that although linear interpolation is a useful tool, we must not use it indiscriminately.

Problems 23

1. Write the following logarithms in standard form:
  (a) $\log 9.017$
  (b) $\log .001372$
  (c) $\log 2476$
  (d) $\log (1.697) \cdot 10^4$
  (e) $\log (3.726) \cdot 10^{-6}$
  (f) $\log e$

2. Find the number x correct to 4 significant digits.
  (a) $\log x = .5521$
  (b) $\log x = 3.9286$
  (c) $\log x = 4.7182 - 5$
  (d) $\log x = -1.8347$

3. Find the number x.
  (a) $10^x = .3976$
  (b) $10^x = e$
  (c) $10^x = 23.14$
  (d) $10^x = .006723$

4. Write as a decimal number:
  (a) $10^{.395}$
  (b) $10^{.1}$
  (c) $\sqrt[5]{10}$
  (d) $\sqrt[4]{160}$
  (e) 10^{-e}
  (f) $10^{-.0013}$

5. We know that $\log_2 8 = 3$ and that $\log_2 16 = 4$. Use linear interpolation to find $\log_2 10$. Is your approximate value too large or too small?

6. Use the tabulated values of $\log 1$ and $\log 1.2$ and interpolate to find $\log 1.1$. Interpolate to find $\log 9.9$ by using the listed values of $\log 9.8$ and $\log 10$. Compare your answers with the tabulated values and discuss your findings.

7. Using $\sqrt{16} = 4$ and $\sqrt{25} = 5$ and linear interpolation, find $\sqrt{18}$. Discuss the accuracy of your result.

8. If $f(x) = 2x - 3$, then $f(2) = 1$ and $f(3) = 3$. Use linear interpolation to find $f(2.5)$. Discuss the accuracy of your result.

9. Let $f(x) = 1/x^2$. Use linear interpolation to find $f(1.5)$ from the values of $f(1)$ and $f(2)$. Also use linear interpolation to find $f(4.5)$ from the values of $f(4)$ and $f(5)$. Discuss the accuracy of your results.

24   COMPUTATIONS WITH LOGARITHMS

At one time, logarithms were studied mainly because they were helpful in simplifying long numerical computations. Today the widespread use of desk calculators and computing machines has removed the necessity of doing complicated computations by hand. This development does not mean that logarithms are no longer important, only that they are important for different reasons. Basic logarithmic computations still have some practical value, and it will increase your mastery of the theory of logarithms if we work a few arithmetical problems with them. There are a number of conventions and short cuts that speed up logarithmic computations, but we won't consider them here. If you ever have to learn them, you can in a relatively short time.

EXAMPLE 24-1.   Calculate the number $\dfrac{(3480)(1265)}{.00143}$.

Solution. One way to proceed is to write

$$\frac{(3480)(1265)}{.00143} = \frac{(3.48) \cdot 10^3(1.265) \cdot 10^3}{(1.43)10^{-3}} = \frac{(3.48)(1.265)10^9}{1.43}$$

and then to calculate the number $N = \dfrac{(3.48)(1.265)}{1.43}$.

According to the rules of logarithms,

$$\log N = \log (3.48)(1.265) - \log (1.43)$$
$$= \log 3.48 + \log 1.265 - \log 1.43.$$

From Table I we have

$$\log N = .5416 + .1021 - .1553 = .4884.$$

Also from Table I we find that $N = 3.079$ and so

$$\frac{(3480)(1265)}{.00143} = (3.079)10^9.$$

We would have had no great difficulty in carrying out the calculation in Example 24-1 without using logarithms. We could not work the following examples, however, without using logarithms.

EXAMPLE 24-2. Find $\sqrt[5]{20}$.

Solution. Let $N = \sqrt[5]{20} = 20^{1/5}$. Then

$$\log N = \frac{\log 20}{5} = \frac{1.3010}{5} = .2602.$$

Thus

$$N = \sqrt[5]{20} = 1.82.$$

EXAMPLE 24-3. Find $\sqrt[5]{.2}$.

Solution. Let $N = (.2)^{1/5}$. Then

$$\log N = \frac{\log .2}{5} = \frac{.3010 - 1}{5}.$$

If we proceed with the arithmetic at this point, we shall find u
$\log N = \frac{-.6990}{5} = -.1398$. But this last number must be written i
standard form before we can solve for N. It is easier to replace th
number $(.3010 - 1)$ with its equivalent expression $(.3010 - 1 + 4 - 4) = (4.3010 - 5)$. Then

$$\log N = \frac{4.3010 - 5}{5} = .8602 - 1.$$

Here $\log N$ is expressed in standard form and we can use Table I to find that $N = \sqrt[5]{.2} = .7248$.

Logarithms also provide us with a convenient way of obtaining an idea of the size of numbers that are quite large.

EXAMPLE 24-4. We mentioned earlier that under favorable conditions a single cell of the bacterium *Escherichia coli* divides into two about every 20 minutes.   If this same rate of division is maintained for 10 hours, how many organisms will be produced from a single cell?

Solution.   The 10-hour interval may be divided into 30 periods of 20 minutes each.   At the end of the first period there are 2 bacteria, at the end of the second there are $2 \cdot 2 = 2^2$, at the end of the third there are 2^3, and so on.   At the end of the 30th period there will be 2^{30} bacteria, which we will call N, the number we were seeking.   Now $\log N = \log 2^{30} = 30 \log 2 = 30(.3010) = 9.0300$.   From the table of logarithms, we see that $N = (1.072)10^9 = 1,072,000,000$, so a single cell is potentially capable of producing about a billion organisms in a 10-hour period.

Problems 24

1. Use logarithms to make the following computations:
   (a) $\dfrac{(375)(1.61)}{(4,678)(.0012)}$
   (b) $\dfrac{(-431)(22)}{681}$
   (c) $\dfrac{32}{\sqrt[5]{21}}$
   (d) $(2^{1/2})^{1/4}$
   (e) $17^{-.6}$

2. Solve for x:
   (a) $10^x = \frac{212}{313}$
   (b) $10^x = 2$

3. Determine which number is larger:
   (a) $25^{7/6}$ or $28^{10/9}$
   (b) 5^π or 157
   (c) 3^{21} or 95^5
   (d) $3^{\sqrt{2}}$ or $2^{\sqrt{3}}$

4. The radioactive isotope C^{11} decomposes rapidly.   If at one instant there is 1 microgram of C^{11}, then t min later there will be A micrograms, where $A = (\frac{1}{2})^{t/20}$.   Find the amount of C^{11} that will be present at the end of 10, 20, and 30 min.

5. If you invest p dollars at 3% interest "compounded annually," at the end of n years you will have accumulated a sum of A dollars.   Express A in terms of p and n.   If you invest \$18.75, how much will you have in your account at the end of 10 years?

6. An angstrom (A) is a unit of length equal to 10^{-8} cm (1 cm is .3937 in.).   The wave length of a certain gamma ray is .6241 A.   Use logarithms to compute the wave length in inches.

7. The time required for a simple pendulum L ft long to make one complete oscillation is t sec, where $t = 2\pi\sqrt{L/32.16}$.   Use logarithms to find the period of a pendulum 3.617 ft long.   (The period is the time required for one complete oscillation.)

8. The volume of a sphere is given by $V = 4\pi r^3/3$.   What is the radius of a sphere that has a volume of 1 cu ft?

25   EXPONENTIAL AND LOGARITHMIC EQUATIONS

We have already observed that Table I may be considered as a table of solutions for equations of the type $10^x = N$, where N is a given positive number.   For example, the solution to the equation $10^x = 2$ is given in the table as $\log 2 = .3010$.   The equation $10^x = 2$ is of the form $a^x = b$, where a and b are given positive numbers.   Of course, the solution to the equation $a^x = b$ can be written as $x = \log_a b$, but we must go a little farther to get a more meaningful answer.   To evaluate this quantity by using Table I, we must recall that $\log_a b = \log b/\log a$ (see Theorem 20-4).

Instead of memorizing the formula relating $\log_a b$ and $\log b$, we can solve the equation $a^x = b$ directly.   Simply take logarithms (to the base 10) of both sides of the equation to obtain $\log a^x = \log b$, and therefore (Theorem 20-2) $x \log a = \log b$.   It follows that $x = \log b/\log a$, as above.

EXAMPLE 25-1.   Solve the equation $2^x = 7$ for x.

Solution.   By taking logarithms of both sides of the equation, we obtain the equation $x \log 2 = \log 7$.   From Table I, $\log 2 = .3010$ and $\log 7 = .8451$.   So our equation becomes $.3010\,x = .8451$.   Hence

$$x = \frac{.8451}{.3010} = 2.808.$$

Remark 1.   Since $2^2 = 4$ and $2^3 = 8$, it should be obvious at the start that the solution to the equation $2^x = 7$ is a number between 2 and 3.

Remark 2.   Since $x \log 2 = \log 7$, it follows that $x = \log 7/\log 2$. It should be emphasized that the expression $\log 7/\log 2$ is a *quotient*. We do not evaluate this quotient by looking up $\log 2$ and $\log 7$ in the table and subtracting; we look up the two numbers and divide.   We can divide with the aid of logarithms, but it still will be division.

EXAMPLE 25-2.   Solve the equation $2^x = 3^{x+1}$ for x.

Solution. We take logarithms of both sides of the equation to obtain the equation

$$x \log 2 = (x + 1) \log 3.$$

Hence

$$x \log 2 - x \log 3 = \log 3,$$

or in other words

$$x = \frac{\log 3}{\log 2 - \log 3}.$$

Using Table I gives

$$x = \frac{.4771}{.3010 - .4771} = \frac{.4771}{-.1761} = -2.709.$$

EXAMPLE 25-3.   Solve the inequality $(.3)^x < \frac{4}{3}$.

Solution. We have already seen in Section 21 that if $M < N$, then $\log_b M < \log_b N$, and conversely. Thus $(.3)^x < \frac{4}{3}$ if, and only if, $\log (.3)^x < \log \frac{4}{3}$. We can then use the rules of logarithms and Table I to solve the inequality in the following manner.

$$x \log (.3) < \log 4 - \log 3,$$

$$x (.4771 - 1) < .6021 - .4771,$$

$$-.5229x < .1250,$$

$$x > -.239.$$

EXAMPLE 25-4.   Solve the equation $I = \frac{E}{R} (1 - e^{-Rt/L})$ for t.

Solution. We can write the equation as

$$\frac{RI}{E} = 1 - e^{-Rt/L} \quad \text{or} \quad e^{-Rt/L} = 1 - \frac{RI}{E}.$$

Then

$$\log e^{-Rt/L} = \log \left(1 - \frac{RI}{E} \right),$$

$$\frac{-Rt}{L} \log e = \log \left(1 - \frac{RI}{E} \right),$$

$$\frac{-Rt}{L} = \frac{\log\left(1 - \dfrac{RI}{E}\right)}{\log e},$$

$$t = \frac{-L \log\left(1 - \dfrac{RI}{E}\right)}{R \log e}.$$

If we use logarithms to the base e, the expression for t takes the simpler form

$$t = \frac{-L}{R} \log_e\left(1 - \frac{RI}{E}\right).$$

EXAMPLE 25-5.   Find x if $2 \log x - \log 10x = 0$.

Solution.   We can use the fundamental properties of logarithms to reduce the problem as follows:

$2 \log x - \log 10x = 2 \log x - \log 10 - \log x = \log x - 1 = 0$.
Therefore, $\log x = 1$, and hence $x = 10$.

EXAMPLE 25-6.   Find x if $x^{\log x} = 100x$.

Solution.   We take logarithms of both sides of the equation to obtain the equation
$$\log (x^{\log x}) = \log 100x.$$
But
$$\log (x^{\log x}) = (\log x)(\log x) = (\log x)^2,$$
and
$$\log 100x = \log 100 + \log x = 2 + \log x.$$
We can therefore write our equation as
$$(\log x)^2 = 2 + \log x,$$
and therefore
$$(\log x)^2 - \log x - 2 = (\log x - 2)(\log x + 1) = 0.$$
It follows that
$$\log x = 2, \quad \text{or} \quad \log x = -1,$$
and hence
$$x = 100, \quad \text{or} \quad x = \tfrac{1}{10}.$$

Problems 25

1. Solve for x.
   (a) $3^x = 2$
   (b) $4^x = \frac{5}{3}$
   (c) $5^x = 17$
   (d) $(.01)^x = 5$

2. Solve for x.
   (a) $3^{1-x} = 2$
   (b) $5^{x+2} = 7^{x-1}$
   (c) $10^{x^2} = 5$
   (d) $5^x = 3$

3. Solve for x.
   (a) $\log (x + 1) - \log x = \frac{1}{2}$ (b) $\log (x^2 - 1) - \log (x + 1) = 2$

4. Show that no number x can be found such that $\log (x - 4) - \log (x + 1) = \log 6$.

5. Use the data in Example 24-4 to determine how long it would take a single cell of *E. coli* to produce 500,000 organisms.

6. A function f is determined by the equation $f(x) = N \cdot 10^{kx}$. What are the numbers N and k if the graph of f contains the points $(0,7)$ and $(1,14)$?

7. A function f is determined by the equation $f(x) = N \log kx$. If the graph of f contains the points $(5,7)$ and $(.5,0)$, what are the numbers k and N?

8. The number of milligrams of radium present at the end of t years is given by the formula $A = A_0 10^{-.000174t}$. What is the initial amount of radium? How long will it take a given sample to reduce to $\frac{1}{2}$ its original size; that is, what is the half-life period?

9. At what interest compounded annually must we invest $100 if we want it to double in 12 years?

10. The intensity I of an x-ray beam after passing through x cm of a certain material is given by $I = I_0 e^{-kx}$, where I_0 is the intensity as the beam enters the material, and k is a constant called the linear coefficient of absorption. Calculate k if the material absorbs $\frac{1}{2}$ the x-ray beam after penetrating 5 cm.

Review Problems, Chapter Three

You should be able to answer the following questions without referring back to the text.

1. Explain why the equation $2^x = -4$ does not have a solution.

2. Let f denote the exponential function with base 10, and let g denote the logarithmic function with base 10. What is the domain of f, the domain of g, the range of f, and the range of g? Which of the following equations are true?

(a) $f(x + y) = f(x)f(y)$ (e) $g(x^p) = pg(x)$
(b) $f(xy) = f(x) + f(y)$ (f) $f[g(x)] = x$
(c) $g(x + y) = g(x)g(y)$ (g) $g[f(x)] = x$
(d) $g(xy) = g(x) + g(y)$ (h) $f(0) = g(10)$

3. If $x = \log_e 10$ and $y = \log e$, what is the value of x/y?

4. How many digits are there in the number 2^{30}?

5. Use logarithms to compute the number $(.218)^{-6.2}$.

6. Which number is larger, e^π or π^e?

7. Solve the equation $(\log x)^2 = \log x^2$.

8. Solve the equation $\log [\log (\log x)] = 0$.

9. Sketch the graph of the equation $y = \log_2 |x|$.

10. For what numbers x is $|\log x| = \log |x|$?

11. Show that $\log x^3 - \log 2x + \log (1/x) = \log (x/2)$.

12. If $\frac{1}{4} \log M - \log N = 2$, express M in terms of N.

13. Sketch the graph of the equation $y = \log 10^x$.

14. If $b^{.6} = 4$, find $\log_4 b$.

15. Express n in terms of the other letters.

   (a) $S = \dfrac{a - ar^n}{1 - r}$ (b) $pv^n = c$ (c) $y^{1/n} = x^n$

16. A light year is the distance traveled by light in one year. If the speed of light is 186,000 miles per second, find the approximate length in miles of 1 light year.

Miscellaneous Problems, Chapter Three

These problems are designed to test your ability to apply your knowledge of exponential and logarithmic functions to somewhat more difficult problems.

1. If a and N are positive numbers and b is a logarithmic base, express the quantity $a^{\log_b N}$ as a power of N.

2. Write the function defined by the equation $y = (2e)^x$ as an exponential function with base e.

3. Is there a number x such that $(\log x)^{-1} = \log x^{-1}$?

4. If $0 < \log x_2 - \log x_1 < 1$, can you conclude that $1 < x_2 - x_1 < 10$?

5. When we write $\log 2 = .3010$, we mean that $.3010$ is the best four-place approximation to $\log 2$. Prove that $\log 2$ is not exactly equal to $.3010$.

6. Let the equation $y = 2^x + 2^{-x}$ define a function f. Sketch the graph of f and show that $f(x) \geq 2$ for all real numbers x.

7. Sketch the graph of the equation $y = \log_{1/2} x$.

8. Can the equation $\log x = x$ have a solution? (*Hint:* Look at the graphs of $y = x$ and $y = \log x$.)

9. Suppose p dollars are invested at i per cent (per year) interest compounded semi-annually. Let A denote the accumulated sum at the end of n interest periods. Express A in terms of p, i, and n. In how many years will an amount of money double if it is invested at 3% compounded semi-annually? At what per cent compounded monthly should money be invested so that it will double in 10 years?

10. Find all the *integers* x and y for which $\log (x + y) = \log x + \log y$.

11. If $a^2 + b^2 = 7ab$, show that $\log [(a + b)/3] = \frac{1}{2}(\log a + \log b)$.

12. Show that $3 \log x + \log (x - 3) = 0$ when x is a real number that satisfies the equation $x^4 - 3x^3 - 1 = 0$.

CHAPTER FOUR

THE TRIGONOMETRIC FUNCTIONS

The word "trigonometry" stems from the Greek words for "triangle measurement," and the subject was originally developed to solve geometrical problems involving triangles. It was found that certain functions, called *trigonometric functions*, were of use in solving such problems. Each trigonometric function was defined by associating with an acute angle a number, the ratio of the lengths of certain sides of a right triangle containing the angle. Thus the domain of a trigonometric function, as it was originally defined, consisted of acute angles, not numbers. But the trigonometric functions have since been extended so that they are also useful in situations in which angles are not involved. The importance of these applica-

tions justifies a non-geometrical approach to the subject of trigonometry.

The trigonometric functions introduced here are functions in the
sense we have already described in Chapter Two; that is, with each
number of one set of numbers will be associated a *number* of another
set.   If you have already studied trigonometry in terms of angles,
some of the procedures we will be following here may seem artificial
to you.   In a sense they are, for they are motivated by geometrical
concepts that we will not discuss until Section 41.   Nevertheless,
you should try to adopt the numerical point of view because it is
the basis for many of the present applications of trigonometry.

26 THE TRIGONOMETRIC POINT

Consider a circle with a radius of 1 and with its center at the origin
of a cartesian coordinate system.   We shall call this circle the **unit
circle.**   Let t be any real number.   Starting at the point with
coordinates $(1,0)$, move $|t|$ units along the circumference of the unit
circle, counter-clockwise if t is positive and clockwise if t is negative
(see Fig. 26-1).   You will arrive at a point on the unit circle that
we shall call the **trigonometric point** $P(t)$.   This procedure defines
a function whose domain is the set of all real numbers and whose
range is the set of points on the unit circle.   Assuming we know what

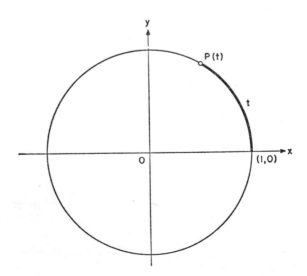

Figure 26-1

$|t|$ units along the circle means, then it should be clear that with every real number t there is associated a trigonometric point $P(t)$.

Let us now try to calculate a few "values" for the function we have defined; that is, let us find some particular points, for example, $P(0)$, $P(1)$, and so on. We will find that it is easier to determine the coordinates of some points than of others. The trigonometric point $P(0)$, for instance, is obviously the point $(1,0)$, but to find the coordinates of the point $P(1)$ we must first measure 1 unit along the arc of the unit circle—a difficult task without a curved ruler. It is more convenient to use tables (which we discuss later) to locate most trigonometric points, in particular $P(1)$. But with some knowledge of the geometry of the circle, we can locate certain particular points directly.

The circumference of the unit circle is $2\pi = 6.2832$ units. Therefore, one-half of the circumference is π units and one-quarter of the circumference is $\pi/2$ units. It now becomes immediately apparent, for example, that $P(\pi)$ is the point $(-1,0)$; $P(\pi/2)$ is the point $(0,1)$, and $P(3\pi/2)$ and $P(-\pi/2)$ both represent the point $(0,-1)$. It should be easy for you to locate the point $P(t)$ if t is any integral multiple of $\pi/2$, for example $7\pi/2$, $-13\pi/2$, and so forth.

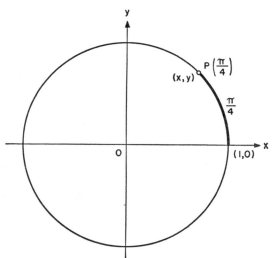

Figure 26-2

If t is any number, the point $P(t)$ is one unit from the origin. Hence if (x,y) are the coordinates of $P(t)$, it follows from the distance formula that

26-1 $$x^2 + y^2 = 1.$$

From this equation we see that if we know one of the coordinates of $P(t)$, we can determine the other coordinate except for its sign.

Let us now locate the trigonometric point $P(\pi/4)$. Since $\pi/4$ is one-eighth of the circumference of the unit circle, the point $P(\pi/4)$ is the mid-point of the arc that joins the points $(1,0)$ and $(0,1)$ (see Fig. 26-2). It is clear from Fig. 26-2 that the point $P(\pi/4)$ is equidistant from the x and y axes; hence $x = y$. Therefore, from Equation 26-1 we see that

$$x^2 + x^2 = 2x^2 = 1.$$

It follows from this equation that $x^2 = \frac{1}{2}$, and since x is clearly positive, $x = 1/\sqrt{2} = \sqrt{2}/2 = y$. Therefore, the coordinates of $P(\pi/4)$ are $(\sqrt{2}/2, \sqrt{2}/2)$. You should be able to find the coordinates of trigonometric points such as $P(3\pi/4)$, $P(5\pi/4)$, and so forth, by locating them on the unit circle and observing that they are symmetrically placed with respect to $P(\pi/4)$.

EXAMPLE 26-1. Find the coordinates of the points $P(3\pi/4)$ and $P(-3\pi/4)$.

Solution. We use the obvious symmetry of Fig. 26-3 and the known coordinates of $P(\pi/4)$ to find that $P(3\pi/4)$ is the point $(-\sqrt{2}/2, \sqrt{2}/2)$ and that $P(-3\pi/4)$ is the point $(-\sqrt{2}/2, -\sqrt{2}/2)$.

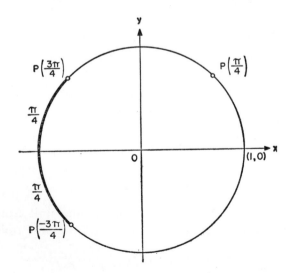

Figure 26-3

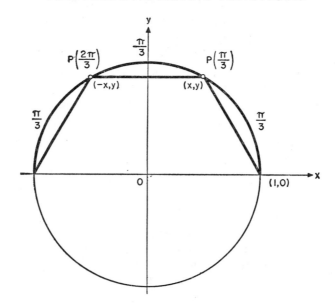

Figure 26-4

We can also locate the trigonometric point $P(\pi/3)$ by simple geometric reasoning. Let (x,y) be the coordinates of the point $P(\pi/3)$. Since the points $P(\pi/3)$ and $P(2\pi/3)$ are symmetrically located with respect to the y-axis (see Fig. 26-4), it is clear that the coordinates of $P(2\pi/3)$ are $(-x,y)$. It is also clear that the chords $\overline{P\left(\dfrac{2\pi}{3}\right)P\left(\dfrac{\pi}{3}\right)}$ and $\overline{P\left(\dfrac{\pi}{3}\right)P(0)}$ are equal because the corresponding arcs are equal. Hence,

26-2 $$\overline{P\left(\frac{2\pi}{3}\right)P\left(\frac{\pi}{3}\right)}^{2} = \overline{P\left(\frac{\pi}{3}\right)P(0)}^{2}.$$

Now $\overline{P\left(\dfrac{2\pi}{3}\right)P\left(\dfrac{\pi}{3}\right)}^{2} = (2x)^2 = 4x^2$ and, according to the distance formula, $\overline{P\left(\dfrac{\pi}{3}\right)P(0)}^{2} = (x-1)^2 + y^2$. Hence, we can write Equation 26-2 as

26-3 $$4x^2 = (x-1)^2 + y^2 = x^2 - 2x + 1 + y^2.$$

If we use Equation 26-1 to simplify Equation 26-3, we obtain the equation $4x^2 = 2 - 2x$, and so

$$4x^2 + 2x - 2 = 2(2x - 1)(x + 1) = 0.$$

There are two solutions to this last equation: $x = \frac{1}{2}$ and $x = -1$. A glance at Fig. 26-4 shows that $x = \frac{1}{2}$ is the solution we are seeking. Now from Equation 26-1 we find

$$y^2 = 1 - x^2 = 1 - \tfrac{1}{4} = \tfrac{3}{4},$$

and hence $y = \sqrt{3}/2$, since Fig. 26-4 shows that y is positive. Thus, $(\frac{1}{2}, \sqrt{3}/2)$ are the coordinates of the trigonometric point $P(\pi/3)$.

The coordinates of $P(\pi/6)$ also can be found by an algebraic method like the one we have just used, but it is easier to use the known coordinates of $P(\pi/3)$ as follows. In Fig. 26-5 the points

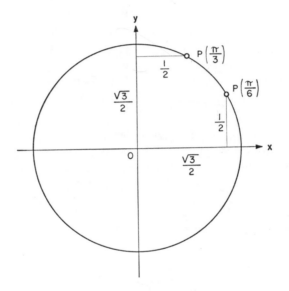

Figure 26-5

$P(\pi/3)$ and $P(\pi/6)$ are shown on the unit circle. It is clear that the arc between the x-axis and $P(\pi/6)$ and the arc between the y-axis and $P(\pi/3)$ are the same length. It then follows that the distance between $P(\pi/6)$ and the x-axis is equal to the distance between $P(\pi/3)$ and the y-axis. In other words, the y-coordinate of $P(\pi/6)$ is equal to the x-coordinate of $P(\pi/3)$. Similarly, the x-coordinate of $P(\pi/6)$ is equal to the y-coordinate of $P(\pi/3)$. Since the coordinates of $P(\pi/3)$ are $(\frac{1}{2}, \sqrt{3}/2)$, it follows that the coordinates of $P(\pi/6)$ are $(\sqrt{3}/2, \frac{1}{2})$. You should now be able to find the coordinates of trigonometric points such as $P(5\pi/6)$, $P(-\pi/6)$, and so forth, by locating them on the unit circle and observing that they are symmetrically placed with respect to $P(\pi/3)$ and $P(\pi/6)$.

Problems 26

1. Determine the coordinates of each of the following trigonometric points:
   (a) $P(2\pi)$ (d) $P(7\pi/2)$
   (b) $P(-3\pi)$ (e) $P(-13\pi/2)$
   (c) $P(5\pi/2)$ (f) $P(21\pi)$

2. Determine the coordinates of each of the following trigonometric points:
   (a) $P(5\pi/4)$ (c) $P(7\pi/4)$
   (b) $P(-\pi/4)$ (d) $P(-9\pi/4)$

3. Determine the coordinates of each of the following trigonometric points:
   (a) $P(2\pi/3)$ (c) $P(4\pi/3)$
   (b) $P(-2\pi/3)$ (d) $P(-4\pi/3)$

4. Determine the coordinates of each of the following trigonometric points:
   (a) $P(-\pi/6)$ (d) $P(-7\pi/6)$
   (b) $P(5\pi/6)$ (e) $P(-11\pi/6)$
   (c) $P(11\pi/6)$ (f) $P(7\pi/6)$

5. Make a careful drawing of the unit circle. By rotating a ruler, or using a piece of string, estimate from your figure the coordinates of $P(1)$.

6. For each of the following points determine the quadrant in which it lies:
   (a) $P(2)$ (d) $P(4)$
   (b) $P(3)$ (e) $P(5)$
   (c) $P(1.5)$ (f) $P(6)$

27   THE TRIGONOMETRIC FUNCTIONS

With each real number t we can associate a pair of real numbers (x,y), the coordinates of the trigonometric point $P(t)$. For example, with $t = 0$ we associate the numbers $(1,0)$; with $t = \pi/4$ we associate the numbers $(\sqrt{2}/2, \sqrt{2}/2)$; and so on. This association leads to the definitions of the six trigonometric functions. These functions are called the **cosine function**, the **sine function**, the **tangent function**, the **cotangent function**, the **secant function**, and the **cosecant function**. The numbers that are associated with a given real number t by these functions are labeled **cos** t, **sin** t, **tan** t, **cot** t, **sec** t, and **csc** t. They are expressed in terms of the coordinates (x,y) of the trigonometric point $P(t)$ by means of the following defining equations.

DEFINITION 27-1. *If the coordinates of the trigonometric point $P(t)$ are (x,y), then*

$$\cos t = x, \qquad\qquad \cot t = \frac{x}{y} \text{ (if } y \neq 0),$$

27-1 $\qquad \sin t = y, \qquad\qquad \sec t = \frac{1}{x} \text{ (if } x \neq 0),$

$$\tan t = \frac{y}{x} \text{ (if } x \neq 0), \qquad \csc t = \frac{1}{y} \text{ (if } y \neq 0).$$

If t is a number for which the x-coordinate of $P(t)$ is 0, then $\tan t$ and $\sec t$ are not defined; that is, t is not in the domain of either the tangent or the secant function. For example, the x-coordinate of $P(\pi/2)$ is 0, so $\pi/2$ is not in the domain of either the tangent or the secant function. Similarly, there are some real numbers not in the domains of the cotangent and cosecant functions, but the domain of both the cosine and sine functions is the set of all real numbers.

EXAMPLE 27-1. Calculate the values of the six trigonometric functions if $t = \pi/3$.

Solution. In the preceding section, we saw that the coordinates of the trigonometric point $P(\pi/3)$ are $(\frac{1}{2}, \sqrt{3}/2)$. Hence, according to Equations 27-1:

$$\cos \frac{\pi}{3} = \frac{1}{2}, \qquad \sec \frac{\pi}{3} = 2,$$

$$\sin \frac{\pi}{3} = \frac{\sqrt{3}}{2}, \qquad \csc \frac{\pi}{3} = \frac{2}{\sqrt{3}},$$

$$\tan \frac{\pi}{3} = \sqrt{3}, \qquad \cot \frac{\pi}{3} = \frac{1}{\sqrt{3}}.$$

EXAMPLE 27-2. Calculate the values of the six trigonometric functions if $t = -3\pi$.

Solution. To locate the trigonometric point $P(-3\pi)$ we must proceed 3π units around the unit circle in a clockwise direction. We find that the coordinates of the point $P(-3\pi)$ are $(-1,0)$. Hence, from Equations 27-1:

$$\cos(-3\pi) = -1, \qquad \tan(-3\pi) = 0,$$

$$\sin(-3\pi) = 0, \qquad \sec(-3\pi) = -1.$$

Since the y-coordinate of $P(-3\pi)$ is 0, the symbols cot (-3π) and csc (-3π) are not defined.

We can establish certain relations among the various trigonometric functions directly from their definitions.   If (x, y) are the coordinates of any trigonometric point $P(t)$, then $x^2 + y^2 = 1$ (Equation 26-1). But according to Equations 27-1, $x = \cos t$ and $y = \sin t$, and therefore we have the basic relation

27-2 $$\cos^2 t + \sin^2 t = 1 \quad \text{for any number } t.$$

Remark.   The notation we used in Equation 27-2 is a shorthand method that avoids the use of parentheses. We use the symbol $\sin^2 t$ instead of $(\sin t)^2$.   This convention is used for all positive exponents and all trigonometric functions, but it is not used with negative exponents.   Thus we do not abbreviate $(\sin t)^{-1}$.   This may seem to be an arbitrary decision to make at the moment, but it will avoid confusion in your later work.

Other relations we can derive from Equations 27-1 are

27-3 $$\tan t = \frac{\sin t}{\cos t},$$

27-4 $$\cot t = \frac{\cos t}{\sin t},$$

27-5 $$\cot t = \frac{1}{\tan t},$$

27-6 $$\sec t = \frac{1}{\cos t},$$

27-7 $$\csc t = \frac{1}{\sin t}.$$

We can prove the validity of these equations very quickly.   For example, tan t is the quotient y/x, where (x, y) are the coordinates of $P(t)$.   But $y = \sin t$ and $x = \cos t$, and so

$$\tan t = \frac{y}{x} = \frac{\sin t}{\cos t}.$$

We can prove the other equations in the same way.   These five equations, together with Equation 27-2, are called the **elementary**

identities.   Each is true for all values of t for which both sides of the equation are defined.

EXAMPLE 27-3.   Show that $\tan^2 t + 1 = \sec^2 t$.

Solution.   This equation is meaningless if the x-coordinate of $P(t)$ is 0, and so we tacitly assume that it is not.   In other words, $\cos t \neq 0$ for those values of t in which we are interested.   Thus we may divide both sides of the elementary identity $\sin^2 t + \cos^2 t = 1$ by $\cos^2 t$ and use other elementary identities to obtain, successively, the equations

$$\frac{\sin^2 t}{\cos^2 t} + 1 = \frac{1}{\cos^2 t},$$

and

27-8 $$\tan^2 t + 1 = \sec^2 t.$$

EXAMPLE 27-4.   Show that $\tan t + \cot t = \csc t \sec t$.

Solution.   From the elementary identities,

$$\tan t + \cot t = \frac{\sin t}{\cos t} + \frac{\cos t}{\sin t}$$

$$= \frac{\sin^2 t + \cos^2 t}{(\sin t)(\cos t)}$$

$$= \frac{1}{(\sin t)(\cos t)}$$

$$= \csc t \sec t.$$

Since every trigonometric point $P(t)$ lies on the unit circle, neither of its coordinates can be greater than 1 in absolute value; that is, both $|x| \leq 1$ and $|y| \leq 1$.   Therefore,

27-9 $$|\cos t| \leq 1 \quad \text{and} \quad |\sin t| \leq 1, \quad \text{for all numbers } t.$$

It then follows from Equations 27-6 and 27-7 that

27-10 $$|\sec t| \geq 1 \quad \text{and} \quad |\csc t| \geq 1, \quad \text{for all numbers } t \text{ in the}$$
domains of these functions.

Using the language of Chapter Two, we can say that the range of both the sine and cosine functions is the set of numbers y that satisfy the inequality $|y| \leq 1$.   The range of both the secant and cosecant functions is the set of numbers y that satisfy the inequality $|y| \geq 1$. The range of both the tangent and cotangent functions is the set of all real numbers.

Problems 27

1. Find the values of the six trigonometric functions if the coordinates of the trigonometric point are:
   (a) $(1/\sqrt{5}, 2/\sqrt{5})$
   (b) $(1/\sqrt{3}, -\sqrt{2/3})$
   (c) $(-1/3, 2\sqrt{2}/3)$
   (d) $(.24, .97)$

2. Estimate the value of each of the following from a sketch of the unit circle.
   (a) sin 1
   (b) cos 3
   (c) cot 1.5
   (d) sec 6.2

3. Make a list of all numbers t that satisfy the inequalities $-2\pi \leq t \leq 2\pi$ for which:
   (a) tan t is undefined
   (b) cot t is undefined
   (c) csc t is undefined
   (d) sec t is undefined

4. Which of the following numbers are positive?
   (a) sin 2
   (b) tan 3
   (c) cos 1.5
   (d) csc 4
   (e) cot 5
   (f) sec 6

5. Show that $1 + \cot^2 t = \csc^2 t$ for any number t in the domain of the cotangent function (see Example 27-3).

6. Complete the following table, which shows the algebraic signs of the trigonometric functions:

	$0 < t < \frac{1}{2}\pi$	$\frac{1}{2}\pi < t < \pi$	$\pi < t < 3\pi/2$	$3\pi/2 < t < 2\pi$
Quadrant in which $P(t)$ lies:	I	II	III	IV
cos t	+	−		
sin t	+	+		
tan t	+	−		
cot t				
csc t				
sec t				

7. Show that each of the following expressions has the value of 1 for all numbers t for which the expressions are defined.
   (a) $\frac{1}{2}(\tan t \csc t \cos t + \cot t \sec t \sin t)$
   (b) $\dfrac{\sec t \csc t}{\tan t + \cot t}$
   (c) $\dfrac{\cos t + \sin^2 t \sec t}{\sec t}$

8. Complete the following table.   (We will make use of this table later.)

t	$\cos t$	$\sin t$	$\tan t$	$\cot t$	$\csc t$	$\sec t$
0	1	0	0	...	...	1
$\dfrac{\pi}{6}$	$\dfrac{\sqrt{3}}{2}$	$\dfrac{1}{2}$	$\dfrac{\sqrt{3}}{3}$	$\sqrt{3}$	2	$\dfrac{2\sqrt{3}}{3}$
$\dfrac{\pi}{4}$	$\dfrac{\sqrt{2}}{2}$	$\dfrac{\sqrt{2}}{2}$	1	1	$\sqrt{2}$	$\sqrt{2}$
$\dfrac{\pi}{3}$	$\dfrac{1}{2}$ .500	$\dfrac{\sqrt{3}}{2}$ .866	$\sqrt{3}$ 1.732	$\dfrac{1}{\sqrt{3}}=\dfrac{\sqrt{3}}{3}$ .577	$\dfrac{2}{\sqrt{3}}=\dfrac{2\sqrt{3}}{3}$ 1.154	2
$\dfrac{\pi}{2}$	0	1	...	0	1	...
$\dfrac{2\pi}{3}$	$-\dfrac{1}{2}$	$\dfrac{\sqrt{3}}{2}$	$-\sqrt{3}$	$\dfrac{\sqrt{3}}{3}$	$\dfrac{2\sqrt{3}}{3}$	-2
$\dfrac{3\pi}{4}$	$-\dfrac{\sqrt{2}}{2}$ $-.707$	$\dfrac{\sqrt{2}}{2}$ .707	-1	-1	$\sqrt{2}$ 1.414	$-\sqrt{2}$ -1.414
$\dfrac{5\pi}{6}$	$-\dfrac{\sqrt{3}}{2}$	$\dfrac{1}{2}$	$-\dfrac{\sqrt{3}}{3}$	$-\sqrt{3}$	2	$-\dfrac{2\sqrt{3}}{3}$
π	-1	0	0	...	...	-1
$\dfrac{7\pi}{6}$	$-\dfrac{\sqrt{3}}{2}$	$-\dfrac{1}{2}$	$\dfrac{\sqrt{3}}{3}$	$\sqrt{3}$	-2	$-\dfrac{2\sqrt{3}}{3}$
$\dfrac{5\pi}{4}$	$-\dfrac{\sqrt{2}}{2}$	$-\dfrac{\sqrt{2}}{2}$	1	1	$-\sqrt{2}$	$-\sqrt{2}$
$\dfrac{4\pi}{3}$	$-\dfrac{1}{2}$	$-\dfrac{\sqrt{3}}{2}$	$\sqrt{3}$	$\dfrac{\sqrt{3}}{3}$	$-\dfrac{2\sqrt{3}}{3}$	-2
$\dfrac{3\pi}{2}$	0	-1	...	0	-1	...
$\dfrac{5\pi}{3}$	$\dfrac{1}{2}$	$-\dfrac{\sqrt{3}}{2}$	$-\sqrt{3}$	$-\dfrac{\sqrt{3}}{3}$	$-\dfrac{2\sqrt{3}}{3}$	2
$\dfrac{7\pi}{4}$	$\dfrac{\sqrt{2}}{2}$	$-\dfrac{\sqrt{2}}{2}$	-1	-1	$-\sqrt{2}$	$\sqrt{2}$
$\dfrac{11\pi}{6}$	$\dfrac{\sqrt{3}}{2}$	$-\dfrac{1}{2}$	$-\dfrac{\sqrt{3}}{3}$	$-\sqrt{3}$	-2	$\dfrac{2\sqrt{3}}{3}$

28   TABLES

We have located the trigonometric point $P(t)$ for numbers such as $t = 0,\ 3\pi/2,\ -\pi,\ \pi/3$, and so forth, by using geometric reasoning. This reasoning enables us to find the corresponding values of the various trigonometric functions from the defining Equations 27-1. If t is a number such that the point $P(t)$ is not easy to locate by geometry, we can find the values of the trigonometric functions from a table. Table II (pp. 395-398) lists values of the trigonometric functions for numbers t such that $0 \leq t \leq 1.60$. We read this table in much the same way as we read the table of logarithms. In particular, we can use linear interpolation to find values of the trigonometric functions for numbers t ($0 \leq t \leq 1.60$) not listed in Table II.

EXAMPLE 28-1.   Find sin .827.

Solution.   We can find the number sin .827 by interpolating between sin .820 and sin .830. From Table II, we see that sin .820 = .7311 and sin .830 = .7379. Thus, sin .827 = sin .820 + .7(.7379 − .7311) = .7311 + .0048 = .7359.

EXAMPLE 28-2.   Find cos 1.262.

Solution.   From the table, we see that cos 1.260 = .3058 and cos 1.270 = .2963. Thus cos 1.262 = cos 1.260 + .2(.2963 − .3058) = .3058 − .0019 = .3039. You should note that .0019 is subtracted, not added, here. This procedure is consistent with the fact that if $0 \leq t_1 < t_2 \leq \pi/2$, then $\cos t_1 > \cos t_2$. This fact follows directly from the definition of $\cos t$ as the x-coordinate of the trigonometric point $P(t)$.

EXAMPLE 28-3.   Find the coordinates of the trigonometric point $P(.73)$.

Solution.   If we use (x, y) to denote the desired coordinates, then $x = \cos .73$ and $y = \sin .73$. With the aid of Table II we find that the coordinates of $P(.73)$ are (.7452, .6669).

There is only one solution to the equation $\log x = .4771$—namely, $x = 3$. But there are many solutions to the equation $\sin t = 0$— for example, $t = 0,\ \pi,\ -\pi,\ 2\pi$, and so forth. It is often true that equations involving trigonometric functions have many solutions, and in Chapter Ten we shall discuss the question of finding *all solutions* of such equations. In this chapter, however, we shall ask only for *a solution* of such equations.

EXAMPLE 28-4. Find a solution to the equation $\tan t = \sqrt{3}$.

Solution. You should remember that $(\frac{1}{2}, \frac{1}{2}\sqrt{3})$ are the coordinates of the trigonometric point $P(\pi/3)$ and therefore $\tan \pi/3 = \sqrt{3}$. Hence, a solution to the equation is $t = \pi/3$. Can you show that $t = 4\pi/3$ is also a solution?

EXAMPLE 28-5. Find a solution to the equation $\cos t = .6241$.

Solution. From Table II we see that

$$\cos .89 = .6294,$$

$$\cos t = .6241,$$

$$\cos .90 = .6216.$$

Since .6241 is $\frac{53}{78} = .7$ of the distance from .6294 to .6216, we conclude that a suitable choice for t is .897.

We end this section with an example that can be solved much more easily by using trigonometric identities than by using tables.

EXAMPLE 28-6. If $0 < t < \pi/2$, and $\tan t = \sqrt{5}/2$, find $\cos t$.

Solution. One way to find $\cos t$ is to compute first the decimal representation of $\sqrt{5}/2$, then use Table II and the given value of $\tan t$ to determine t, and finally again use the table to find $\cos t$. But it is much easier to use some trigonometric identities to solve this problem. From Equation 27-8,

$$\sec^2 t = 1 + \tan^2 t = 1 + \tfrac{5}{4} = \tfrac{9}{4}.$$

Thus,

$$\cos^2 t = 1/\sec^2 t = \tfrac{4}{9}.$$

Since $0 < t < \pi/2$, we know that $\cos t > 0$, and hence it follows from the last equation that $\cos t = \tfrac{2}{3}$.

Problems 28

1. With the aid of Table II find the following numbers:
   (a) tan .732
   (b) sec .904
   (c) csc 1.301
   (d) cot $\frac{1}{8}$
   (e) sin $\frac{3}{8}$
   (f) cos $\frac{7}{8}$

2. Which is larger, cos .333 or cos $\frac{1}{3}$?

3. What can you conclude from Table II concerning t, sin t, and tan t for numbers t that satisfy the inequalities $0 \le t \le .05$?

4. How do you explain the fact that Table II shows that the value of sec t is the same for all numbers t that satisfy the inequalities $0 \le t \le .03$?

5. Explain why the values of the cosine, tangent, cotangent, and secant functions are listed in Table II with negative signs for the numbers 1.58, 1.59, and 1.60.

6. Find a number t that will satisfy each of the following equations:
   (a) sin $t = \frac{1}{2}$
   (b) cos $t = \frac{1}{2}$
   (c) tan $t = .1716$
   (d) cot $t = 15$
   (e) sec $t = 1.652$
   (f) csc $t = 1$

7. If $0 < t < \frac{1}{2}\pi$, and sin $t = \frac{1}{4}$, find cos t.

8. If $\frac{1}{2}\pi < t < \pi$, and cos $t = -\sqrt{3}/3$, find tan t.

9. Use the values of sin .85 and cos .85 listed in Table II to test the identity $\sin^2 t + \cos^2 t = 1$.

10. With the aid of Table II find the value of each of the following expressions. (*Hint:* Use elementary identities to simplify the expression first.)
   (a) $\sqrt{1 - \cos^2 .56}$
   (b) $\sqrt{\sec^2 .79 - 1}$
   (c) $(\tan 1.4 \cos 1.4 - \csc 1.4) \csc 1.4$
   (d) $\dfrac{\sec .32}{\tan .32 + \cot .32}$

29 FUNCTIONAL VALUES FOR ANY NUMBER t

Just as we were able to find the logarithms of any positive number by using only a table of logarithms of numbers between 1 and 10, so we can find all values of the trigonometric functions by using only a table of values corresponding to numbers t such that $0 \le t \le \pi/2$. (Table II contains values of t between 0 and 1.60, and $\pi/2 = 1.5708$ approximately.)

Each trigonometric point $P(t)$ is joined to whichever point is closer to it—$(1,0)$ or $(-1,0)$—by an arc of the unit circle whose length does not exceed one-fourth of the circumference of the circle. In other words, the length of the shorter arc of the unit circle that joins $P(t)$ to the x-axis is never greater than $\pi/2$. We shall call the length of this arc the **reference number associated with the num-**

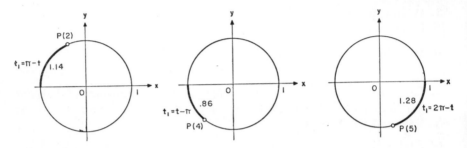

Figure 29-1

ber t and denote it by t_1. For example (see Fig. 29-1), if $t = 2$, then $t_1 = \pi - t = 1.14$; if $t = 4$, then $t_1 = 4 - \pi = .86$; if $t = 5$, then $t_1 = 2\pi - 5 = 1.28$, where we have used the approximation $\pi = 3.14$.

Since t_1 is a number between 0 and $\pi/2$, its trigonometric point $P(t_1)$ lies in the first quadrant. In order to find the relationship

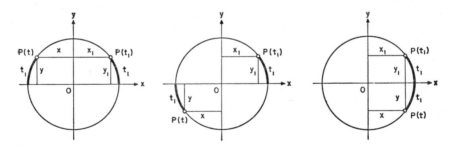

Figure 29-2

between the coordinates (x_1, y_1) of $P(t_1)$ and the coordinates (x, y) of $P(t)$, let us examine the drawings in Fig. 29-2. You should be able to convince yourself that in every case either $x = x_1$ or $x = -x_1$, and that either $y = y_1$ or $y = -y_1$. We can summarize the relationships between the coordinates of the points $P(t)$ and $P(t_1)$ by the equations

29-1 $|x| = x_1$ and $|y| = y_1$.

It then follows from these last equations and from the definitions of the trigonometric functions that *the values of the trigonometric functions or the numbers t and t_1 are the same, except possibly for their signs.* To be precise,

29-2 $|T(t)| = T(t_1)$,

where T may stand for any trigonometric function. To show, for example, that $|\tan t| = \tan t_1$, we need only note that by definition $\tan t = y/x$. Hence,

$$|\tan t| = \frac{|y|}{|x|} = \frac{y_1}{x_1} = \tan t_1.$$

The values of the trigonometric functions for t_1 are listed in Table II, and therefore we can determine the absolute values of the trigonometric functions for any number t as soon as we find the reference number t_1. To find the actual values, we need only notice the quadrant in which $P(t)$ lies and affix the proper sign.

EXAMPLE 29-1.   Find sin 4.

Solution. The trigonometric point $P(4)$ lies in the third quadrant so $\sin 4 < 0$. The associated reference number is $t_1 = 4 - \pi = .86$. According to Equation 29-2 and Table II,

$$|\sin 4| = \sin .86 = .7578.$$

Therefore, $\sin 4 = -.7578$.

EXAMPLE 29-2.   Find sec $-31\pi/4$.

Solution. We obtain the point $P(-31\pi/4)$ by proceeding $31\pi/4 = 7\pi + 3\pi/4$ units around the unit circle from the point $(1,0)$ in a clockwise direction (Fig. 29-3). The point is in the first quadrant and the reference number is $t_1 = \pi/4$. Hence, sec $(-31\pi/4) = $ sec $\pi/4 = \sqrt{2}$.

Our method for finding the values of the trigonometric functions for any number t consists of four steps:

    (i) Determine the quadrant in which $P(t)$ lies;
    (ii) Find the reference number t_1 associated with t;
    (iii) Use Table II to find $T(t_1) = |T(t)|$;
    (iv) Affix the proper algebraic sign.

If t is a number between -2π and 2π, it is easy to locate $P(t)$. If t is not a number between -2π and 2π, and if the location of $P(t)$ is not obvious, we might proceed in the manner illustrated by the following two examples.

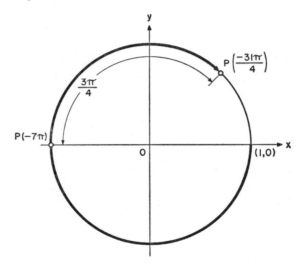

Figure 29-3

EXAMPLE 29-3.   Locate $P(60)$, find the reference number t_1 associated with $t = 60$, and find the value of cos 60.

Solution. To locate the trigonometric point $P(60)$ we must proceed 60 units around the unit circle in a counter-clockwise direction starting from the point (1,0). Since the circumference of the unit circle is $2\pi = 6.283$ units, it is apparent that we will traverse the entire circumference a number of times. To discover the exact number of complete revolutions, we divide 60 by 2π, using the process of "long division."

$$
\begin{array}{r}
9. \\
6.283\overline{\smash{)}60.000} \\
56.547 \\
\hline
3.453
\end{array}
$$

Thus we may write $60 = 9 \cdot (6.283) + 3.453$. This result means that to locate the point $P(60)$ we must proceed nine times around the unit circle and then 3.453 units in a counter-clockwise direction.   It follows that the point $P(3.453)$ is the same as the point $P(60)$.   It is clear that $P(3.453)$ is in the third quadrant so $t_1 = 3.453 - \pi = 3.453 - 3.142 = .311$.   With the aid of Table II we find that $\cos 60 = -\cos .311 = -.9520$.

EXAMPLE 29-4.   Find $\tan (-26)$.

Solution.   The first step in locating $P(-26)$ is to use "long division" to write $-26 = -4 \cdot (6.283) - .868$.   This result means that we are to proceed four times around the unit circle and then .868 units in a *clockwise* direction.   The point $P(-.868)$ is therefore the same as the point $P(-26)$.   Since $-\pi/2 = -1.571$, we see that $P(-.868)$ is in the fourth quadrant and that $t_1 = .868$.   Thus, we have $\tan (-26) = -\tan .868 = -1.180$.

Problems 29

1. With the aid of Table II evaluate the following (use $\pi = 3.14$):
    (a) $\sin 3.56$ (d) $\cot 4.75$
    (b) $\cos 2.79$ (e) $\sec -3.95$
    (c) $\tan -5.41$ (f) $\csc 6.19$

2. Evaluate the following:
    (a) $\cos 13\pi/3$ (f) $\tan -27\pi/4$
    (b) $\sin 17\pi/6$ (g) $\csc 43\pi/6$
    (c) $\cot 22\pi/3$ (h) $\sin -61\pi/2$
    (d) $\cos -35\pi/6$ (i) $\tan 59\pi/6$
    (e) $\sec 41\pi/4$ (j) $\cos 71\pi/2$

3. With the aid of Table II find the coordinates of each of the following trigonometric points (use $\pi = 3.142$ and $2\pi = 6.283$):
    (a) $P(2)$ (f) $P(20)$
    (b) $P(3)$ (g) $P(-\frac{1}{2})$
    (c) $P(4)$ (h) $P(-\sqrt{2})$
    (d) $P(5)$ (i) $P(3\sqrt{2})$
    (e) $P(6)$ (j) $P(-3\sqrt{3}/2)$

4. With the aid of Table II evaluate the following (use $\pi = 3.142$ and $2\pi = 6.283$):
    (a) $\tan 7$ (e) $\sec 45$
    (b) $\sin -10$ (f) $\csc -30$
    (c) $\cos 14$ (g) $\sin 60$
    (d) $\cot 21$ (h) $\cos -45$

5. Determine which is larger:
   — (a) cos 5 or cos 6   (c) tan 10 or tan 11
   — (b) sin 5 or sin 6   (d) cos 10 or cos 11

6. Find a number t such that $\pi < t < 3\pi/2$ and:
   (a) $\cos t = -\tfrac{1}{2}$ (c) $\sin t = -\tfrac{1}{2}$
   (b) $\tan t = \sqrt{3}$ (d) $\tan t = \tfrac{1}{2}$

7. Find a number t such that $3\pi/2 < t < 2\pi$ and $3 \sin t + 4 \cos t = 0$.

8. One end of a shaft is fastened to a piston that moves vertically. The other end is connected to a point P on the rim of the wheel by means of prongs as shown in Fig. 29-4. Let the radius of the wheel be 1 ft, and

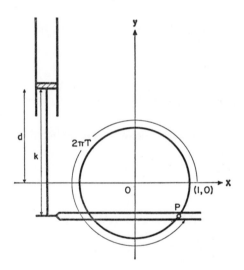

Figure 29-4

suppose that the shaft is k ft long, as shown in the figure. Let the wheel rotate counter-clockwise at the rate of 1 rps; that is, P moves 2π fps around a unit circle. A coordinate system is introduced as shown in the figure.
   (a) Find a formula for the distance d ft between the bottom of the piston and the x-axis T sec after P is at the point (1,0).
   (b) Locate the piston when T is $\tfrac{7}{8}$, $\tfrac{10}{3}$, and $13/\pi$.

9. A piston is connected to the rim of a wheel as shown in Fig. 29-5. The radius of the wheel is 1 ft and the length of the connecting rod $\overline{PQ}$ shown in the figure is 3 ft. The wheel rotates counter-clockwise at the rate of 1 rps. A coordinate system is introduced as shown in the figure.

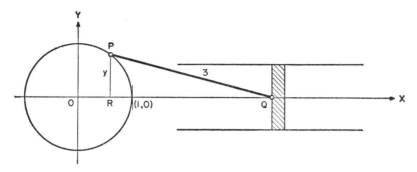

Figure 29-5

(a) Show that T seconds after the point P is at the point $(1,0)$, the x-coordinate of the point Q is given by the equation
$$x = \sqrt{9 - \sin^2 2\pi T} + \cos 2\pi T.$$
(*Hint:* Find the distance $\overline{RQ}$ by means of the Pythagorean Theorem.)

(b) Find the position of the point Q when T is $\frac{1}{3}$, $\frac{11}{3}$, and $\frac{4}{5}$.

30   GRAPHS OF THE TRIGONOMETRIC FUNCTIONS

To locate the trigonometric point $P(t)$ for a given number t, we start at the point $(1,0)$ and proceed $|t|$ units around the unit circle in the appropriate direction. We locate the point $P(t + 2\pi)$ by first laying off $|t|$ units on the circumference of the circle and then proceeding 2π units (one complete revolution). It is apparent therefore that $P(t)$ *and* $P(t + 2\pi)$ *represent the same point.* It follows that for any number t,

30-1 $$T(t + 2\pi) = T(t),$$

where T may represent any one of the six trigonometric functions. For example, $\sin (t + 2\pi) = \sin t$. From Equation 30-1 it follows that the graph of any trigonometric function need only be plotted for values of t in an interval with a length of 2π; the complete graph will consist of duplications of this portion.

To plot the graph of the sine function we shall first choose values of t between and including 0 and 2π. (Any other interval of length 2π would do just as well.) From the values of the sine function that we calculated in Exercise 8 of Problems 27, we can find 17 points on this portion of the graph.   We can find additional points from Table II by using the methods we discussed in the preceding section. We plot a number of these points and join them smoothly to form the heavy portion of the curve shown in Fig. 30-1.   The remainder of the graph of the sine function consists of duplications of this part of the graph.

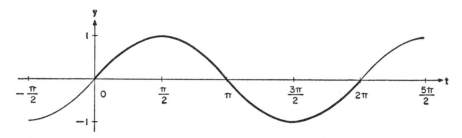

Figure 30-1

We can plot the graph of the cosine function in the same way that we plotted the graph of the sine function.   The graph of the cosine function is shown in Fig. 30-2, and the graph of the cosecant function in Fig. 30-3.   Since csc $t = 1/\sin t$, we have drawn a dashed line sine curve in Fig. 30-3 to show how it is related to the cosecant curve.

There is a fundamental difference between the graph of the tangent

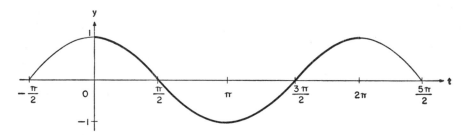

Figure 30-2

function and the graphs shown in Figs. 30-1, 30-2, and 30-3.   Suppose we plot the graph of the equation $y = \tan t$ for values of t in an interval of length 2π—for example, from $t = -\frac{1}{2}\pi$ to $t = 3\pi/2$. We get the heavy curve shown in Fig. 30-4.   The remainder of the graph of the tangent function is simply a reproduction of this portion. But it is obvious from the figure that we need only have plotted that

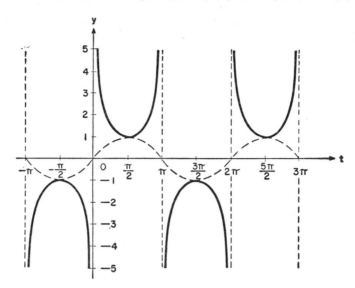

Figure 30-3

portion of the graph that corresponds to values of t between $-\frac{1}{2}\pi$ and $\frac{1}{2}\pi$.   *The graph of the tangent function repeats every π units.*

Up to this point we have used the letter t rather than the letter x to denote a number in the domain of a trigonometric function in order to avoid confusion with the x-coordinate of the trigonometric point $P(t)$.   When there is no danger of such confusion, we often use the letter x to denote a number in the domain.   In particular

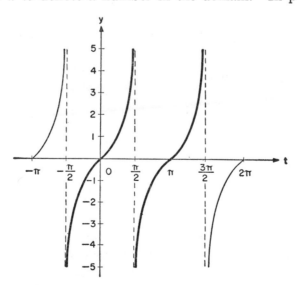

Figure 30-4

we frequently use the letter x instead of t when dealing with graphs since we usually label the horizontal coordinate axis as the x-axis rather than the t-axis.

The graphs display certain properties of the trigonometric functions that we shall study analytically in a later section. It is clear, for example, that the cosine and sine curves are the "same" except for their positions relative to the y-axis. For example, if we "shift" the sine curve $\frac{1}{2}\pi$ units to the left, it will fall directly over the cosine curve.

A graph is **symmetric with respect to the y-axis** if for each point (x,y) on the graph the point $(-x,y)$ is also on the graph. In geometrical terms this statement means that for every point P on the graph there is a point Q on the graph such that the y-axis is the perpendicular bisector of the segment $\overline{PQ}$. When a graph is symmetric with respect to the y-axis, we say that the part of the graph to the left of the y-axis is the **reflection** about the y-axis of the part of the graph to the right. Figure 30-2 shows at a glance that the graph of the cosine function is symmetric with respect to the y-axis.

A graph is **symmetric with respect to the origin** if for each point (x,y) on the graph the point $(-x,-y)$ is also on the graph. Geometrically this sentence means that for every point P on the graph there is a point Q on the graph such that the origin is the mid-point of the segment $\overline{PQ}$. Figures 30-1 and 30-4 show clearly that the graphs of both the sine and tangent functions are symmetric with respect to the origin.

Figures 30-1 to 30-4 also illustrate some properties of the trigonometric functions that are developed in a course in calculus. You should become familiar with the graphs shown in these figures and be able to make a quick sketch of the graph of any trigonometric function.

Problems 30

1. Sketch a graph of the secant function.
2. Sketch a graph of the cotangent function.
3. Discuss the symmetry of the graphs of the cotangent, secant, and co-secant functions.
4. Use the graphs to find the following numbers:
    (a) sin 5
    (b) cos 2
    (c) tan -1
    (d) csc 2

5. If the graph of the equation $y = f(x)$ is symmetric with respect to the y-axis, how are the numbers $f(x)$ and $f(-x)$ related?

6. If the graph of the equation $y = f(x)$ is symmetric with respect to the origin, how are the numbers $f(x)$ and $f(-x)$ related?

7. From Fig. 30-1 it is clear that the sine function is an **increasing function** if $0 < t < \pi/2$. That is, if $0 < t_1 < t_2 < \frac{1}{2}\pi$, then $\sin t_1 < \sin t_2$. Figure 30-2 indicates that the cosine function is a **decreasing function** for the interval $0 < t < \frac{1}{2}\pi$. That is, if $0 < t_1 < t_2 < \frac{1}{2}\pi$, then $\cos t_1 > \cos t_2$. In each of the following cases determine whether the function is increasing or decreasing for the interval indicated:
   (a) The tangent function in the interval $0 < t < \frac{1}{2}\pi$,
   (b) The sine function in the interval $\frac{1}{2}\pi < t < \pi$,
   (c) The cosine function in the interval $\frac{1}{2}\pi < t < \pi$,
   (d) The sine function in the interval $-\pi < t < -\frac{1}{2}\pi$,
   (e) The cotangent function in the interval $0 < t < \frac{1}{2}\pi$.

8. Determine which of the following statements are true:
   (a) If $-\frac{1}{2}\pi < t_1 < t_2 < \frac{1}{2}\pi$, then $\sin t_1 < \sin t_2$,
   (b) If $0 < t_1 < t_2 < \pi$, then $\cos t_1 > \cos t_2$,
   (c) If $30\pi < t_1 < t_2 < 61\pi/2$, then $\sin t_1 < \sin t_2$,
   (d) If $0 < t_1 < t_2$, then $\tan t_1 < \tan t_2$.

9. Graph the equation $y = \sin 2x$ in the interval $0 < x < \pi$.

10. Graph the equation $y = 2 \cos x$ in the interval $0 < x < \pi$.

11. Sketch the graph of the equation $y = \cos t + \sin t$ by plotting the graphs of the equations $y = \cos t$ and $y = \sin t$ on the same axes and adding y-coordinates.

12. Graph the equations $y = x$ and $y = \sin x$ on the same axes to convince yourself that $\sin x < x$ if $x > 0$.

13. Graph the equations $y = x$ and $y = \cos x$ on the same axes. Find an approximate solution to the equation $x = \cos x$ by finding the x-coordinate of the point of intersection of the two graphs. Check your answer by using Table II.

31   THE ADDITION FORMULAS

If f is a given function, a formula relating the numbers $f(u)$, $f(v)$, and $f(u + v)$ is called an **addition formula**. For the function f that is determined by the direct variation formula $f(x) = mx$, the addition formula is $f(u + v) = f(u) + f(v)$. If f is an exponential function, $f(x) = b^x$, the addition formula is $f(u + v) = f(u)f(v)$. In this section we will begin the task of finding addition formulas for the trigonometric functions.

Let u and v be any two numbers and $P(u)$ and $P(v)$ be the corresponding trigonometric points. Figure 31-1 is drawn for particular numbers u and v, but the following argument is applicable to any pair of numbers. With the number $u - v$ is associated the trigonometric point $P(u - v)$, and it is clear that the arc joining the points $P(0)$ and $P(u - v)$ is the same length as the arc joining $P(u)$ and $P(v)$—namely, $|u - v|$ units. We know from geometry that the corresponding chords are therefore also of equal length. The lengths of these chords may be expressed in terms of the coordinates of their end points as follows. According to the definitions of the sine and

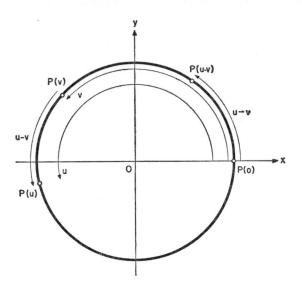

Figure 31-1

cosine functions, the coordinates of any trigonometric point $P(t)$ are $(\cos t, \sin t)$. Therefore the coordinates of $P(u)$ are $(\cos u, \sin u)$, the coordinates of $P(v)$ are $(\cos v, \sin v)$, and the coordinates of $P(u - v)$ are $[\cos (u - v), \sin (u - v)]$. The coordinates of $P(0)$ are, of course, $(1,0)$. Then according to the distance formula,

$$\overline{P(u)P(v)}^2 = (\cos u - \cos v)^2 + (\sin u - \sin v)^2,$$

$$= \cos^2 u - 2 \cos u \cos v + \cos^2 v + \sin^2 u$$

$$- 2 \sin u \sin v + \sin^2 v.$$

An application of the fundamental identity $\sin^2 t + \cos^2 t = 1$ yields

31-1 $$\overline{P(u)P(v)}^2 = 2 - 2\cos u \cos v - 2\sin u \sin v.$$

Similarly,

$$\overline{P(0)P(u - v)}^2 = [\cos (u - v) - 1]^2 + \sin^2 (u - v)$$
$$= \cos^2 (u - v) - 2\cos (u - v)$$
$$+ 1 + \sin^2 (u - v),$$

and so

31-2 $$\overline{P(0)P(u - v)}^2 = 2 - 2\cos (u - v).$$

Since the two chords are the same length, we can equate the right-hand sides of Equations 31-1 and 31-2 to obtain the equation

$$2 - 2\cos (u - v) = 2 - 2\cos u \cos v - 2\sin u \sin v.$$

A slight simplification leads to the identity

31-3 $$\cos (u - v) = \cos u \cos v + \sin u \sin v.$$

Note, in particular, that $\cos (u - v)$ is *not* the same as $\cos u - \cos v$.

EXAMPLE 31-1.   Find $\cos \pi/12$.

Solution.   We can write $\pi/12 = \pi/3 - \pi/4$ and therefore can apply Equation 31-3 to obtain

$$\cos \frac{\pi}{12} = \cos \left(\frac{\pi}{3} - \frac{\pi}{4} \right)$$

$$= \cos \frac{\pi}{3} \cos \frac{\pi}{4} + \sin \frac{\pi}{3} \sin \frac{\pi}{4}$$

$$= \left(\frac{1}{2} \right) \left(\frac{\sqrt{2}}{2} \right) + \left(\frac{\sqrt{3}}{2} \right) \left(\frac{\sqrt{2}}{2} \right)$$

$$= \frac{\sqrt{2}(1 + \sqrt{3})}{4}.$$

Equation 31-3 is the fundamental formula from which we will derive a great deal of information about the trigonometric functions, including further addition formulas.   For example, since the formula must be valid for any two numbers u and v, it must be valid if $u = \pi/2$.

Thus,

$$\cos\left(\frac{\pi}{2} - v\right) = \cos\frac{\pi}{2}\cos v + \sin\frac{\pi}{2}\sin v.$$

We already know that $\cos(\pi/2) = 0$ and $\sin(\pi/2) = 1$, so it follows that

31-4 $$\cos\left(\frac{\pi}{2} - v\right) = \sin v,$$

and *this equation is true for any number v.*

A similar identity is valid for the sine function. Let u be any number and consider the number $\sin(\pi/2 - u)$. According to Equation 31-4 the sine of a number v is the cosine of $\pi/2 - v$. Hence if we let $v = \pi/2 - u$, then $\sin(\pi/2 - u) = \cos[\pi/2 - (\pi/2 - u)]$. Since $\pi/2 - (\pi/2 - u) = u$, it follows that

31-5 $$\sin\left(\frac{\pi}{2} - u\right) = \cos u,$$

and *this equation is true for any number u.*

EXAMPLE 31-2.   If u and v are two numbers such that $u + v = \pi/2$, show that $\sin^2 u + \sin^2 v = 1$.

Solution. Since $u + v = \pi/2$, $v = \pi/2 - u$. Therefore $\sin v = \cos u$ (Equation 31-5), and

$$\sin^2 u + \sin^2 v = \sin^2 u + \cos^2 u = 1.$$

We have seen enough examples of functions to know that for a given function f, $f(-x)$ and $-f(x)$ do not necessarily represent the same number. In the case of the sine function, however, they do.

31-6 $$\sin(-v) = -\sin v, \quad \text{for every number } v.$$

The proof of this assertion follows readily from the identities we have just studied. From Equations 31-4 and 31-3 we see that

$$\sin(-v) = \cos\left[\frac{\pi}{2} - (-v)\right] = \cos\left(v + \frac{\pi}{2}\right) = \cos\left[v - \left(\frac{-\pi}{2}\right)\right]$$

$$= \cos v \cos\frac{-\pi}{2} + \sin v \sin\frac{-\pi}{2}.$$

But since $\cos(-\pi/2) = 0$ and $\sin(-\pi/2) = -1$, this last equation reduces to Equation 31-6.

In Section 30 we observed that the graph of the sine function was symmetric with respect to the origin. Equation 31-6 is the analytic statement of this fact. For if the point (x,y) is on the graph of the sine function—that is, if $y = \sin x$—then $\sin(-x) = -\sin x = -y$ so that the point $(-x,-y)$ is also on the graph (see Exercise 6 of Problems 30).

But $\cos(-v)$ and $-\cos v$ are in general not the same number; indeed,

31-7 $\cos(-v) = \cos v$ for every number v.

This fact is established by setting $u = 0$ in Equation 31-3 to obtain

$$\cos(0 - v) = \cos(-v) = \cos 0 \cos v + \sin 0 \sin v.$$

Since $\cos 0 = 1$ and $\sin 0 = 0$, this last equation reduces to Equation 31-7.

In geometric terms, Equation 31-7 tells us that the graph of the cosine function is symmetric with respect to the y-axis. For if the point (x,y) is on the graph of the equation $y = \cos x$, then the point $(-x,y)$ is also on the graph since $\cos(-x) = \cos x = y$ (see Exercise 5 of Problems 30).

EXAMPLE 31-3.   What is the relation between the numbers $\tan v$ and $\tan(-v)$?

Solution.   We have

$$\tan(-v) = \frac{\sin(-v)}{\cos(-v)} = \frac{-\sin v}{\cos v} = -\tan v.$$

Problems 31

1. Show that the following equations are true for any number t.
   (a) $\cos(\pi - t) = -\cos t$ (c) $\cos(t - \pi) = -\cos t$
   (b) $\cos(2\pi - t) = \cos t$

2. Let t be a number such that $0 \le t \le 2\pi$. Let t_1 be the reference number associated with t (see Section 29). Using the results of Problem 1 show that $\cos t_1 = |\cos t|$.

3. Discuss the equation that results when you let $v = u$ in Equation 31-3.

4. Use Equation 31-3 to find a formula for $\cos(u + \tfrac{1}{2}\pi)$.

5. Utilizing the fact that $\pi/12 = \pi/4 - \pi/6$, find the exact value of $\cos \pi/12$. Compare your result with the result of Example 31-1.

6. Compute the exact value of $\cos 5\pi/12$.

7. Show that $\csc (\frac{1}{2}\pi - u) = \sec u$ and that $\tan (\frac{1}{2}\pi - u) = \cot u$.

8. Find the relation between the numbers $\cot t$ and $\cot (-t)$, $\sec t$ and $\sec (-t)$, and $\csc t$ and $\csc (-t)$.

9. Use Equation 31-5 to find the exact value of $\sin 5\pi/12$.

10. Show that $|\sin t| = |\sin |t||$. Will the equation be valid if we replace the sine function with any trigonometric function; that is, does $|T(t)| = |T(|t|)|$, where T can be any trigonometric function?

11. Show that $\cos (v - \frac{1}{2}\pi) = \sin v$ for any number v. From this equation what can you say about the graphs of the sine and cosine functions?

12. Show that the graph of $y = \sin x \cos x$ is symmetric with respect to the origin.

13. Show that the graph of $y = \sin x + \cos x$ is not symmetric with respect to either the y-axis or the origin.

14. Use Equations 31-5 and 31-6 to show that $\sin (u - \frac{1}{2}\pi) = -\cos u$.

15. Let u and v be numbers such that $u + v = \pi$. Compute the value of each of the following expressions:
(a) $\cos u + \cos v$ (b) $\sin^2 u + \cos^2 v$

16. Find a solution to each of the following equations:
(a) $\cos \pi/6 = \sin x$
(b) $\cos (\frac{1}{2}\pi - t) = \cos \frac{1}{2}\pi - \cos t$
(c) $\cos 2x = \sin \pi/3$
(d) $\sin \frac{1}{2}x = \cos \frac{3}{2}$

17. A function f such that $f(-x) = f(x)$ for all numbers x in the domain of f is called an **even function.** For example, the cosine function is an even function. Determine which of the following equations define even functions.
(a) $f(x) = \csc x$ (c) $f(x) = x^2$ (e) $f(x) = x^2 + x$
(b) $f(x) = \sec x$ (d) $f(x) = x^3$ (f) $f(x) = x \sin x$

18. A function f with the property that $f(-x) = -f(x)$ for all numbers x in the domain of f is called an **odd function.** For example, the sine function is an odd function. Determine which of the following equations define odd functions.
(a) $f(x) = \tan x$ (c) $f(x) = x^3$ (e) $f(x) = x \cos x$
(b) $f(x) = \csc x$ (d) $f(x) = x^3 + x$ (f) $f(x) = \sin (\cos x)$

19. What can you say about the symmetry of the graph of an even function? An odd function?

32 FURTHER ADDITION FORMULAS

With the aid of the results we found in the preceding section, we can derive further addition formulas. Since $\cos (u + v) = \cos [u - (-v)]$, we may apply Equation 31-3 to this latter expression and obtain the equation

$$\cos (u + v) = \cos [u - (-v)] = \cos u \cos (-v) + \sin u \sin (-v).$$

We already know that $\cos (-v) = \cos v$ and $\sin (-v) = -\sin v$, so

32-1 $\cos (u + v) = \cos u \cos v - \sin u \sin v.$

We expand $\sin (u + v)$ by first noting from Equation 31-4 that

$$\sin (u + v) = \cos \left[\frac{\pi}{2} - (u + v) \right] = \cos \left[\left(\frac{\pi}{2} - u \right) - v \right]$$

and then by expanding this latter expression in accordance with Equation 31-3:

$$\sin (u + v) = \cos \left[\left(\frac{\pi}{2} - u \right) - v \right]$$

$$= \cos \left(\frac{\pi}{2} - u \right) \cos v + \sin \left(\frac{\pi}{2} - u \right) \sin v.$$

Since $\cos \left(\frac{\pi}{2} - u \right) = \sin u$, and $\sin \left(\frac{\pi}{2} - u \right) = \cos u$, we see that

32-2 $\sin (u + v) = \sin u \cos v + \cos u \sin v.$

This equation leads directly to the expansion of $\sin (u - v)$, for

$$\sin (u - v) = \sin [u + (-v)] = \sin u \cos (-v) + \cos u \sin (-v).$$

If we replace $\cos (-v)$ with $\cos v$, and $\sin (-v)$ with $-\sin v$, we obtain the equation

32-3 $\sin (u - v) = \sin u \cos v - \cos u \sin v.$

There are so many identities of the type we have developed in this section and preceding ones that it's difficult to keep them all in mind. The key facts to memorize are the formulas for $\sin (u + v)$ and cos $(u + v)$ plus the equations sin $(-v) = -\sin v$ and cos $(-v) =$ cos v. With this information, and a knowledge of the values of the trigonometric functions for $t = 0$, $\pi/2$, and so on, it should be easy for you to derive the other formulas we have discussed and many more.

EXAMPLE 32-1.   Show that sin $(\frac{1}{2}\pi + t) = \cos t$ for every number t.

Solution. According to Equation 32-2, sin $(\frac{1}{2}\pi + t) = \sin \frac{1}{2}\pi \cos t + \cos \frac{1}{2}\pi \sin t$. But sin $\frac{1}{2}\pi = 1$ and cos $\frac{1}{2}\pi = 0$, and therefore sin $(\frac{1}{2}\pi + t) = \cos t$.

EXAMPLE 32-2.   Find an expression for tan $(u + v)$.

Solution. According to an elementary identity, tan $(u + v) = \dfrac{\sin (u + v)}{\cos (u + v)}$. When we expand the numerator and denominator we get

$$\tan (u + v) = \frac{\sin u \cos v + \cos u \sin v}{\cos u \cos v - \sin u \sin v}.$$

If neither cos $u = 0$ nor cos $v = 0$, we can divide both the numerator and the denominator of the fraction on the right by the product cos u cos v to obtain a formula that involves only the tangent function:

$$\tan (u + v) = \frac{\dfrac{\sin u \cos v}{\cos u \cos v} + \dfrac{\cos u \sin v}{\cos u \cos v}}{\dfrac{\cos u \cos v}{\cos u \cos v} - \dfrac{\sin u \sin v}{\cos u \cos v}},$$

so that

$$\tan (u + v) = \frac{\tan u + \tan v}{1 - \tan u \tan v}.$$

EXAMPLE 32-3.   Find the exact value of sec $7\pi/12$.

Solution. Since $\dfrac{7\pi}{12} = \dfrac{\pi}{3} + \dfrac{\pi}{4}$, we have

$$\sec \frac{7\pi}{12} = \frac{1}{\cos \dfrac{7\pi}{12}} = \frac{1}{\cos \left(\dfrac{\pi}{3} + \dfrac{\pi}{4} \right)}$$

$$= \frac{1}{\cos \dfrac{\pi}{3} \cos \dfrac{\pi}{4} - \sin \dfrac{\pi}{3} \sin \dfrac{\pi}{4}}$$

$$= \frac{1}{\left(\frac{1}{2}\right)\left(\frac{\sqrt{2}}{2}\right) - \left(\frac{\sqrt{3}}{2}\right)\left(\frac{\sqrt{2}}{2}\right)} = \frac{2\sqrt{2}}{1 - \sqrt{3}}$$

$$= -\sqrt{2}(1 + \sqrt{3}).$$

Problems 32

1. Derive a formula for $\cot (u + v)$.

2. Derive a formula for $\tan (u - v)$.

3. Verify the following identities:
   (a) $\sin (\pi + t) = -\sin t$ (d) $\sec (t + 3\pi/2) = \csc t$
   (b) $\tan (\pi - u) = -\tan u$ (e) $\csc (\pi - x) = \csc x$
   (c) $\sin (3\pi/2 - t) = -\cos t$ (f) $\tan (\frac{1}{2}\pi + t) = -\cot t$

4. Find the exact value of each of the following:
   (a) $\sin \pi/12$ (c) $\cos 13\pi/12$
   (b) $\sin 7\pi/12$ (d) $\tan 7\pi/12$

5. Use Table II and the addition formulas to evaluate the following:
   (a) $\sin \frac{1}{2} \cos 1 + \cos \frac{1}{2} \sin 1$
   (b) $\cos .3 \cos .1 - \sin .3 \sin .1$
   (c) $\sin 3 \cos 2 - \cos 3 \sin 2$

6. If $\sin u = \frac{3}{5}$, $\sin v = \frac{4}{5}$, and $0 < u < v < \frac{1}{2}\pi$, evaluate the following:
   (a) $\sin (u + v)$ (c) $\cos (u + v)$
   (b) $\sin (u - v)$ (d) $\tan (u + v)$

7. Simplify each of the following expressions:
   (a) $\cos (u + v) \cos v + \sin (u + v) \sin v$
   (b) $\sin (u - v) \cos v + \cos (u - v) \sin v$
   (c) $\frac{1}{2}[\sin (x + y) + \sin (x - y)] \csc x$

8. Derive a formula for $\sin (x + y + z)$.

9. If $x + y + z = \pi$, show that $\cos z + \cos x \cos y - \sin x \sin y = 0$.

10. Find an expression for $\sin (\sin x + \sin y)$.

33   VALUES OF THE TRIGONOMETRIC FUNCTIONS
FOR MULTIPLES OF t

It is easy to see that the numbers $\sin 2t$ and $2 \sin t$ are not the same for every number t. If $t = \pi/2$, for example, we see that $\sin 2t = \sin \pi = 0$, while $2 \sin t = 2 \sin \frac{1}{2}\pi = 2$. To find an expression for $\sin 2t$, we need only replace each of the numbers u and v in Equation 32-2 with the same number t. We then obtain the identity

$$\sin (t + t) = \sin t \cos t + \cos t \sin t.$$

This identity reduces to the equation

33-1 $$\sin 2t = 2 \sin t \cos t.$$

We can derive a formula for $\cos 2t$ in a similar manner. From Equation 32-1 we have

$$\cos (t + t) = \cos t \cos t - \sin t \sin t,$$

and hence,

33-2 $$\cos 2t = \cos^2 t - \sin^2 t.$$

We can write this equation in different forms by using the identity $\cos^2 t + \sin^2 t = 1$; in particular,

33-3 $$\cos 2t = 1 - 2 \sin^2 t \quad \text{and}$$

33-4 $$\cos 2t = 2 \cos^2 t - 1.$$

The identities that result when these last two equations are solved for $\sin^2 t$ and $\cos^2 t$ are particularly useful for certain operations in calculus. They are

33-5 $$\sin^2 t = \frac{1 - \cos 2t}{2} \quad \text{and}$$

33-6 $$\cos^2 t = \frac{1 + \cos 2t}{2}.$$

EXAMPLE 33-1.   Find the exact value of $\sin \dfrac{\pi}{8}$.

Solution. We have not discussed the values of the trigonometric functions for $t = \pi/8$, but we do know the values for $2t = \pi/4$. So we replace t by $\pi/8$ in Equation 33-5 to obtain

$$\sin^2 \frac{\pi}{8} = \frac{1 - \cos \dfrac{\pi}{4}}{2} = \frac{1}{2} \left(1 - \frac{\sqrt{2}}{2} \right) = \frac{1}{4} (2 - \sqrt{2}).$$

The number $\sin \dfrac{\pi}{8}$ is positive and hence $\sin \dfrac{\pi}{8} = \frac{1}{2}\sqrt{2 - \sqrt{2}}$.

Equations 33-5 and 33-6 give only the squares of the numbers $\sin t$ and $\cos t$. If we want to find the numbers themselves, we must, by locating the quadrant in which the trigonometric point $P(t)$ lies, determine the correct sign. A corresponding formula for $\tan t$ is more complete. If we multiply the numerator and denominator of the right member of the equation $\tan t = \sin t/\cos t$ by $2 \cos t$, we obtain

$$\tan t = \frac{2 \sin t \cos t}{2 \cos^2 t}.$$

From Equation 33-1 the numerator is $\sin 2t$, and, from Equation 33-6, the denominator is $1 + \cos 2t$. Hence,

33-7
$$\tan t = \frac{\sin 2t}{1 + \cos 2t}.$$

EXAMPLE 33-2.   Use Equation 33-7 to find the exact value of $\tan 5\pi/8$.

Solution.   By setting $t = 5\pi/8$ in Equation 33-7 we obtain

$$\tan \frac{5\pi}{8} = \frac{\sin \dfrac{5\pi}{4}}{1 + \cos \dfrac{5\pi}{4}} = \frac{-\dfrac{\sqrt{2}}{2}}{1 - \dfrac{\sqrt{2}}{2}} = \frac{-\sqrt{2}}{2 - \sqrt{2}}$$

$$= \frac{-\sqrt{2}(2 + \sqrt{2})}{(2 - \sqrt{2})(2 + \sqrt{2})} = \frac{-\sqrt{2}}{2}(2 + \sqrt{2}) = -(\sqrt{2} + 1).$$

EXAMPLE 33-3.   Find the maximum value of the product $\sin t \cos t$.

Solution.   According to Equation 33-1, $\sin t \cos t = \frac{1}{2} \sin 2t$. The maximum value assumed by $\sin 2t$ is 1. Hence the maximum value of the product $\sin t \cos t$ is $\frac{1}{2}$. (The maximum value occurs when $2t = \pi/2$ or $t = \pi/4$, for instance.)

Problems 33

1. Derive a formula for $\tan 2t$.

2. Derive a formula for $\cot 2t$.

3. Derive a formula for $\tan^2 t$ by "dividing Equation 33-5 by Equation 33-6."

— 4. Find the exact value of each of the following:
    (a) $\cos \pi/8$ (c) $\tan \pi/8$
    (b) $\sin 5\pi/8$ (d) $\cos 5\pi/8$

5. Use Equation 33-6 and the fact that $2(\pi/12) = \pi/6$ to find the exact value of $\cos \pi/12$. Compare your answer with the result of Example 31-1.

6. Derive an identity for $\sin 3t$.

7. Find the exact value of $\sin \pi/16$.

8. Simplify the following expressions:
   (a) $(\sin x + \cos x)^2 - \sin 2x$ (c) $\sin^2 2t - \cos^2 2t$
   (b) $\sin^2 2t/(1 + \cos 2t)^2 + 1$ (d) $(\sin 2t)(\cos 2t)$

9. If t satisfies the inequalities $0 < t < \frac{1}{2}\pi$, and if $\sin t = \frac{3}{5}$, find the exact value of each of the following:
   (a) $\sin 2t$ (b) $\cos 2t$ (c) $\sin 3t$

10. Find a number x such that $\sin x \neq 0$ and $\sin 2x = \sin x$.

11. With the aid of Table II and the formulas given in this section, evaluate the following:
   (a) $\sin \frac{1}{2} \cos \frac{1}{2}$ (c) $\cos^2 \frac{2}{5} - \cos^2 (\frac{1}{2}\pi - \frac{2}{5})$
   (b) $2 \cos^2 .3$ (d) $(1 + \cos 2) \csc 2$

12. If $0 < t < \frac{1}{4}\pi$, and if $z = a \sin 2t$, express each of the following expressions in terms of z and a:
   (a) $\sin 4t$ (c) $\sin t$
   (b) $\cos 4t$ (d) $\tan t$

34 SUMMARY OF TRIGONOMETRIC IDENTITIES

We have developed several relationships among the trigonometric functions in the last few sections. In this section, we will summarize these relationships.

First we list eight elementary identities that we can obtain directly from the definitions of the trigonometric functions.

34-1

$$\csc t = \frac{1}{\sin t}, \qquad \cot t = \frac{\cos t}{\sin t},$$

$$\sec t = \frac{1}{\cos t}, \qquad \sin^2 t + \cos^2 t = 1,$$

$$\cot t = \frac{1}{\tan t}, \qquad \tan^2 t + 1 = \sec^2 t,$$

$$\tan t = \frac{\sin t}{\cos t}, \qquad \cot^2 t + 1 = \csc^2 t.$$

Some of the following equations are marked with an asterisk (*). You should be able to obtain the remaining relations by using these equations and the elementary identities.

The basic addition formulas are:

$$\text{(*)} \quad \sin (u \pm v) = \sin u \cos v \pm \cos u \sin v,$$

34-2

$$\text{(*)} \quad \cos (u \pm v) = \cos u \cos v \mp \sin u \sin v,$$

$$\tan (u \pm v) = \frac{\tan u \pm \tan v}{1 \mp \tan u \tan v}.$$

The basic relations involving the trigonometric functions of $-t$ are:

$$\text{(*)} \quad \sin (-t) = -\sin t,$$

34-3

$$\text{(*)} \quad \cos (-t) = \cos t,$$

$$\tan (-t) = -\tan t.$$

The following equations state the basic relations involving the trigonometric functions of $2t$.

$$\sin 2t = 2 \sin t \cos t,$$

34-4

$$\cos 2t = \cos^2 t - \sin^2 t = 1 - 2 \sin^2 t = 2 \cos^2 t - 1,$$

$$\tan 2t = \frac{2 \tan t}{1 - \tan^2 t}.$$

You will frequently find it useful to express Relations 34-4 in the following form:

$$\sin^2 t = \frac{1}{2} (1 - \cos 2t),$$

34-5

$$\cos^2 t = \frac{1}{2} (1 + \cos 2t),$$

$$\tan t = \frac{\sin 2t}{1 + \cos 2t} = \frac{1 - \cos 2t}{\sin 2t}.$$

All of the above relations are "identities" in the sense that they are valid for any numbers t, u, and v, for which the functions involved are defined. Such identities are used principally to change the form of an expression involving trigonometric functions to a simpler or more useful form.

EXAMPLE 34-1.   Simplify the expression $\sin t \left(\dfrac{\cot t}{\sec t} + \csc t \right)$.

Solution.   We can use the elementary identities to simplify the given expression in the following manner:

$$\sin t \left(\frac{\cot t}{\sec t} + \csc t \right) = \sin t \cdot \frac{\cos t}{\sin t} \cdot \cos t + 1$$

$$= \cos^2 t + 1.$$

EXAMPLE 34-2.   Write the expression $(\sin 2t / \sin t) - (\cos 2t / \cos t)$ in a form that involves only trigonometric functions of t.

Solution.

$$\frac{\sin 2t}{\sin t} - \frac{\cos 2t}{\cos t} = \frac{2 \sin t \cos t}{\sin t} - \frac{2 \cos^2 t - 1}{\cos t}$$

$$= 2 \cos t - 2 \cos t + \sec t = \sec t.$$

EXAMPLE 34-3.   Simplify the expression $\csc 2t + \cot 2t$.

Solution.

$$\csc 2t + \cot 2t = \frac{1}{\sin 2t} + \frac{\cos 2t}{\sin 2t}$$

$$= \frac{1 + \cos 2t}{\sin 2t}$$

$$= \frac{2 \cos^2 t}{2 \sin t \cos t}$$

$$= \frac{\cos t}{\sin t} = \cot t.$$

EXAMPLE 34-4.   If $0 < x < 2\pi$, show that $\sin \frac{1}{2} x = \sqrt{(1 - \cos x)/2}$.

Solution.   We substitute $x = 2t$ in the formula $\sin^2 t = \frac{1}{2}(1 - \cos 2t)$ to obtain the equation $\sin^2 \frac{1}{2} x = \frac{1}{2}(1 - \cos x)$.   Thus we find that either $\sin \frac{1}{2} x = \sqrt{\frac{1}{2}(1 - \cos x)}$, or $\sin \frac{1}{2} x = -\sqrt{\frac{1}{2}(1 - \cos x)}$.   From the inequalities $0 < x < 2\pi$, it follows that $0 < \frac{1}{2} x < \pi$, so that $\sin \frac{1}{2} x > 0$, and the equation we are seeking then follows.

Problems 34

1. Simplify the following expressions:
    (a) $\csc t - \cot t \cos t$ (c) $\sin^2 u/(1 - \cos u) - 1$
    (b) $\tan x \sin x + \cos x$ (d) $\tan t \,(1 + \cot^2 t)/(1 + \tan^2 t)$

2. Let t satisfy the inequalities $0 < t < \frac{1}{2}\pi$. Express each of the following in terms of $\sin t$:
    (a) $\sec t$ (c) $\cot t$
    (b) $\tan t$ (d) $\csc 2t$

3. Simplify the following expressions:
    (a) $[(2 \sin^2 t - 1)/\sin t \cos t] + \cot 2t$
    (b) $(\sec t + \tan t)/(\cos t - \tan t - \sec t)$
    (c) $\sin t \cot t \,(\sec t - 1)/(1 - \cos t)$
    (d) $\sin x/(\sec x + 1) + \sin x/(\sec x - 1)$

4. Show that $\sqrt{1 + 2 \sin x \cos x} = |\sin x + \cos x|$.

5. Find a solution to the equation $\tan^2 x + \sec^2 x = 3$.

6. Write each of the following expressions in terms of trigonometric functions of $2t$:
    (a) $(\sin^3 t - \cos^3 t)/(\sin t - \cos t)$
    (b) $(\cos t - 1)^2 - (\sin t - 1)^2 + 2(\cos t - \sin t)$
    (c) $(\tan t + \cot t)/(\cot t - \tan t)$
    (d) $(\sec 2t - 1)(1 - 2 \sin^2 t)$

7. Write a formula for $\tan \frac{1}{2}x$ (see Example 34-4).

8. Verify the following identities:
    (a) $\sin (u + v) + \sin (u - v) = 2 \sin u \cos v$
    (b) $\sin (u + v) - \sin (u - v) = 2 \cos u \sin v$
    (c) $\cos (u - v) + \cos (u + v) = 2 \cos u \cos v$
    (d) $\cos (u - v) - \cos (u + v) = 2 \sin u \sin v$

9. The identities listed in the previous problem express a sum as a product, and hence are called the **factoring identities**. They can be written in a form that is sometimes more useful by substituting $x = u + v$ and $y = u - v$. Then $u = \frac{1}{2}(x + y)$ and $v = \frac{1}{2}(x - y)$ so that the identity in Problem 8(a) is transformed into the identity
$$\sin x + \sin y = 2 \sin \tfrac{1}{2}(x + y) \cos \tfrac{1}{2}(x - y).$$
Derive similar formulas for the following sums and differences:
    (a) $\sin x - \sin y$ (b) $\cos x + \cos y$ (c) $\cos x - \cos y$

10. With the aid of the formulas of the preceding exercise, find a number x such that $\sin x \neq 0$, and such that $\sin x + \sin 2x = 0$.

11. Show that $\dfrac{\sin 2x + \sin 2y}{\cos 2x + \cos 2y}$ can be replaced by $\tan (x + y)$.

12. Show that $\dfrac{\cos x + \sin x}{\cos x - \sin x}$ can be replaced by $\tan 2x + \sec 2x$.

35 PERIODICITY

We have already remarked that the graphs of the trigonometric functions "repeat" themselves every 2π units. This situation stems from the fact that $T(x + 2\pi) = T(x)$ for every trigonometric function T and every number x. We have also learned that the graph of the tangent function repeats itself every π units. In other words,

$$\tan (x + \pi) = \tan x \quad \text{for every number } x.$$

We can also establish this fact by using an addition formula (Equations 34-2) and the value $\tan \pi = 0$, which give us

$$\tan (x + \pi) = \frac{\tan x + \tan \pi}{1 + \tan x \tan \pi} = \tan x.$$

A function whose graph "repeats" itself is called a **periodic function**. More precisely *a function f is periodic if there is a number p such that $f(x + p) = f(x)$ for all numbers x in the domain of f.* If there is a *smallest* positive number p for which this last equation is valid, then p is called the **period** of f. The sine and cosine functions, for example, are periodic with period 2π, and the tangent function is periodic with period π.

> EXAMPLE 35-1. Show that the function f that is defined by the equation $f(x) = |\sin x|$ is periodic with period π.

Solution. We first show that $f(x + \pi) = f(x)$ for all numbers x.

$$f(x + \pi) = |\sin (x + \pi)|$$

$$= |\sin x \cos \pi + \cos x \sin \pi|$$

$$= |-\sin x| = |\sin x| = f(x).$$

In order to prove that π is the *period* of f we must also show that if p is the *smallest positive number* for which $|\sin (x + p)| = |\sin x|$, then $p = \pi$. Since we require that the equation $|\sin (x + p)| = |\sin x|$ be valid for all values of x, it must, in particular, be valid when $x = 0$.

Therefore p must be a positive number such that $|\sin (0 + p)| = |\sin 0|$; that is, $|\sin p| = 0$. The smallest positive number that satisfies this last equation is clearly $p = \pi$.

Figure 35-1 shows the graph of the equation $y = \sin 2x$. From the graph it is clear that the function g that is defined by the equation $g(x) = \sin 2x$ is a periodic function with period π. That is, a "cycle"

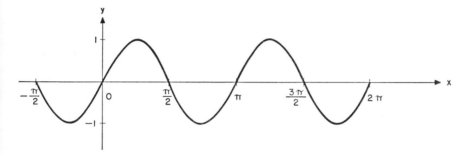

Figure 35-1

of the graph is completed in intervals π units long, and not in any smaller interval. Analytically we have

$$g(x + \pi) = \sin 2(x + \pi) = \sin (2x + 2\pi) = \sin 2x = g(x).$$

Notice that the period of the function g defined by the equation $g(x) = \sin 2x$ is one-half the period of the function f defined by the equation $f(x) = \sin x$. We can generalize this remark as follows.

THEOREM 35-1. *If a function f is periodic with period p, and if the function g is defined by the equation $g(x) = f(ax)$, where $a > 0$, then g is a periodic function with period p/a.*

It is easy to show that $g(x + p/a) = g(x)$. We have, from the definition of the function g,

$$g(x + p/a) = f[a(x + p/a)] = f(ax + p).$$

Since f is periodic with period p, $f(ax + p) = f(ax)$. But $f(ax) = g(x)$, so $g(x + p/a) = g(x)$. It is also true that the smallest positive number h for which $g(x + h) = g(x)$ for all numbers x in the domain of g is $h = p/a$, but we omit the proof.

EXAMPLE 35-2.   What is the period of the function g that is defined by the equation $g(x) = \tan 4\pi x$?

Solution.   This example illustrates the situation that is described in Theorem 35-1.   Here the function f is the tangent function, and the number a is 4π.   Since the period p of the tangent function f is π, the period of the function g is $p/a = \pi/4\pi = \frac{1}{4}$.

EXAMPLE 35-3.   Sketch the graph of the equation $y = \cos \pi x$.

Solution.   The period of the function g defined by the equation $g(x) = \cos \pi x$ is $2\pi/\pi = 2$.   We therefore need only plot the portion of the graph in the interval from $x = 0$ to $x = 2$ to get a complete picture of the way this function behaves.   Figure 35-2 shows the result.

You will observe that the curve in Fig. 35-2 is merely the graph of the cosine function so "compressed" that an entire cycle is com-

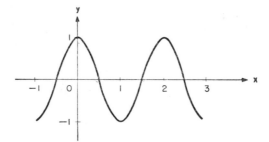

Figure 35-2

pleted in intervals 2 units long.   Similarly, the graph of the equation $y = \sin ax$, where a is a positive number, is simply a sine curve either horizontally compressed or elongated so that an entire cycle is completed in every interval of length $2\pi/a$.   Hence to quickly obtain a sketch of the graph of the equation $y = \sin ax$ we need only plot a very few points, for example, the points $(0,0)$, $(\pi/2a,1)$, $(\pi/a,0)$, $(3\pi/2a,-1)$, and $(2\pi/a,0)$ and join them by a "sine-type" curve. You should have no trouble sketching graphs of equations of the form $y = T(ax)$, where T may be any trigonometric function and a any positive number.

The trigonometric functions are not the only periodic functions. The "saw-tooth" wave (Example 35-4) that is sometimes encountered in electronics problems also falls into this category.

EXAMPLE 35-4.   Sketch the graph of the function f that is determined by the equation $f(x) = x - [x]$, where $[x]$ represents the greatest integer that does not exceed x (see Section 11).

Solution. If $x \geq 0$, then $f(x)$ is simply the "fractional part" of x. Thus $f(\pi) = \pi - [\pi] = 3.142 - 3 = .142$, $f(\sqrt{2}) = .414$, and $f(3) = 0$.   It is therefore easy to see that the graph of f, for non-negative values of x, may be obtained by repeating the part of the graph that corresponds to values of x between 0 and 1.   You will not find it difficult to convince yourself that the part of the graph to the left of the y-axis may also be obtained by reproducing the heavy part of the graph in Fig. 35-3.   Thus f is periodic with period 1.

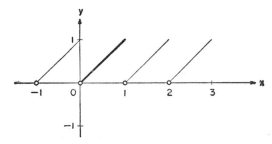

Figure 35-3

If a function is defined only for values of x lying between two given numbers, we often wish to consider its **periodic extension**.   This is a new function whose domain is the set of all real numbers and whose graph consists of repetitions of the graph of the original function.

EXAMPLE 35-5.   Let f be the function whose domain is the set of numbers x such that $-1 \leq x \leq 1$ and for which $f(x) = |x|$.   If F is the periodic extension of f, sketch the graph of F and find $F(2)$, $F(\pi)$, and $F(-\tfrac{5}{3})$.

Solution. The heavy part of the curve in Fig. 35-4 is the graph of f. The entire curve, which is obtained by repeating this portion, is the

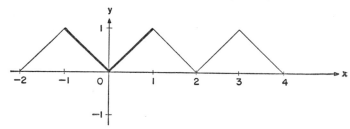

Figure 35-4

graph of F.   It is easy to see that F is a periodic function with period 2. From Fig. 35-4 we see that $F(2) = 0$ and that

$$F(\pi) = F(3.14 - 4) = f(-.86) = .86.$$

Similarly,

$$F(-\tfrac{5}{3}) = F(-\tfrac{5}{3} + 2) = f(\tfrac{1}{3}) = \tfrac{1}{3}.$$

Problems 35

1. Determine which of the following equations define periodic functions:
   (a) $y = x \sin x$ (c) $f(x) = \sin x - \cos x$
   (b) $y = 3x + 1$ (d) $f(x) = 4$

2. Let f be a periodic function with period p.   Show that $f(x - p) = f(x)$ and that $f(x + 2p) = f(x)$.

3. Sketch a graph of the functions that are defined by each of the following equations and determine the period:
   (a) $y = \sin 2\pi x$ (d) $y = \cos \tfrac{1}{2}x$
   (b) $y = \cot 4x$ (e) $y = 2 \sin x$
   (c) $y = \tan \pi x$ (f) $y = [x] - x$

4. Show that $f(t) = \sin^2 t$ defines a periodic function while $f(t) = \sin t^2$ does not.

5. Let f be the function defined by the following equations:
$$f(x) = -1 \quad \text{if} \quad -1 < x < 0,$$
$$f(x) = 1 \quad \text{if} \quad 0 < x < 1.$$
Sketch the graph of the function F which is the periodic extension of f, and find $F(3.5)$, $F(-16/3)$, and $F(201.7)$.   This graph is an example of a "square" wave.

6. Determine the periods of the functions that are defined by each of the following equations:
   (a) $y = \cos^2 x - \sin^2 x$ (c) $y = 2 \tan x/(1 - \tan^2 x)$
   (b) $y = \sin 2x/(1 + \cos 2x)$ (d) $y = 2 \cos^2 4x - 1$

7. A function f has the following properties: (i) it is periodic with period 4, (ii) if $-2 \le x \le 0$, $f(x) = -\tfrac{1}{2}x$, (iii) if $0 \le x \le 2$, $f(x) = \tfrac{1}{2}x$.   Sketch the graph of f and find $f(7)$.

8. Let f be the function whose domain is the set of all positive integers and for which $f(n)$ is the integer in the nth decimal place in the decimal expansion of $\tfrac{1}{7}$.   What is the range of f?   Is f periodic, and if so, what is its period?

9. Let f and g be periodic functions whose periods arc p and q respectively. Is the function F periodic in the following equations?

(a) $F(x) = f(x)g(x)$ (c) $F(x) = f(x^2)$

(b) $F(x) = [f(x)]^2$ (d) $F(x) = f[g(x)]$

36 BOUNDEDNESS AND AMPLITUDE

The graphs of the sine and cosine functions illustrate the fact that $-1 \leq \sin x \leq 1$ and $-1 \leq \cos x \leq 1$ for every real number x. The graph of the tangent function shows that $\tan x$ can be any real number. This contrast between the graphs of the sine and cosine functions and the graph of the tangent function illustrates the property of **boundedness**. The sine and cosine functions are bounded above and bounded below in accordance with the following definition.

DEFINITION 36-1. *A function f is **bounded above** if a number M can be found such that $f(x) \leq M$ for all numbers x in the domain of f. A function f is **bounded below** if a number m can be found such that $f(x) \geq m$ for all numbers x in the domain of f.*

We see that $\sin x$ is bounded above, since $\sin x \leq 1$ for all x, and bounded below, since $\sin x \geq -1$ for all x. Thus in Definition 36-1, the number M could be 1 and m could be -1. Or M could be 2, for it is certainly true that $\sin x \leq 2$. The number 1, however, is the smallest possible choice we can make for M, and the number -1 is the largest possible choice we can make for m in this example.

When a function is bounded above, the *smallest* number M such that $f(x) \leq M$ for all numbers x in the domain of f is called the **least upper bound** of f. If f is bounded below, the *largest* number m such that $f(x) \geq m$ for all numbers x in the domain of f is called the **greatest lower bound** of f.

The least upper bound of the sine function is 1, and the greatest lower bound of the sine function is -1. The tangent function is not bounded and hence has no least upper bound or greatest lower bound.

DEFINITION 36-2. *The **amplitude** of a bounded periodic function f is the number $\frac{1}{2}(M - m)$, where M and m are the least upper and greatest lower bounds of f.*

The amplitude of the sine function is thus $\frac{1}{2}[1 - (-1)] = 1$. We do not say that the tangent function has an amplitude because it is not bounded.

EXAMPLE 36-1. Determine the amplitude of the function f that is defined by the equation $f(x) = x - [x]$ (see Example 35-4).

Solution.   We see from Fig. 35-3 that the least upper bound of f is 1, and the greatest lower bound of f is 0.   Note that there is no number x for which $f(x)$ *equals* 1, but that 1 is nevertheless the smallest number M such that $f(x) \leq M$ for all values of x.   The amplitude of f is therefore $\frac{1}{2}(1 - 0) = \frac{1}{2}$.

In the preceding section we saw that the graph of the equation $y = \sin ax$, where $a > 0$, had the same appearance as the graph of the sine curve, except that it was either horizontally compressed or elongated.   The graph of the equation $y = A \sin x$ is also a "sine-type" curve since it can be obtained by multiplying the y-coordinate of each point of the graph of the sine function by the number A. This multiplication either vertically compresses or elongates the sine curve.   If $A < 0$, the multiplication also reflects the sine curve about the x-axis.   Since the amplitude of the sine curve is 1, the amplitude of the graph of the equation $y = A \sin x$ is $|A|$.   The graphs of the equations $y = 2 \sin x$ and $y = \frac{1}{2} \sin x$ are compared with a dashed-line sine curve in Fig. 36-1.

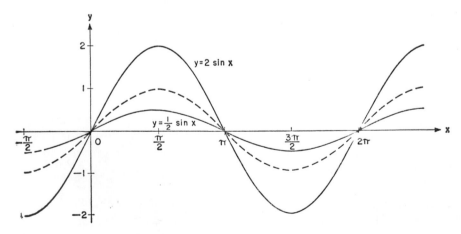

Figure 36-1

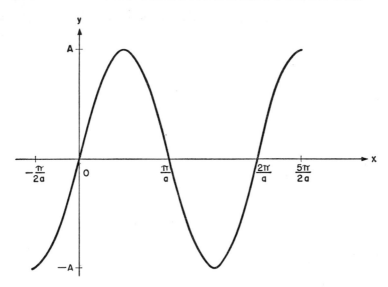

Figure 36-2

EXAMPLE 36-2.   Discuss the graph of an equation of the form $y = A \sin ax$, where a is a positive number.

Solution.   The graph of this equation is a sine curve that is either compressed or elongated both vertically and horizontally.   We saw in the preceding section that the graph of the equation $y = \sin ax$ is a "sine-type" curve with the period $2\pi/a$.   If we multiply the y-coordinate of each point of this graph by A, we obtain the graph of $y = A \sin ax$, which has an amplitude of $|A|$.   A typical graph of an equation of the form $y = A \sin ax$ is shown in Fig. 36-2.   (In the figure it is assumed that $A > 0$.)

EXAMPLE 36-3.   Graph the equation $y = |\sin x|$.

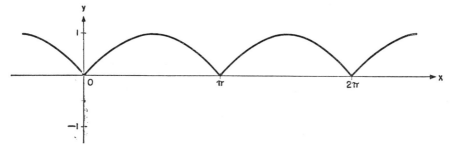

Figure 36-3

Solution. For those numbers x for which $\sin x$ is positive, the graph of the equation $y = |\sin x|$ is the same as the graph of the equation $y = \sin x$. For numbers x for which $\sin x$ is negative, the graph of the equation $y = |\sin x|$ is identical to the graph of the equation $y = -\sin x$—that is, it is the graph of the equation $y = \sin x$ reflected about the x-axis. Figure 36-3 illustrates the fact, already shown in Example 35-1, that the period of the curve is π. The least upper and greatest lower bounds are 1 and 0, respectively. The amplitude is therefore $\frac{1}{2}$.

Problems 36

1. Sketch the graphs of each of the following equations:
   - (a) $y = \frac{1}{2} \cos x$
   - (b) $y = -4 \sin x$
   - (c) $y = \pi \cos 2\pi x$
   - (d) $y = -\dfrac{\sin \pi x}{3}$

2. Determine the least upper bound and/or the greatest lower bound when they exist for the functions defined by the following equations:
   - (a) $y = 2x + 3$
   - (b) $y = 1/x^2$
   - (c) $y = 2^x$
   - (d) $y = \sec x$
   - (e) $y = \log x$
   - (f) $y = 1/|x|$

3. Determine the amplitude in each of the following cases:
   - (a) $f(x) = -5 \sin \pi x$
   - (b) $f(x) = 4 \sin x \cos x$
   - (c) The function F in Example 35-5
   - (d) The function F of Exercise 5 of Problems 35
   - (e) The function f of Exercise 7 of Problems 35

4. Graph the function defined by the equation $y = .001 \tan x$. Is it bounded?

5. Graph the function defined by the equation $y = 2^{\sin x}$. What is its amplitude and period?

6. Graph the following equations. In each case determine the amplitude.
   - (a) $y = 3 \sin 4\pi x$
   - (b) $y = -.1 \cos \pi x$
   - (c) $y = .4 \sin \frac{1}{4}\pi x$
   - (d) $y = 5 \cos 10\pi x$

7. Graph the function f and determine its amplitude if $f(x) = 2 \sin^2 2\pi x$.

8. Criticize the following statement. "The amplitude of a bounded periodic function is its maximum value."

9. Criticize the following statement. "The least upper bound of a function is the largest number in the range of the function."

37   THE EQUATION y = A sin (ax + b)

Trigonometric functions are useful in solving problems involving vibrations and oscillations.   For example, if you could measure the voltage drop across the terminals of an ordinary electrical outlet you might find that the voltage t seconds after the start of your measurements is given by the equation $E = 155 \sin 120\pi t$.   The amplitude of the function defined by this equation is 155 and the period of the function is $2\pi/120\pi = \frac{1}{60}$.   The reciprocal of the period of a periodic function is called the **frequency** of the function.   The frequency represents the number of cycles (or the fraction of a cycle) completed by the graph of the function in a vertical band 1 unit wide.   In our example we see that the frequency of ordinary household voltage is 60 cycles per second.

The voltage equation mentioned in the preceding paragraph is correct only if the initial measurement is made when the voltage is 0 and increasing—that is, $E = 0$ when $t = 0$, and $E > 0$ for values of t slightly greater than 0.   If the first measurement is made at any other point in the cycle, we would find that the equation expressing E would have the form $E = 155 \sin (120\pi t + b)$, where the value of b depends on the point in the cycle at which the initial measurement is made.   This equation is of the type $y = A \sin (ax + b)$, where a is a positive number.   The graph of such an equation is the same as the graph of the equation $y = A \sin ax$, except that it is shifted along the x-axis.   The graph of the equation $y = A \sin (ax + b)$ is a sine-type curve whose amplitude is $|A|$ and whose period is $2\pi/a$.   Notice that $y = 0$ at the point at which $ax + b = 0$—that is, at the point $x = -b/a$.   The number $-b/a$ is called the **phase shift**.   The phase shift represents the number of units that the graph of the equation $y = A \sin ax$ must be shifted along the x-axis in order to coincide with the graph of the equation $y = A \sin (ax + b)$.   This shift is to the left when the phase shift is negative and to the right if the phase shift is positive.

EXAMPLE 37-1.   Sketch the graph of the equation $y = 2 \sin (x + 1)$.

Solution.   This graph is a sine-type curve with an amplitude of 2 and a period of 2π.   Notice that $y = 0$ when $x + 1 = 0$—that is, when

$x = -1$. The phase shift is -1 so that the graph of $y = 2 \sin x$ must be shifted -1 units—that is, one unit to the left—to obtain the graph of the equation $y = 2 \sin (x + 1)$. The graph is shown in Fig. 37-1.

In Section 30, where we first studied the graphs of the trigonometric functions, we learned that the sine and cosine curves were the same in the sense that they can be made to coincide by shifting one along the x-axis. We now see exactly what this statement means, for ac-

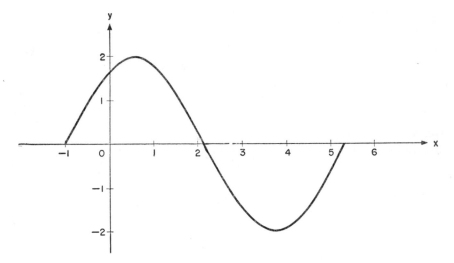

Figure 37-1

cording to Example 32-1, $\cos x = \sin (x + \frac{1}{2}\pi)$, and so the graph of the cosine function is the same as the graph of the equation $y = \sin (x + \frac{1}{2}\pi)$. But the graph of this last equation is merely a sine curve with a phase shift of $-\frac{1}{2}\pi$ units—that is, a sine curve shifted $\frac{1}{2}\pi$ units to the left.

EXAMPLE 37-2. Sketch the graph of the equation $y = 2 \sin (2x - \pi)$.

Solution. This curve has the same form as the graph of the equation $y = 2 \sin 2x$, so its amplitude is 2 and its period is $2\pi/2 = \pi$. In this example the phase shift is $\pi/2$ so we obtain the graph of the equation $y = 2 \sin (2x - \pi)$ by shifting the curve $y = 2 \sin 2x$ along the x-axis $\pi/2$ units. Figure 37-2 shows the graph.

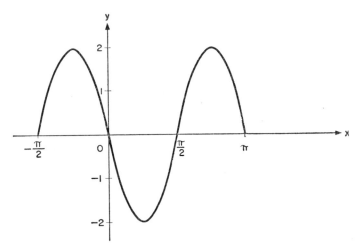

Figure 37-2

The trigonometric functions are also used to describe certain mechanical phenomena. Suppose a particle is moving along a straight line. Let t represent the number of units of time that have elapsed since the particle started moving, and let S be the corresponding number of units that the particle has been displaced from some "position of equilibrium" on the line. If the moving particle is always acted upon by a force that is directed toward the point of equilibrium and whose magnitude is proportional to the displacement from that point, then the resulting motion is called **simple harmonic motion,** and the equation connecting S and t has the form $S = A \sin (at + b)$. These remarks are illustrated by the following example.

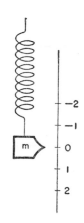

Figure 37-3

Suppose a mass of m grams is suspended from a spring and that a number scale originating at the rest position of the mass is placed as shown in Fig. 37-3. Now if the mass is pulled down A units and then released, it will oscillate up and down about the rest position. Assuming no frictional losses, the number of units S of displacement from the rest position t seconds after release is given by an equation of the form

37-1
$$S = A \sin \left(\sqrt{\frac{k}{m}}\, t - \frac{\pi}{2} \right),$$

where k is a positive number that measures the "stiffness" of the spring—the "stiffer" the spring, the larger is k. We really need calculus to derive Equation 37-1 from mechanical principles, so let us just accept the result and attempt to read some information from it. We see that:

(i) The amplitude of the vibration is A units; the displacement of the mass is always between $-A$ and A units from the rest position.

(ii) The period of the motion is $2\pi/\sqrt{k/m} = \sqrt{4\pi^2 m/k}$ seconds per oscillation. The frequency is $\sqrt{k/4\pi^2 m}$ oscillations per second. This formula shows that the stiffer the spring and the lighter the mass, the more rapid is the vibration.

We neglect the effects of friction and air resistance in deriving Equation 37-1. According to that equation, the mass would go on forever oscillating between the same limits. Actually, of course, friction and air resistance do act on the mass and the oscillations grow smaller as time goes on. When we include these other forces in our calculations, we are dealing with a type of motion called *damped vibration*. A typical equation used to describe such a motion has the form

$$y = A^{-rt} \sin (at + b),$$

where $r > 0$. You will probably encounter this equation in your subsequent work in mathematics, and you will want to investigate it further at that time.

Problems 37   *Tuesday 1 d 2 a d d 3 c*

1. Sketch the graph of each of the following equations:
   (a) $y = \sin (x + 3\pi/2)$ (c) $y = \cos (x - \frac{1}{2}\pi)$
   (b) $y = \tan (x + \frac{1}{2}\pi)$ (d) $y = \sin (x + \pi/6)$

2. Sketch the graph of each of the following equations. In each case determine the frequency and phase shift.
   (a) $y = \sin (2\pi x + \pi)$ (c) $y = \cos (2\pi x - \pi)$
   (b) $y = \sin (\frac{1}{2}x + 3)$ (d) $y = \tan (\pi x - 4)$

3. Sketch the graph of each of the following equations. In each case determine the frequency, phase shift, and amplitude.
   (a) $y = 4 \sin (3x - \frac{1}{2}\pi)$ (c) $y = 3 \cos (2\pi x - 4\pi)$
   (b) $y = \dfrac{\sin (\frac{1}{2}\pi x + 1)}{2}$ (d) $y = -\frac{1}{4} \cos (\pi x - 3\pi)$

4. Sketch the graph of the equation $y = |2 \sin (\pi x - \frac{1}{2}\pi)|$ and determine the frequency, phase shift, and amplitude.

5. If displacement is related to time by the equation $S = B \cos (ct + d)$, is the resulting motion simple harmonic motion? In other words, can you find numbers A, a, and b such that $B \cos (ct + d) = A \sin (at + b)$?

6. (a) Let $A > 0$, and suppose that $y = -A \sin (ax + b)$. Show that you can find numbers c and d such that $y = A \sin (cx + d)$ so that it is no restriction to suppose that $A > 0$ in the equation $y = A \sin (ax + b)$.

   (b) Find an equation of the form $y = A \sin (ax + b)$, where $A > 0$, which is equivalent to the equation $y = -2 \sin (2\pi x + 1)$.

7. (a) Explain why it is no restriction to assume that $a > 0$ in the equation $y = A \sin (ax + b)$. (*Hint:* Show that if $a < 0$, then numbers B, c, and d can be found such that $c > 0$ and $B \sin (cx + d) = A \sin (ax + b)$).

   (b) Find an equation of the form $y = A \sin (ax + b)$, where A and a are *positive* numbers, which is equivalent to the equation $y = 3 \sin (-5x + 2)$.

8. (a) Explain why a complete discussion of the equation $y = A \sin (ax + b)$ automatically includes a discussion of the equation $y = A \cos (ax + b)$.

   (b) Write an equation of the form $y = A \sin (ax + b)$ that is equivalent to the equation $y = 2 \cos (2\pi x + \pi)$.

9. Find numbers B, c, and d, such that for given numbers A, a, and b,
$$A \cot (ax + b) = B \tan (cx + d).$$

10. Calculate the frequency of the motion if a mass of $m = 50$ is displaced slightly from its equilibrium position when attached to a spring with a stiffness constant k of 1000.

11. Let a charge of Q_0 coulombs be introduced onto the plates of a condenser with a capacitance of C farads. The condenser is placed in a circuit with a coil that has an inductance of L henrys. If the resistance of the circuit is negligible, the charge Q on the condenser t seconds after it is placed in the circuit is given by the equation
$$Q = Q_0 \sin \left(\frac{t}{\sqrt{LC}} + \frac{1}{2}\pi \right).$$
Calculate the frequency associated with this circuit if $L = .1$ henry and $C = 10^{-4}$ farad.

38   SPECIAL GRAPHING METHODS

Formulas that define functions often consist of the sum of a number of terms.   One device for plotting the graph of such functions is by the "addition of y-coordinates" (see Exercise 11 of Problems 30). The following examples illustrate this method.

EXAMPLE 38-1.   Graph the equation $y = \sin x + \sin 2x$.

Solution.   With what we already know about graphs of the trigonometric functions, we can easily graph the equations $y = \sin x$ and $y = \sin 2x$ separately.   The results are shown as the broken-line curves in Fig. 38-1.   We obtain the graph of the equation $y = \sin x + \sin 2x$

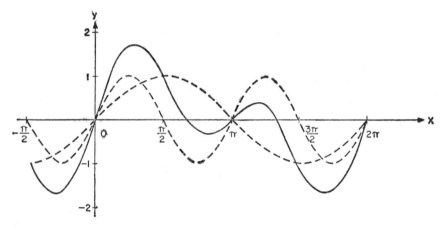

Figure 38-1

by simply adding the y-coordinates of corresponding points on the dashed curves with the aid of some drawing instruments such as a pair of dividers or a compass.   The result is the solid-line curve of Fig. 38-1.

EXAMPLE 38-2.   Graph the equation $y = x + \cos 2\pi x$.

Solution.   If we graph the two equations $y = x$ and $y = \cos 2\pi x$ and then add the corresponding y-coordinates, the solid curve of Fig. 38-2 results.   This is the graph we are seeking.

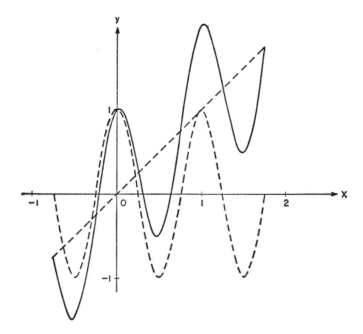

Figure 38-2

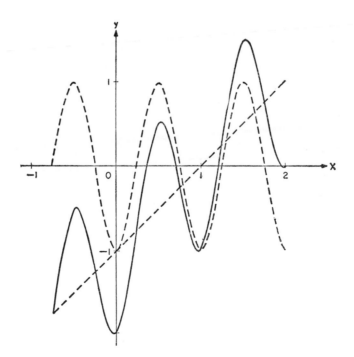

Figure 38-3

EXAMPLE 38-3. Graph the equation $y = x - 2\cos^2 \pi x$.

Solution. We first use the identity $2\cos^2 \pi x = 1 + \cos 2\pi x$ (see Equation 34-5) to write the given equation as $y = x - 1 - \cos 2\pi x = (x - 1) + (-\cos 2\pi x)$. We can now graph the equations $y = x - 1$ and $y = -\cos 2\pi x$ separately. The results are shown as broken-line curves in Fig. 38-3. We then obtain the graph of the given equation by adding y-coordinates of corresponding points, which yields the solid-line curve of Fig. 38-3.

The most general function that expresses simple harmonic motion is determined by an equation of the form $y = B \sin ax + C \cos ax$, where $a > 0$. We can plot the graph of this function by adding y-coordinates, but we can get a better understanding of the function from the following theorem.

THEOREM 38-1. *For any given values of B, C, and a, a positive number A and a number b ccn be found such that*

$$B \sin ax + C \cos ax = A \sin (ax + b)$$

for all values of x.

Proof. To prove this theorem, we need only find numbers A and b for which the above equation is an identity. Let $A = \sqrt{B^2 + C^2}$.

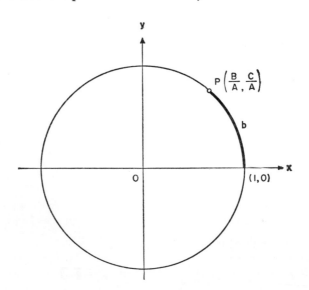

Figure 38-4

Then $A^2 = B^2 + C^2$ and $(B/A)^2 + (C/A)^2 = 1$. It follows that the point P with coordinates $(B/A, C/A)$ is a point on the unit circle (see Fig. 38-4). Let b be any number such that P is the trigonometric point of b. We could choose, for example, b as the distance measured along the unit circle in the counter-clockwise direction from the point $(1,0)$ to the point P. According to the definition of the trigonometric functions, $\sin b = C/A$ and $\cos b = B/A$, and hence,

38-1 $B = A \cos b$ and $C = A \sin b.$

Now using an addition formula (Equations 34-2) we may write $A \sin (ax + b) = A \cos b \sin ax + A \sin b \cos ax$. If we replace the numbers $A \cos b$ and $A \sin b$ with the values B and C from Equations 38-1, the identity $A \sin (ax + b) = B \sin ax + C \cos ax$ is established.

> EXAMPLE 38-4.   Two alternating current generators produce currents that are given, in terms of the time t, by the equations
>
> $$i_1 = \sqrt{3} \sin 120\pi t \quad \text{and} \quad i_2 = -\cos 120\pi t.$$
>
> If the output of the second is added to the output of the first, find the maximum current output, when it occurs, and determine the phase shift produced.
>
> *Solution.*   The combined current is given by the equation
>
> $$i = \sqrt{3} \sin 120\pi t - \cos 120\pi t.$$
>
> In this case, $A = \sqrt{3 + 1} = 2$. The point P has coordinates $(\sqrt{3}/2, -\frac{1}{2})$. Thus $\sin b = -\frac{1}{2}$ and $\cos b = \sqrt{3}/2$, so b can be chosen as $-\pi/6$. The total current can therefore be represented by the equation $i = 2 \sin (120\pi t - \pi/6)$. It follows that the maximum current is 2 and that the current experiences a phase shift of $\frac{1}{720}$ units of time. The maximum value of i occurs when $120\pi t - \pi/6 = \pi/2 + k \cdot 2\pi$ (k can be any integer), and hence when $t = \frac{1}{180} + k/60$.

Problems 38

1. Graph the following equations:
   (a) $y = \cos x + \cos 2x$
   (b) $y = \sin 2x + \cos x$
   (c) $y = \cos 2x - \sin x$
   (d) $y = \sin x + |\sin x|$

2. Graph the following equations:
   (a) $y = x + \sin 2\pi x$
   (b) $y = 2x - \cos 2\pi x$
   (c) $y = 3x + 2 - \sin 2\pi x$
   (d) $y = [x] + \sin 2\pi x$

3. Graph the following equations:
   (a) $y = \sin^2 \pi x - x$
   (b) $y = 3 + \sin^2 \pi x - \cos^2 \pi x$

4. Use graphs to determine the number of solutions that exist for each of the following equations:
   (a) $x = \tan \pi x$ (b) $x^2 = \sin 2\pi x$

5. Graph the equation $y = \log_{10} x + \cot \pi x$.

6. Graph the equation $y = 2^x + \sin 2\pi x$.

7. Graph the following equations (see Exercise 8 of Problems 34):
   (a) $y = 2 \sin 4\pi x \cos 2\pi x$ (c) $y = \cos 2x \sin x$
   (b) $y = 2 \sin 3x \sin x$ (d) $y = \cos 10x \cos 5x$

8. Using an identity from Equations 34-5, graph the equation $y = \sin 2\pi x \tan \pi x$. Before you plot the point on the graph corresponding to $x = \frac{1}{2}$, reexamine the original equation.

9. Graph the equation $13y = 5 \sin 2\pi x + 12 \cos 2\pi x$ by first writing an equivalent equation of the form $y = A \sin (ax + b)$.

10. Assuming $t \geq 0$, find when, for the first time, the combined current in Example 38-4 is zero.

11. Prove the following theorem: For any given values of B, C, and a, a positive number A and a number b can be found such that
$$B \sin ax + C \cos ax = A \cos (ax + b).$$

39 ANGLES

Let O be any point in the plane, and assume that a half-line originates at this point. Suppose P is some point on the half-line. Now rotate the half-line about the point O to a new position, and let Q be a point on the new half-line. The rotation generates an **angle** that we will call the angle POQ (see Fig. 39-1). The half-line passing through OP is the **initial side**, the half-line passing through OQ is the **terminal side**, and the point O is the **vertex** of the angle POQ.

If we take the vertex O to be the origin of a cartesian coordinate

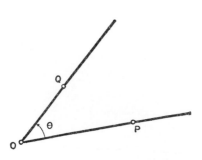

Figure 39-1

system and the initial half-line to be the positive *x*-axis, then the
angle is in **standard position** (see Fig. 39-2).   An angle generated
by rotating the initial side in the counter-clockwise direction is called
a **positive angle** and one gen-
erated by rotating the initial side
in the clockwise direction is
called a **negative angle.** We
will label angles with Greek let-
ters such as θ, ϕ, α, β, and γ.

If *t* is a given real number, let
us plot the trigonometric point
$P(t)$ on the unit circle and consider the angle $P(0)OP(t) = \theta$
(see Fig. 39-3).   The number *t*
may be used as a *measure* of this
angle.   We have an angle of *t*
units.   The unit of angular measurement in this system is called a
radian.   Thus θ is an angle that

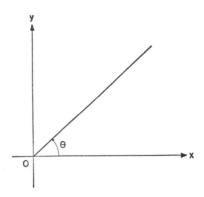

Figure 39-2

measures *t* radians.   An angle of 1 radian is the angle $P(0)OP(1)$.
That is, *the angle subtended by a unit arc of a unit circle is an angle of*
1 *radian*.   A right angle is an angle of $\pi/2$ radians, a straight angle
is an angle of π radians, and so on.   If θ is a given angle, we find its
measure in radians by placing it in standard position and finding

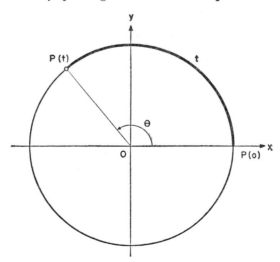

Figure 39-3

the number t whose trigonometric point is the point where the terminal side of θ intersects the unit circle.

Just as lengths are measured in different units, such as feet, yards, and rods, so angles are also measured in different units. Another common unit of angular measurement, besides the radian, is the **degree** (°). If the half-line generating an angle makes one complete revolution, it forms an angle of 360°. Knowing this fact, we can easily find the relationship between radians and degrees. Since a straight angle measures 180° and also π radians, it is clear that $1° = \pi/180$ radians and 1 radian $= (180/\pi)°$. On the basis of these facts we can write the following formulas. *If θ is an angle that measures A degrees and also t radians, then*

39-1
$$A = \frac{180}{\pi} t \quad \text{or} \quad t = \frac{\pi}{180} A.$$

You should have no trouble converting from one system of units to the other if you remember the single fact that π **radians** $= 180°$.

EXAMPLE 39-1. If θ is an angle of 30°, find its measure in radians.

Solution. From Equations 39-1, $t = (\pi/180) 30 = \pi/6$ radians.

EXAMPLE 39-2. If θ is an angle that measures 4 radians, find its measure in degrees.

Solution. From Equations 39-1, $A = (180/\pi)4 = 229°$.

If θ is an angle that measures t_1 radians and ϕ is an angle that measures t_2 radians, then the angle $\theta + \phi$ is the angle that measures $t_1 + t_2$ radians. If k is any real number, the angle $k\theta$ is the angle

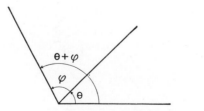

Figure 39-4

that measures kt_1 radians. These definitions correspond to the intuitive geometric definitions that are illustrated in Fig. 39-4.

Problems 39

1. Complete the following table:

Radian measure of θ:	0	$\dfrac{\pi}{6}$	$\dfrac{\pi}{4}$	$\dfrac{\pi}{3}$	$\dfrac{1}{2}\pi$	$\dfrac{2\pi}{3}$	$\dfrac{3\pi}{4}$	$\dfrac{5\pi}{6}$	π
Degree measure of θ:	0°	30°	45	60°	90°	120	135°	150°	180°

2. Find the radian measure of an angle θ if it measures
   (a) 225°   (c) 330°   (e) 105.2°
   (b) 240°   (d) 40°   (f) 361.47°

3. Find the degree measure of an angle θ to the nearest tenth of a degree if its radian measure is
   (a) $\pi/12$ (c) 3   (e) .712
   (b) $-5\pi/6$ (d) $\frac{1}{2}$ (f) $\frac{13}{3}$

4. Angles also are measured in minutes (') and seconds ("). These units are related to the degree unit by the equations $1° = 60'$ and $1' = 60''$. Find the degree-minute-second measure to the nearest second if an angle measures
   (a) 27.2°   (c) 1 radian   (e) 3.1 radians
   (b) 163.36°   (d) .612 radian   (f) -5 radians

5. Find the radian measure of an angle that measures
   (a) 1°   (c) 1''   (e) 148° 37'
   (b) 1'   (d) 34° 22'   (f) 25° 31' 14''

6. In what sense are the angles that measure 40° and 400° the "same"? In what respects are they different?

7. Use Table II to sketch angles of 1, 2, and 3 radians.

8. Suppose that the circumference of the unit circle is divided into 7 equal parts by 7 equally spaced points. If two successive division points are joined to the origin, what is the degree-minute-second measure of the resulting angle?

9. Determine which of the following represents the measure of the larger angle:
   (a) 1.3 radians or 78°   (c) 58 radians or $(58)^{2°}$
   (b) 123° or 2.2 radians

10. What is the degree measure of the acute angle formed by the x-axis and the line that joins the origin to the trigonometric point $P(3)$.

11. Let θ and φ be angles of 25° and 42°.   If the angle $\theta + \varphi$ is in standard position, find the coordinates of the point where the unit circle intersects the terminal side of the angle $\theta + \varphi$.

40 SOME FACTS ABOUT CIRCLES

The unit circle has a radius of 1 and its center is at the origin.   Now suppose we look at a circle whose center is also at the origin, but whose radius is a positive number r not necessarily equal to 1 (see Fig. 40-1).   Just as we considered the point $(1,0)$ as an "initial" point on the unit circle, here we consider the corresponding point $(r,0)$ as an "initial" point.   If s is any real number, we determine

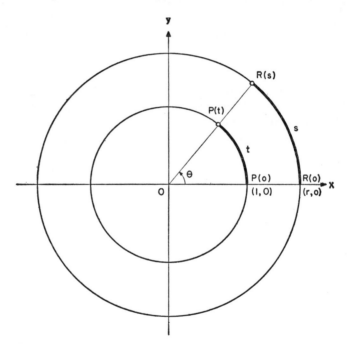

Figure 40-1

the point $R(s)$ by starting at the point $(r,0)$ and proceeding $|s|$ units along the circumference of the circle in the counter-clockwise direction if s is positive, and clockwise if s is negative.   The process of locating the point $R(s)$ can be described as follows.   We rotate the positive x-axis about the origin, counter-clockwise or clockwise depending on whether s is positive or negative, until the point $(r,0)$ has moved $|s|$ units.   During this process the point $(1,0)$ will be moved $|t|$ units around the unit circle to a point $P(t)$.   Let us find the relation between the numbers s and t.

The arcs $\overparen{R(0)R(s)}$ and $\overparen{P(0)P(t)}$ determine the same central angle θ. From plane geometry we know that the lengths of these arcs are therefore in the same ratio as the radii of the two circles, so that $|s|/|t| = r/1$ or $|s| = r|t|$.   Since s and t both have the same sign we have

40-1 $$s = rt.$$

The number t in Equation 40-1 is the radian measure of the central angle θ.   Thus Equation 40-1 says, "*The arc length s on a circle of radius r subtended by a central angle of t radians is equal to rt.*"
We may also write Equation 40-1 as

$$t = \frac{s}{r}.$$

In this form the equation says, "*The radian measure t of a central angle θ is the quotient of the subtended arc s and the radius of the circle.*"
The length s of the arc joining the points $R(0)$ and $R(s)$ is $(|s|/2\pi r)$ times the circumference of the circle.   Again, from geometry, we know that the area of the segment $R(0)OR(s)$ (see Fig. 40-2) is therefore $(|s|/2\pi r)$ times the area of the entire circle.   If K denotes the area of this segment, then

40-2 $$K = \frac{|s|}{2\pi r}\,\pi r^2 \quad \text{or} \quad K = \frac{1}{2}\,r|s|.$$

Note the similarity between Equation 40-2 and the formula for the area of a triangle (area equals one-half the base times the altitude).
Since $s = rt$, Formula 40-2 may also be written as

40-3 $$K = \frac{1}{2}\,r^2|t|.$$

Formulas 40-2 and 40-3 actually give the total area "swept out" by the line segment $OR(0)$ as $R(0)$ is moved $|s|$ units along the circle of radius r.   For example, if $s = 3\pi r$—that is, $1\frac{1}{2}$ times the circumference—Equation 40-2 gives $K = (\frac{3}{2})\pi r^2$ or $1\frac{1}{2}$ times the area of the circle.   If we drop the absolute value signs in Equations 40-2 and 40-3, the new formulas state that the area swept out by the segment

$OR(0)$ is positive if $OR(0)$ rotates in a counter-clockwise direction and negative if $OR(0)$ rotates in a clockwise direction.   It is sometimes convenient to adopt this convention.

If a point moves along the arc of a circle of radius r at a constant velocity v, then this velocity is given by the equation $v = s/T$, where T represents the number of units of time required to traverse s units of distance.   The quotient s/T measures the rate at which

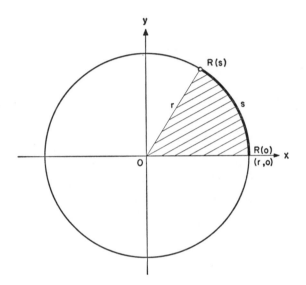

Figure 40-2

distance changes with time.   If, for example, s is measured in feet and T in seconds, then v is measured in feet per second.   As the point moves around the circle, the angle between the radius through the point and any fixed radius will change.   If this angle measures 0 units initially and t units at time T, then the angular velocity ω of the point is given by the equation $\omega = t/T$.   When t represents the radian measure of the angle, then angular velocity is measured in radians per unit of time.   We can easily obtain the relation between the linear velocity v and the angular velocity ω (measured in radians per unit of time).   Since $s = rt$, we have $v = s/T = rt/T = r(t/T) = r\omega$, and hence

40-4 $v = r\omega.$

You should notice that v will be *negative* when the motion is clockwise.

EXAMPLE 40-1.   A fly sits on the tip of the minute hand of a clock. If the hand is 4 inches long, how fast is the fly moving in miles per hour, assuming that the clock keeps perfect time?

Solution.   The angular velocity of the minute hand is -2π radians per hour (ω is negative since the minute hand obviously moves in a clockwise direction).   Thus the linear velocity of the fly is $v = -8\pi$ inches per hour or $v = -8\pi/(12\cdot5280) = -.0003967$ miles per hour.

Problems 40

1. Find the length of the circular arc and the area of the circular segment generated by a central angle of measure t in a circle of radius r if:
   (a) $r = 5$, $t = 5\pi/12$ radians   (c) $r = 1/\pi$, $t = 165°$
   (b) $r = .5$, $t = 36°$ (d) $r = 2$, $t = 715°$

2. A circle with a radius of 2 contains a central angle θ that intercepts an arc 5 units long.   What is the measure of θ in radians? In degrees?

3. A wheel 6 in. in diameter is rotating at the rate of 50 rpm.   Find the velocity in fps of a point on the rim of the wheel.

4. The latitude of Columbus, Ohio, is 40° north.   Assuming that the earth is a sphere with a radius of 3960 miles, calculate the distance from Columbus to the North Pole.

5. A protractor is to be marked at 1° intervals.   Find what the radius of the protractor must be if the graduating marks are to be $\frac{1}{16}$ in. apart around the rim.

6. The outside diameter of the wheel of a car is 20 in.   Find the number of revolutions the wheel makes in 1 sec if the car is traveling 60 mph.

7. Draw a sketch to show that the arc and chord subtended by a small central angle θ are almost the same length.   Use this fact to calculate the sun's diameter, assuming the sun to be 93 million miles from the earth and as seen from the earth to subtend an angle of 32'.

8. Two concentric circles have radii r and R in. ($r < R$).   Two half-lines drawn from the center form a central angle that measures t radians. Find a formula for the area between the inner and outer circle bounded by the two half-lines.   Can you express this area entirely in terms of the lengths of its edges?

9. The radius of the front wheel of a child's tricycle is 10 in. and the rear wheels each have a radius of 6 in.   The pedals are fastened to the front wheels by arms that are 7 in. long.   How far does a pedal travel when the rear wheels make 1 revolution?

10. At a distance of 10 ft, the smallest velocity that the average eye can detect is about .005 fps. How long must the minute hand of a clock be made in order for the average person to see it move when he is standing 10 ft from the clock?

11. A piston is connected to the rim of a wheel as shown in Fig. 29-5. The radius of the wheel is r ft, the length of the connecting rod is L ft, and the angular velocity of the wheel is ω radians per sec. A coordinate system is introduced as shown in the figure. Find an expression for the x-coordinate of the point Q if the point P is at the point $(r,0)$ when $T = 0$.

41   TRIGONOMETRIC FUNCTIONS OF ANGLES

We have defined the trigonometric functions in terms of correspondences between sets of *numbers*. With a real number t there are associated six numbers, the values of the six trigonometric functions. This numerical approach is justified by the fact that this is the form in which you will encounter the trigonometric functions in calculus and in many practical situations. In the next few sections we shall adopt a more traditional viewpoint and consider some of the geometrical aspects of trigonometry. Our first step will be to define the trigonometric functions of angles.

With every angle θ we can associate a real number t, the measure of the angle in radians. The sine function then associates with t the number sin t. In this way to every angle there corresponds a number, sin t. This correspondence defines a function whose domain is the set of angles. The number associated with the angle θ by this function is written sin θ. In other words, we define sin $\theta =$ sin t, where t is the radian measure of the angle θ. We follow the same procedure for the other trigonometric functions.

Definition 41-1. *If θ is an angle that measures t radians, then*

$$T(\theta) = T(t),$$

where T may be any one of the six trigonometric functions.

Example 41-1. Find cos θ if θ is an angle that measures 1.3 radians.

Solution. By definition, cos $\theta =$ cos 1.3. From Table II we find that cos 1.3 = .2675, and therefore cos $\theta =$ .2675.

Example 41-2.   Find tan 30°.

Solution.   The expression tan 30° is merely an abbreviation for "tan θ and θ measures 30°." An angle of 30° measures $30\pi/180 = \pi/6$ radians and hence tan 30° $= \tan \pi/6 = 1/\sqrt{3}$.

Table III, in the back of this book, lists values of the trigonometric functions for angles measured in degrees. We find from the table, for example, that sin 1° = .0175. You should note that sin 1 = .8415, so sin 1 and sin 1° are not the same number.

Table III lists values of the trigonometric functions only for angles between 0° and 90°. To find the values for other angles we modify the procedure we used in Section 29 to find the values of trigonometric functions for numbers not listed in Table II. Let θ be any angle in standard position (see Fig. 41-1). Then according to Definition

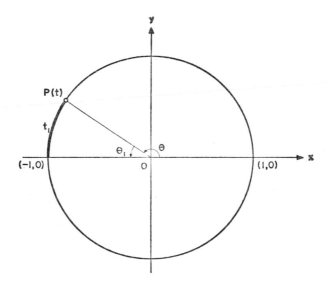

Figure 41-1

41-1, $T(\theta) = T(t)$, where t is the radian measure of θ and T may be any trigonometric function. Now to find $T(t)$ we first must find the reference number t_1 associated with t. This number measures the distance along the unit circle between the trigonometric point $P(t)$ and the nearest point on the x-axis. In terms of angles, the quantity that corresponds to the reference number t_1 is the **reference angle θ_1**. This angle is the *positive acute angle between the terminal side*

of θ and the x-axis.   Its radian measure is t_1.   Therefore $T(\theta_1) = T(t_1)$.
We saw earlier that $|T(t)| = T(t_1)$, and hence $|T(\theta)| = T(\theta_1)$.   The
number $T(\theta_1)$ may be found from Table II if θ_1 is measured in radians
and from Table III if θ_1 is measured in degrees.   The sign of $T(\theta)$
is determined by the quadrant in which the terminal side of θ lies.
The steps in finding $T(\theta)$ for a given angle θ may be summarized as
follows.

   (i) Locate the quadrant in which the terminal side of θ lies.
   (ii) Calculate the reference angle θ_1.
   (iii) Use Table II or Table III to find $T(\theta_1) = |T(\theta)|$.
   (iv) Affix the proper sign to obtain $T(\theta)$.

EXAMPLE 41-3.   Find cos 1059°.

Solution.   Since $1059 = 2 \cdot 360 + 339$, we see that an angle of 1059°
is generated by rotating the positive x-axis (in a counter-clockwise
direction) two complete revolutions, and then through an angle of 339°.
The terminal side of the angle therefore lies in the fourth quadrant and
the reference angle $\theta_1 = 360° - 339° = 21°$.   Hence, from Table III,
$|\cos 1059°| = \cos 21° = .9336$.   The cosine of an angle whose terminal
side lies in the fourth quadrant is positive, so we finally have cos 1059°
$= .9336$.

EXAMPLE 41-4.   Find csc $(-130°)$.

Solution.   The terminal side of an angle of $-130°$ lies in the third
quadrant   and   the   reference   angle $\theta_1 = 180° - 130° = 50°$.   We
therefore see that csc $(-130°) = -\csc 50°$.   The number csc 50° is
not listed in Table III, but we know that $\csc 50° = 1/\sin 50°$, and
hence csc $(-130°) = -1/\sin 50° = -1.305$.

All the identities and formulas we have previously derived are
still valid when numbers such as t, u, and so forth, are replaced by
angles θ, φ, and the like.   For example, if θ and φ are any two angles,
then

$$\sin (\theta + \varphi) = \sin \theta \cos \varphi + \cos \theta \sin \varphi.$$

We see from Fig. 41-1 that the terminal side of an angle θ in standard position intersects the unit circle at the point $P(t)$, where t is
the radian measure of θ.   The coordinates of $P(t)$ are (cos t, sin t).

Therefore, since $\cos t = \cos \theta$ and $\sin t = \sin \theta$, *the terminal side of an angle θ in standard position intersects the unit circle at the point $(\cos \theta, \sin \theta)$.* Now let θ be an angle in standard position (see Fig. 41-2) and suppose that P with coordinates (x, y) is any point on the terminal side of θ. The distance $\overline{OP}$ is $r = \sqrt{x^2 + y^2}$. If we drop perpendiculars from the points $(\cos \theta, \sin \theta)$ and (x, y) to the x-axis, two similar

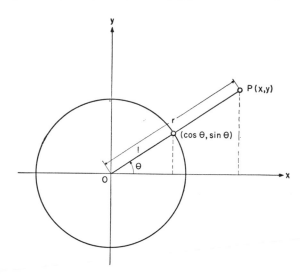

Figure 41-2

triangles are formed and we see that $x/r = \cos \theta/1$ and $y/r = \sin \theta/1$ so that $x = r \cos \theta$ and $y = r \sin \theta$. These remarks are summarized in the following useful theorem.

THEOREM 41-1. *If P is a point r units from the origin on the terminal side of an angle θ in standard position, then the coordinates of P are given by the equations*

41-1 $x = r \cos \theta \quad \text{and} \quad y = r \sin \theta.$

EXAMPLE 41-5. A point P on a circle of radius 5 is on the terminal side of a 36-degree angle in standard position. Find the coordinates of P.

Solution. From Theorem 41-1 and Table III, it follows that the coordinates of P are

$$x = 5 \cos 36° = 5(.8090) = 4.045,$$
$$y = 5 \sin 36° = 5(.5878) = 2.939.$$

The next theorem gives another interpretation of the results we obtained in the preceding paragraph.

THEOREM 41-2. *If P is a point r units from the origin on the terminal side of an angle θ, and if the coordinates of P are (x, y), then the values of the trigonometric functions for the angle θ are given by the equations*

$$\sin \theta = \frac{y}{r}, \qquad \cot \theta = \frac{x}{y},$$

41-2

$$\cos \theta = \frac{x}{r}, \qquad \sec \theta = \frac{r}{x},$$

$$\tan \theta = \frac{y}{x}, \qquad \csc \theta = \frac{r}{y}.$$

Proof. The first two equations are simply restatements of Equations 41-1. We can establish the other equations by using the first two equations and the elementary trigonometric identities. For example, $\tan \theta = \sin \theta / \cos \theta = (y/r)/(x/r) = y/x$.

Equations 41-2 are usually used in elementary textbooks to *define* the trigonometric functions.

Problems 41

1. Use Table III to evaluate each of the following:
   - (a) sin 40.6°
   - (b) cos 125°
   - (c) tan 95°
   - (d) cot −261.4°
   - (e) sin 3° 21′
   - (f) cos 698°
   - (g) sec −21°
   - (h) sin 37° 1′ 1″
   - (i) csc −705° ʹ

2. Determine which is the larger number:
   - (a) cos 3° or cos 3
   - (b) cot 1° or cot 1
   - (c) sin 7° or sin 7
   - (d) tan 4° or tan 4

3. Find the six trigonometric functions of the angle θ if the angle is in standard position and the coordinates of a point on the terminal side of the angle are:
   - (a) (2,3)
   - (b) (−1,2)
   - (c) (3,−5)
   - (d) (−1,−$\frac{3}{2}$)
   - (e) (12,13)
   - (f) (10,24)

4. Find the degree measure of the smallest positive angle in standard position such that the coordinates of a point on the terminal side of the angle are:
   - (a) (3,4)
   - (b) (1,5)
   - (c) (−6,2)
   - (d) (1,−2.2)

5. Make a sketch of the unit circle showing a small central angle θ that measures t radians. Explain why the figure suggests that $\sin \theta = t$ (approximately). Does $\sin 1° = 1$ (approximately)?

6. Use an addition formula and the fact that $15° = 45° - 30°$ to calculate $\cos 15°$. Compare your result with the value listed in Table III.

7. Use Theorem 41-1 to calculate the coordinates of a point P that is on a circle of radius 5 if P is on the terminal side of an angle in standard position that measures:
  (a) 35°   (c) 192°
  (b) 122°   (d) 303°

8. Make use of Table III to draw a careful sketch of a central angle in a unit circle that measures:
  (a) 57°   (c) −85°
  (b) 13°   (d) 261°

9. A circle of radius 4 with its center at the origin is divided into 5 equal arcs by 5 points—P_1, P_2, P_3, P_4, and P_5. The point P_1 is on the terminal side of an angle θ in standard position and the points are numbered in the order in which they appear as the circle is traversed in a counter-clockwise direction. What are the coordinates of P_4?

10. A fly on a sheet of coordinate paper starts at the point (3,4), proceeds by a straight line path to the nearest point on the unit circle, and then follows the arc of the circle to the point (1,0). How far did the fly walk?

42   RIGHT-TRIANGLE TRIGONOMETRY

As we said earlier, the subject of trigonometry was originally de-veloped to solve geometrical problems involving triangles. In partic-

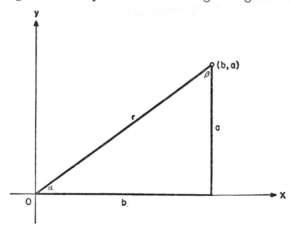

Figure 42-1

ular, the trigonometric functions were defined in terms of the ratios of the lengths of sides of a right triangle.   Let us denote the two acute angles of a right triangle by α and β, label the lengths of the sides opposite these angles a and b respectively, and let r represent the length of the hypotenuse of the triangle.   Place the vertex of the angle α at the origin of a cartesian coordinate system and the side of length b along the x-axis so that the triangle appears as in Fig. 42-1. The coordinates of the vertex of β are therefore (b,a).   Since the angle α is in standard position, we may use Theorem 41-2 to write the equations

42-1
$$\sin \alpha = \frac{a}{r}, \qquad \csc \alpha = \frac{r}{a},$$

$$\cos \alpha = \frac{b}{r}, \qquad \sec \alpha = \frac{r}{b},$$

$$\tan \alpha = \frac{a}{b}, \qquad \cot \alpha = \frac{b}{a}.$$

Using words instead of letters may help you remember these equations.   *If α is an acute angle of a right triangle*, then

42-2
$$\sin \alpha = \frac{\text{side opposite } \alpha}{\text{hypotenuse}}, \qquad \csc \alpha = \frac{\text{hypotenuse}}{\text{side opposite } \alpha},$$

$$\cos \alpha = \frac{\text{side adjacent } \alpha}{\text{hypotenuse}}, \qquad \sec \alpha = \frac{\text{hypotenuse}}{\text{side adjacent } \alpha},$$

$$\tan \alpha = \frac{\text{side opposite } \alpha}{\text{side adjacent } \alpha}, \qquad \cot \alpha = \frac{\text{side adjacent } \alpha}{\text{side opposite } \alpha}.$$

It is easy to verify that $T(\alpha) = \text{co-}T(\beta)$, where T may be replaced by any trigonometric function and co-T by the corresponding cofunction.   For example,

$$\sin \alpha = \frac{\text{side opposite } \alpha}{\text{hypotenuse}} = \frac{\text{side adjacent } \beta}{\text{hypotenuse}} = \cos \beta.$$

This equality and the fact that α and β are complementary angles accounts for the terminology of co-functions.   The word "cosine," for example, is an abbreviation for "complement's sine."

Equations 42-2 are the original definitions of the trigonometric functions.   They are extremely useful for solving certain problems that can be stated in geometrical terms, so you should not neglect them.   Traditionally, the study of trigonometry begins with a study of the trigonometric functions of acute angles as defined by Equa- tions 42-2.   Then the functions are defined for angles other than acute angles, identities are established, and so on.

The right-triangle definitions also provide a convenient memory device for obtaining the values of the trigonometric functions for certain angles—namely, 30°, 45°, and 60°.   Let P be a point on the circle of radius 2 with its center at the origin.   If P is on the terminal side of a 30-degree angle in standard position, it follows from Theorem 41-1 that the coordinates of P are:

$$x = 2 \cos 30° = 2 \cos \frac{\pi}{6} = 2 \left(\frac{\sqrt{3}}{2} \right) = \sqrt{3},$$

$$y = 2 \sin 30° = 2 \sin \frac{\pi}{6} = 2 \left(\frac{1}{2} \right) = 1.$$

If we drop a perpendicular to the x-axis from P (see Fig. 42-2), we obtain a right triangle with sides whose lengths are 1, $\sqrt{3}$, and 2. The acute angles of this triangle measure 30° and 60°.   This triangle, together with Equations 42-2, form a convenient device for remem-

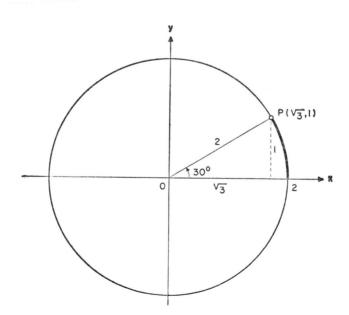

Figure 42-2

bering the values of the trigonometric functions of angles that measure 30° and 60°.   For example, it is clear from Fig. 42-2 that tan 60°
= $\sqrt{3}/1 = \sqrt{3}$.

Many practical triangle problems can be solved by right-triangle
trigonometry.   A typical example of such a problem is the following.

EXAMPLE 42-1.   From a certain point on a level plain at the foot of a
mountain, the angle of elevation of the peak is 45°.   From a point
2000 feet away, the angle of elevation of the peak is 30°.   How high
above the plain is the peak of the mountain?

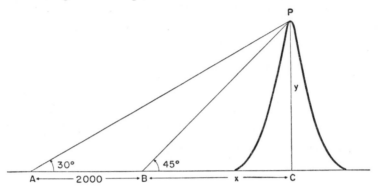

Figure 42-3

Solution.   The situation is illustrated in Fig. 42-3.   Triangles *APC*
and *BPC* are right triangles, so we immediately obtain two equations
using Equations 42-2,

$$\tan 45° = \frac{y}{x},$$

and $$\tan 30° = \frac{y}{x + 2000}.$$

Since tan 45° = 1 and tan 30° = $1/\sqrt{3}$, these equations become

$$y = x,$$

and $$x + 2000 = \sqrt{3}y.$$

When we solve these last two equations for *y*, we get:

$$y = \frac{2000}{\sqrt{3} - 1} = 2732 \text{ feet.}$$

EXAMPLE 42-2. If t is a number such that $0 < t < \pi/2$, show that

$$\cos t < \frac{t}{\sin t} < \frac{1}{\cos t}.$$

Solution.   Figure 42-4 shows the distance t laid off on the unit circle. The central angle measures t radians, so $T(\theta) = T(t)$ for any trigonometric function T.   The point P is the trigonometric point of t and R

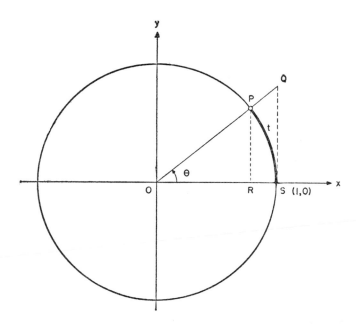

Figure 42-4

is the foot of the perpendicular dropped from P to the x-axis. The coordinates of the point S are $(1,0)$, and the segment QS is drawn perpendicular to the x-axis. Clearly, then,

42-3   *Area triangle POR < Area circular segment POS*
                    < Area triangle QOS,

and we shall now find expressions for each of these areas. Since $\cos \theta = \cos t = \overline{OR}/1$, the base of the triangle POR is $\overline{OR} = \cos t$. Similarly, the altitude of triangle POR is $\overline{PR} = \sin t$. The area of triangle POR is therefore $\frac{1}{2} \sin t \cos t$. According to Equation 40-2, the area of the circular segment POS is $\frac{1}{2}t$. Triangle QOS is a right triangle with base $\overline{OS} = 1$. Now $\tan \theta = \tan t = \overline{QS}/1$, and hence the altitude is $\overline{QS} = \tan t$. The area of triangle QOS is therefore

$\frac{1}{2}$ tan t. We may now write Inequalities 42-3 as

$$\tfrac{1}{2} \sin t \cos t < \tfrac{1}{2}t < \tfrac{1}{2} \tan t.$$

If we divide each term of these inequalities by $\frac{1}{2} \sin t$, we get the result we are seeking. You will encounter these inequalities again when you study calculus.

Problems 42

1. Let P be a point on the circle of radius 2 with its center at the origin. If P is on the terminal side of a 45-degree angle in standard position, use Theorem 41-1 to find the coordinates of P. If we drop a perpendicular from P to the x-axis, a triangle is formed that will help us remember the values of the trigonometric functions of the angle that measures 45°.

2. Complete the following table. (You should be able to work this problem without referring to the text.)

θ	$\sin \theta$	$\cos \theta$	$\tan \theta$
0			
30°			
45°			
60°			
90°			
120°			
135°			
150°			
180°			

3. Find the angles of a right triangle if the lengths of two of the sides of the triangle are:
   (a) $a = 3, b = 4$ (c) $a = 7, r = 25$
   (b) $a = 5, b = 12$ (d) $a = 8, r = 17$

4. Find the lengths of the sides of a right triangle if the measure of one angle and the length of one side are:
   (a) $a = 5, \beta = 40°$ (c) $b = 8.21, \alpha = 26° 31'$
   (b) $a = 3, \alpha = 10°$ (d) $r = 7, \alpha = 64° 17'$

5. At a time when the angle of elevation of the sun (measured from the horizontal) measures 50°, the length of the shadow of a tree is 75 ft. What is the height of the tree?

6. Find the measure of an angle α of a right triangle if:
   (a) $\sin \alpha = \cos (\alpha + 45°)$ (c) $\sec \tfrac{1}{2}\alpha = \csc 2\alpha$
   (b) $\tan \alpha = \cot 2\alpha$ (d) $\sin (\alpha + 25°) = \cos (\alpha - 25°)$

7. Can you construct a right triangle with an angle α such that sin $(35° + \alpha)$ = cos $(35° - \alpha)$?

8. Two airplanes fly around the world, one at a constant latitude of 40° and the other at a constant latitude of 35°. Both complete the trip in the same time. Compute the ratio of their speeds.

9. When a man who is 5 ft tall looks toward the top of a building, his line of vision makes an angle of 35° with the horizontal. For a man 6 ft tall in the same spot, the angle of elevation is only 32°. How high is the building?

10. Determine the length of an uncrossed belt running around two pulleys whose radii are 4″ and 8″ and whose centers are 24″ apart.

11. Determine the length of the belt in the preceding problem if the belt is crossed once.

43   THE LAW OF SINES

There are certain relations among the lengths of the sides and the trigonometric functions of the angles of a triangle that aid in the solution of practical geometrical problems. We will consider one of these relations, the **Law of Sines,** in this section.

THEOREM 43-1 (**Law of Sines**). *Let* α, β, *and* γ *be the angles of a triangle and a, b, and c be the lengths of the sides opposite the respective angles.* Then

$$\frac{\sin \alpha}{a} = \frac{\sin \beta}{b} = \frac{\sin \gamma}{c}.$$

Written out, the Law of Sines states that *the ratio of the sine of an angle of a triangle to the length of the opposite side is the same for all angles of the triangle.*

   Proof. We will now show that $(\sin \alpha)/a = (\sin \beta)/b$. Consider two ways of placing the triangle with respect to a cartesian coordinate system. First, place the vertex of the angle α at the origin with the side of length c extending along the positive x-axis (see Fig. 43-1). Then turn the triangle over so that the vertex of β is at the origin and the side of length c again extends along the positive x-axis (Fig. 43-2). In the first case, the vertex of γ will fall at some point P and in the second case at some point Q. The essential thing to ob-

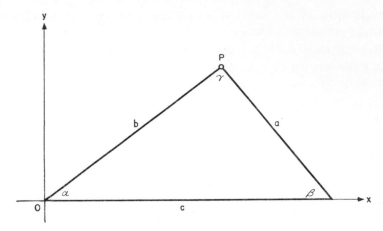

Figure 43-1

serve is that the points *P and Q have the same y-coordinate*—namely, the altitude of the triangle. In Fig. 43-1 the angle α is in standard position, and in Fig. 43-2 the angle β is in standard position. According to Theorem 41-1, the y-coordinate of P is $b \sin \alpha$, and the y-coordinate of Q is $a \sin \beta$. Hence $b \sin \alpha = a \sin \beta$, and so $\sin \alpha / a = \sin \beta / b$. Since we used no special properties of the angles α and β in establishing this equation, we have really shown that the ratio of the sine of an angle of a triangle to the length of the opposite side is the same for all angles of the triangle. We have therefore proved the Law of Sines.

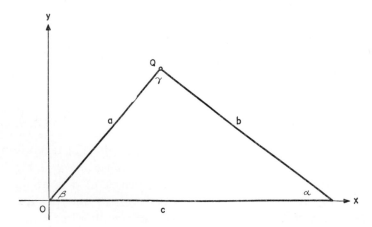

Figure 43-2

The lengths of the sides of a triangle and the size of its angles cannot be assigned arbitrarily. For example, the sum of the angles of a triangle must measure 180°, and therefore if we know what two angles measure, we can find the measure of the third. If, in addition to knowing two angles of a triangle, we also know the length of one side, then we can use the Law of Sines to find the lengths of the other two sides. This procedure is illustrated in the following example.

EXAMPLE 43-1. Let $\alpha = 45°$, $\beta = 75°$, and $c = 10$. Find a, b, and γ.

Solution. Since $\alpha + \beta + \gamma = 180°$, $\gamma = 180° - 120° = 60°$.
According to the Law of Sines, $\sin \alpha / a = \sin \gamma / c$, so

$$a = \frac{c \sin \alpha}{\sin \gamma} = \frac{(10) \sin 45°}{\sin 60°} = \frac{(10)\sqrt{2}/2}{\sqrt{3}/2} = \frac{10\sqrt{2}}{\sqrt{3}}.$$

Similarly,

$$b = \frac{c \sin \beta}{\sin \gamma} = \frac{10 \sin 75°}{\sin 60°}.$$

We find the value of $\sin 75°$ by writing $\sin 75° = \sin (30° + 45°)$ and using an addition formula:

$$\sin 75° = \frac{1 + \sqrt{3}}{2\sqrt{2}}.$$

Thus

$$b = \frac{\frac{10(1 + \sqrt{3})}{2\sqrt{2}}}{\frac{\sqrt{3}}{2}} = \frac{10(1 + \sqrt{3})}{\sqrt{6}}.$$

If we know the lengths of two sides of a triangle and the measure of the angle opposite one of the sides, then we can determine the remaining side and angles by using the Law of Sines.

EXAMPLE 43-2. Let $\alpha = 30°$, $a = 10$, and $c = 15$. Find β, γ, and b.

Solution. Since $\sin \gamma / c = \sin \alpha / a$, we have $\sin \gamma = c \sin \alpha / a$. Thus

$$\sin \gamma = \frac{15 \sin 30°}{10} = \frac{15}{20} = \frac{3}{4}.$$

Now there are two angles between 0° and 180° for which $\sin \gamma = \frac{3}{4}$. These angles are $\gamma = 48° 36'$ or $\gamma = 131° 24'$. In case $\gamma = 48° 36'$, then $\beta = 101° 24'$ and $b = a \sin \beta / \sin \alpha = 20(.98) = 19.6$. In case $\gamma = 131° 24'$, then $\beta = 18° 36'$ and $b = 20(.32) = 6.4$. These two possibilities are shown in Fig. 43-3.

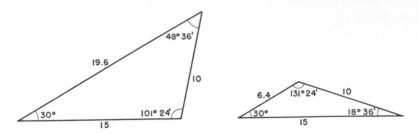

Figure 43-3

If two numbers a and c and an angle α are given, there may be one, two, or no triangles that have one side of length a, another of length c, and the angle α opposite the side of length a. We should therefore be careful in solving problems such as Example 43-2. Frequently a sketch will immediately make the situation clear. Figure 43-4 shows that it is impossible to construct a triangle in which $a < c$ and α is obtuse. If α is acute and $a < c$, the problem becomes more compli-

Figure 43-4

cated. Figure 43-5 illustrates the possibilities of one, two, or no solutions. We find which of these situations exists when we calculate $\sin \gamma = c \sin \alpha / a$. If $\sin \gamma = 1$, then γ is a right angle and there is just one suitable triangle. If $\sin \gamma < 1$, then there are two possible choices for γ, as there were in Example 43-2. But if it should appear

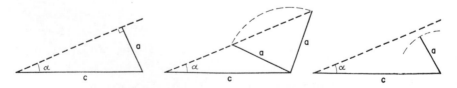

Figure 43-5

that sin γ is greater than 1, then there are no triangles that satisfy the given conditions.

If you are interested, you might try to analyze all the possibilities in this so-called *ambiguous case* and then check your results against those found in a standard trigonometry book. Our purpose here was to call your attention to the fact that complications may arise in this type of problem.

Problems 43

1. Interpret the Law of Sines if one of the angles, say γ, is a right angle.
2. Find the remaining parts of a triangle if:
   (a) $\gamma = 75°$, $\beta = 30°$, $a = 5$
   (b) $\alpha = 42°$, $\gamma = 76°$, $b = 18$
   (c) $\alpha = 33°\ 30'$, $\beta = 50°\ 48'$, $c = 12.4$
   (d) $\beta = 2\alpha$, $\gamma = 2\beta$, $a = 1.6$
3. Either show that no triangle exists or find the missing parts of all triangles such that:
   (a) $a = 4$, $b = 5$, $\alpha = 30°$
   (b) $a = 12$, $c = 6$, $\gamma = 67°$
   (c) $b = 20$, $c = 26$, $\beta = 148°$
   (d) $a = 23.8$, $b = 31.4$, $\alpha = 23°\ 40'$
4. Show that if $\beta = 2\alpha$, then $\cos \alpha = b/2a$.
5. City A is directly south of city B, but there are no direct airline flights from A to B. Planes first fly 143 miles from city A to city C, which is 51° east of north from A, and then fly 212 miles to city B. What is the straight-line distance between A and B?
6. Observers in cities A and B, which are 5 miles apart, see an object in the sky above the line on the ground joining the cities. The angle of elevation at A is 23° and the angle of elevation at B is 31°. What is the altitude of the object?
7. The diagonal of a parallelogram is 10 in. long. At one end the diagonal makes angles of 33° and 25° with the sides of the parallelogram. Find the lengths of the sides of the parallelogram.
8. In order to measure the distance between two points A and B on opposite sides of a canyon, a third point C is chosen so that the following measurements can be made: $\overline{CA} = 175$ ft, and $\overline{CB} = 212$ ft. At B, the angle ABC is 47°. Compute the distance $\overline{AB}$.
9. Four ships, A, B, C, and D, are at sea in the following relative positions. B is on a line between A and C, B is due north of D, and D is due west

of C. The distance between B and D is 2 miles. From D, the angle BDA measures 40°, and from C the angle BCD measures 25°. What is the distance between A and D?

10. Let D be a point on the side c of a triangle ABC such that CD bisects the angle γ. Use the Law of Sines to prove that $\overline{AD}/\overline{DB} = b/a$.

44   THE LAW OF COSINES

In this section, we shall discuss a generalization of the Pythagorean Theorem called the **Law of Cosines**. You will find many applications of this important law in your study of mathematics.

THEOREM 44-1 (**Law of Cosines**). *Let a, b, and c be the lengths of the sides of a triangle and label the angle opposite the side of length a by α.* Then

44-1 $$a^2 = b^2 + c^2 - 2bc \cos \alpha.$$

Written out, the Law of Cosines states that *the square of the length of a given side of a triangle is equal to the sum of the squares of the lengths of the other two sides minus twice the product of the lengths of the other sides and the cosine of the angle between them.*

Proof. We place the triangle so that the vertex of the angle α falls at the origin of a cartesian coordinate system and the side of length c lies along the positive x-axis (see Fig. 44-1). It is clear

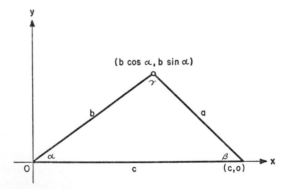

Figure 44-1

that the coordinates of the vertex of the angle β are $(c,0)$. Since the angle α is in standard position, Theorem 41-1 tells us that the coordinates of the vertex of γ are $(b \cos \alpha, b \sin \alpha)$. The distance between the vertices of β and γ is a, and according to the distance formula

$$a^2 = (b \cos \alpha - c)^2 + (b \sin \alpha)^2$$

$$= b^2 \cos^2 \alpha + b^2 \sin^2 \alpha + c^2 - 2bc \cos \alpha.$$

Since

$$b^2 \cos^2 \alpha + b^2 \sin^2 \alpha = b^2 (\cos^2 \alpha + \sin^2 \alpha) = b^2 \cdot 1 = b^2,$$

our equation reduces to Equation 44-1 and the Law of Cosines is established.

If α is a right angle, then $\cos \alpha = 0$ and Equation 44-1 simply re-states the Theorem of Pythagoras.

If we know the lengths of two sides of a triangle and the measure of the angle between them, then we can use the Law of Cosines to find the length of the remaining side and the magnitudes of the other angles.

EXAMPLE 44-1.   If $\gamma = 60°$, $a = 12$, and $b = 5$, find c, α, and β.

Solution.   According to the Law of Cosines,

$$c^2 = 12^2 + 5^2 - 2 \cdot 12 \cdot 5 \cdot \cos 60°.$$

Since $\cos 60° = \frac{1}{2}$, we have

$$c^2 = 144 + 25 - 2 \cdot 12 \cdot 5 \cdot \tfrac{1}{2} = 109,$$

and hence $c = \sqrt{109}$.   We can also use the Law of Cosines to find the angles α and β.   For example, from Equation 44-1

$$2bc \cos \alpha = b^2 + c^2 - a^2,$$

so that

$$\cos \alpha = \frac{b^2 + c^2 - a^2}{2bc} = \frac{134 - 144}{10\sqrt{109}} = \frac{-1}{\sqrt{109}} = -.0958.$$

From Table III we find that $\cos 84° \, 30' = .0958$, and therefore

$$\alpha = 180° - 84° \, 30' = 95° \, 30'. \quad \text{Then}$$

$$\beta = 180° - (95° \, 30' + 60°) = 24° \, 30'.$$

To find the angles of a triangle when all the sides are given, we can again use the Law of Cosines.

EXAMPLE 44-2. Find the angles of a triangle if the lengths of the sides are 5, 6, and 8.

Solution. Let $a = 5$, $b = 6$, and $c = 8$. Then

$$\cos \alpha = \frac{(6)^2 + (8)^2 - (5)^2}{2(6)(8)} = \frac{25}{32} = .7812$$

$$\cos \beta = \frac{(5)^2 + (8)^2 - (6)^2}{2(5)(8)} = \frac{53}{80} = .6625$$

$$\cos \gamma = \frac{(5)^2 + (6)^2 - (8)^2}{2(5)(6)} = \frac{-1}{20} = -.0500$$

With the aid of Table III we find $\alpha = 38° \ 37'$, $\beta = 48° \ 30'$, and $\gamma = 92° \ 52'$. Note that $\alpha + \beta + \gamma = 179° \ 59'$ rather than 180°, but this result is not surprising since we did some "rounding off" in our calculations.

EXAMPLE 44-3. If a, b, and c are the lengths of the sides of a triangle, show that α is an acute angle if, and only if, $b^2 + c^2 > a^2$.

Solution. Since α is an angle of a triangle, it must measure between 0° and 180°. Such an angle is acute if, and only if, its cosine is positive. According to the Law of Cosines, $\cos \alpha = (b^2 + c^2 - a^2)/2bc$, and this quotient is positive if, and only if, $b^2 + c^2 - a^2 > 0$—that is, if, and only if, $b^2 + c^2 > a^2$.

Problems 44

1. Find the remaining parts of a triangle if:
   (a) $a = 3$, $b = 2$, $\gamma = 60°$ (d) $b = 6$, $c = 9$, $\alpha = 53°$
   (b) $b = 4$, $c = \sqrt{3}$, $\alpha = 30°$ (e) $a = 9$, $b = 4$, $\gamma = 93° \ 15'$
   (c) $b = 7$, $c = \sqrt{2}$, $\alpha = 135°$ (f) $a = 2$, $c = 2$, $\beta = 45°$

2. Determine the angles of a triangle if the lengths of the sides are:
   (a) 5, 7, and 8   (c) 28, 45, and 53
   (b) 15, 25, and 30   (d) 4, 5, and 10

3. A metal frame is constructed in the form of an isosceles trapezoid. Both base angles measure 80°, the length of the base is 7 ft, and both sides are 5 ft long. Determine the length of a bar to be used as a diagonal brace.

4. In order to measure the distance between two points A and B on opposite sides of a building, a third point C is chosen such that the following measurements can be made: $\overline{CA} = 215$ ft, $\overline{CB} = 371$ ft, and the angle ACB measures 56° at C. What is the distance between A and B?

5. Use the Law of Cosines to prove that a triangle does not exist whose side lengths would satisfy the inequality $a > b + c$.

6. A man is at a point directly south of factory A and on a line southwest from factory B. He hears the noon whistle of factory B 5 sec after noon, and the noon whistle of factory A 7 sec after noon. Assuming the velocity of sound to be 1100 fps, what is the distance between the factories?

7.   (a) If the lengths of the sides of an isosceles triangle are a, b, and b, use the Law of Cosines to show that $a^2 = 2b^2(1 - \cos \alpha)$.
   (b) A perpendicular dropped from the vertex A of angle α to the side of length a bisects the angle α and also the side of length a. Thus from right-triangle trigonometry, $a = 2b \sin \frac{1}{2}\alpha$. Show that the two equations for the length a are consistent.

8. A pilot intends to fly from city A to city B, a distance of 150 miles. He starts 15° off his course, and proceeds 50 miles before discovering his error. How much should he alter his course and how far must he fly to reach B?

9. Let (x_1, y_1) and (x_2, y_2) be two points in the plane. Label the lengths of the line segments that join the points to the origin as r_1 and r_2 and let θ be the angle between these segments ($0 \leq \theta \leq 180°$). Show that $\cos \theta = (x_1 x_2 + y_1 y_2)/r_1 r_2$. What can you conclude if $x_1 x_2 + y_1 y_2 = 0$?

10. Determine the angles of a triangle if the vertices of the triangle are the following points:
   (a) (0,0), (2,0), and (2,3)
   (b) (0,0), (1,0), and (2,−5)
   (c) (0,0), (1,1), and (−1,3)
   (d) (1,2), (−2,1), and (−1,−2)
   (e) (2,−1), (−3,1), and (1,4)

45   AREA FORMULAS

If a triangle is placed with the vertex of the angle α at the origin of a cartesian coordinate system and with the side of length c extending along the positive x-axis as shown in Fig. 45-1, then α is in standard position and according to Theorem 41-1 the y-coordinate of the vertex of γ is $b \sin \alpha$. This number is the length of the altitude of the triangle. Since the area of a triangle is one-half the product of the base and the altitude, we see that the area A of the triangle is given by the equation

45-1
$$A = \frac{1}{2} bc \sin \alpha.$$

We have shown that *the area of a triangle is equal to one-half the product of the lengths of any two sides and the sine of the included angle.*

By using the relation $b = (c \sin \beta)/\sin \gamma$ from the Law of Sines, we can write Equation 45-1 as

45-2
$$A = c^2 \frac{\sin \alpha \sin \beta}{2 \sin \gamma}.$$

Equation 45-2 expresses the area of a triangle in terms of the sines of all three angles and the length of one side.

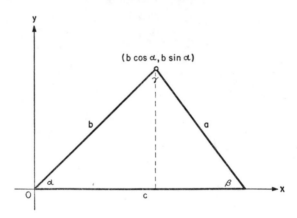

Figure 45-1

If we square both sides of Equation 45-1, we get the equations

45-3
$$A^2 = \frac{b^2c^2}{4} \sin^2 \alpha = \frac{b^2c^2}{4} (1 - \cos^2 \alpha).$$

Now, from the Law of Cosines,

$$\cos \alpha = \frac{b^2 + c^2 - a^2}{2bc},$$

so

$$1 - \cos^2 \alpha = 1 - \frac{(b^2 + c^2 - a^2)^2}{4b^2c^2}$$

$$= \frac{4b^2c^2 - (b^2 + c^2 - a^2)^2}{4b^2c^2}.$$

The numerator of this fraction is the difference of two squares, and if we use the identity $A^2 - B^2 = (A + B)(A - B)$, with $A = 2bc$ and $B = b^2 + c^2 - a^2$, we have

$$1 - \cos^2 \alpha = \frac{(2bc + b^2 + c^2 - a^2)(2bc - b^2 - c^2 + a^2)}{4b^2c^2}$$

$$= \frac{[(b + c)^2 - a^2][a^2 - (b - c)^2]}{4b^2c^2}$$

$$= \frac{(b + c + a)(b + c - a)(a + b - c)(a - b + c)}{4b^2c^2}.$$

When we substitute this expression in Equation 45-3, we obtain the equation

45-4 $$A^2 = \frac{(a + b + c)(a + b - c)(b + c - a)(c + a - b)}{16}.$$

This equation expresses *the area of a triangle in terms of the lengths of its sides.* We can put it in a simpler form by introducing the **semiperimeter** $s = \dfrac{1}{2}(a + b + c)$ of the triangle. You can easily verify the following equations:

45-5
$$2s = (a + b + c), \qquad 2(s - b) = c + a - b,$$
$$2(s - a) = b + c - a, \qquad 2(s - c) = a + b - c.$$

When we introduce these quantities into Equation 45-4 it becomes

45-6 $$A = \sqrt{s(s - a)(s - b)(s - c)}.$$

Let us now inscribe a circle in a triangle (Fig. 45-2). Suppose that the point P is the center of the circle and that r is its radius.

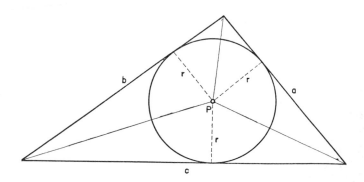

Figure 45-2

We divide the triangle into three smaller triangles by joining the point P to each of the vertices; we find the area of the large triangle by adding the areas of the small triangles. Since the radius of the inscribed circle is perpendicular to a side of the large triangle at its point of contact, the altitude of each of these interior triangles is r. We therefore see that

$$A = \tfrac{1}{2}ra + \tfrac{1}{2}rb + \tfrac{1}{2}rc = r\tfrac{1}{2}(a + b + c), \quad \text{so}$$

45-7 $$A = rs.$$

By equating the right-hand sides of Equations 45-6 and 45-7, we find that the radius of the inscribed circle is given by the formula

45-8 $$r = \sqrt{\frac{(s - a)(s - b)(s - c)}{s}}.$$

If you search through other trigonometry books, particularly older ones, you will uncover many other formulas that connect the sides and the trigonometric functions of the angles of a triangle.

Problems 45

1. Find the area of a triangle if:
   (a) $b = 14,\ c = 5,\ \alpha = 30°$ (c) $a = 5,\ c = 7.2,\ \beta = 71°$
   (b) $a = 10,\ b = 20,\ \gamma = 179°$ (d) $b = 1.5,\ c = 4,\ \alpha = \dfrac{5\pi}{7}$ radians

2. Find the area of a triangle if:
   (a) $c = 3,\ \beta = 40°,\ \gamma = 60°$
   (b) $a = 2,\ \alpha = 60°,\ \beta = 75°$
   (c) $b = 11,\ \alpha = 1$ radian, $\beta = 1.5$ radians
   (d) $c = 3.2,\ \alpha = 16°,\ \beta = 31°\ 45'$

3. Find the area of a triangle and the radius of the inscribed circle if:
   (a) $a = 2,\ b = 3,\ c = 4$ (c) $a = \log 2,\ b = \log 3,\ c = \log 5$
   (b) $a = 2,\ b = 7,\ c = 8$ (d) $a = \sqrt{2},\ b = 2,\ c = 3$

4. If two triangles are similar, the ratio of the length of any side of one triangle to the length of the corresponding side of the other is a constant k. How are the areas related? How are the radii of the inscribed circles related?

5. Equation 45-6 expresses the area of a triangle in terms of the lengths of its sides (angles are not involved). Is it possible to express the area of a triangle in terms of its angles only?

6. Find the length of the longest side of a triangle whose area is 10 and whose angles measure 30°, 50°, and 100°.

7. A field is in the shape of a parallelogram. The lengths of two of the sides are 5 rods and 7 rods. The length of the longer diagonal is 10 rods. Find the area of the field.

8. Let a circle of radius r be inscribed in a triangle ABC and let x, y, and z denote the lengths of the segments from the points of contact of the inscribed circle to the vertices A, B, and C. Show that the area of the triangle is given by the equation $A = r(x + y + z)$. From this equation deduce the equation $A = r^2(\cot \frac{1}{2}\alpha + \cot \frac{1}{2}\beta + \cot \frac{1}{2}\gamma)$.

9. Show that the area of an isosceles triangle is a maximum if the angle between the two equal sides is a right angle.

10. Let B and C be fixed points, l a line parallel to BC, and A a point on l. Show that the product
$$[(\overline{AC} + \overline{AB})^2 - \overline{BC}^2][\overline{BC}^2 - (\overline{AC} - \overline{AB})^2]$$
has a constant value for any choice of the point A.

11. Let P be the point of contact between the inscribed circle of radius r and the side of length b of a triangle ABC. Show that $\overline{AP} = s - a$, and thus deduce the equation $\tan \frac{1}{2}\alpha = r/(s - a)$. This equation can be used to find the angles of a triangle when the lengths of the three sides are given.

Review Problems, Chapter Four

You should be able to answer the following questions without referring back to the text.

1. Is there a number t such that $\sin t = \frac{1}{4}$ and $\cos t = \frac{3}{4}$?

2. What can you say about the numbers t_1 and t_2 if $\sin^2 t_1 + \cos^2 t_2 \neq 1$?

3. Which of the following inequalities are true for all numbers t for which the functions are defined?

(a) $|\sin^2 t| \leq 1$

(b) $-1 \leq \sin t \cos t \leq 1$

(c) $|\sin t \sec t| \leq 1$

(d) $|\sin t + \cos t| \leq 2$

(e) $|\tan t + \cot t| \geq 1$

(f) $\left|\cos^2 t + \dfrac{\tan^2 t}{\sec^2 t}\right| \leq 1$

4. If $\csc t = 1.5$, find the values of the other five trigonometric functions of t.

5. With the aid of Table II evaluate the following:

(a) $\sin (\sin 1)$ (b) $\cos (\tan 1.6)$ (c) $\sec (\cos 3)$

6. Graph the equation $y = \sqrt{1 - \sin^2 x}$.

7. Find the coordinates of the point $P(t)$ if you know that:
  (a) $\sin t = \frac{3}{5}$ and $\frac{1}{2}\pi < t < \pi$ (b) $\cos t = \frac{12}{13}$ and $\sin t < 0$.

8. If $\tan t = \frac{3}{4}$, find $\sin 2t$.

9. If $0 < u < v < \frac{1}{2}\pi$, $\cos u = \frac{3}{5}$, and $\sin v = \frac{12}{13}$, find $\cos (u + v)$ and $\sin (v - u)$.

10. A ferris wheel with a radius of 12 ft revolves at the rate of 3 rpm.   Assume that the rays of the sun are parallel, and that the sun is directly overhead.   Find a formula that gives the position of the shadow of a given rider t minutes after he passes the lowest point of the wheel.

11. What is the domain of the function that is defined by the equations:
  (a) $y = \log (\sin x)$ (b) $y = \sin (\log x)$

12. Which is larger?
  (a) $\sin (\cos 1)$ or $\cos (\sin 1)$ (b) $\cos (\log 1)$ or $\log (\cos 1)$

13. Solve for x:
  (a) $\sin [\sin (\sin x)] = 0$ (b) $\cos (\cos x) = 0$

14. A steel bar measures 2 ft at room temperature.   It is then fastened at both ends and heated so that it expands .1 in.   Assume that the ends stay fixed and that the bar buckles in the middle so that an isosceles triangle is formed by the bar and the line joining the end points.   Determine the height of this isosceles triangle.

15. Show that $\cos 2t = \cos^4 t - \sin^4 t$.

16. If n is a positive integer, find
  (a) $\sin n\pi$
  (b) $\cos n\pi$
  (c) $\sin \dfrac{(2n + 1)}{2} \pi$
  (d) $\cos \frac{1}{2}(2n + 1)\pi$

17. If the radius of the earth is 3960 miles, what is the distance between two parallels of latitude that are 1° apart?

18. Find the area of a circle inscribed in a regular pentagon if the length of the sides is 1 in.

19. Show that the area of a regular polygon with n sides each of length a is $\frac{1}{4}na^2 \cot (\pi/n)$.

Miscellaneous Problems, Chapter Four

These problems are designed to test your ability to apply your knowledge of trigonometric functions to somewhat more difficult problems.

1. Determine whether the following equations have graphs that are: (a) symmetric with respect to the y-axis, (b) symmetric with respect

It is particularly advantageous to write complex numbers in trigonometric form when we multiply or divide. Suppose that u and v are two complex numbers whose trigonometric forms are $u = r\,(\cos\theta + i\sin\theta)$ and $v = s\,(\cos\phi + i\sin\phi)$. Then by straight-forward multiplication their product is

$$uv = rs\,[\cos\theta\cos\phi - \sin\theta\sin\phi) + i\,(\sin\theta\cos\phi + \cos\theta\sin\phi)].$$

From the addition Formulas 34-2 we have

$$\cos\theta\cos\phi - \sin\theta\sin\phi = \cos(\theta + \phi),\quad\text{and}$$

$$\sin\theta\cos\phi + \cos\theta\sin\phi = \sin(\theta + \phi).$$

Hence,

48-2 $$uv = rs\,[\cos(\theta + \phi) + i\sin(\theta + \phi)].$$

Written out, Equation 48-2 states that *the product of two complex numbers is the complex number whose absolute value is the product of the absolute values of the factors, and whose argument is the sum of the arguments of the factors.*

EXAMPLE 48-2. Let z be a complex number. Find the trigonometric form of the product iz.

Solution. Suppose the trigonometric form of the number z is $z = r\,(\cos\theta + i\sin\theta)$. Since $i = 1\,(\cos 90° + i\sin 90°)$, $iz = r\,[\cos(\theta + 90°) + i\sin(\theta + 90°)]$. Thus we obtain the complex number iz from the complex number z by rotating the line joining z and the origin 90° in a counter-clockwise direction.

EXAMPLE 48-3. If $z = r\,(\cos\theta + i\sin\theta)$, express z^2 in trigonometric form.

Solution. The absolute value of z^2 is r^2, and the argument of z^2 is $\theta + \theta = 2\theta$. Hence, $z^2 = r^2\,(\cos 2\theta + i\sin 2\theta)$.

To find the quotient u/v of the two complex numbers $u = r\,(\cos\theta + i\sin\theta)$ and $v = s\,(\cos\phi + i\sin\phi)$, where $s \neq 0$, we find the complex number $w = t\,(\cos\psi + i\sin\psi)$ such that $u = vw$. Hence, if we use Equation 48-2 we see that t and ψ should be chosen so that

48-3 $$r\,(\cos\theta + i\sin\theta) = st\,[\cos(\phi + \psi) + i\sin(\phi + \psi)].$$

Now it is clear that *two complex numbers are equal if, and only if,*

(i) *their absolute values are equal,*

(ii) *their arguments are equal or differ by a multiple of 360°.*

Thus, we must have

$$r = st$$

$$\theta = \phi + \psi + k \cdot 360° \quad (k \text{ may be any integer}).$$

So we have $t = r/s$ and $\psi = \theta - \phi - k \cdot 360°$. Since $T(\theta - \phi - k \cdot 360°) = T(\theta - \phi)$, the trigonometric form of the quotient u/v can be written as

48-4
$$\frac{u}{v} = \frac{r}{s} [\cos (\theta - \phi) + i \sin (\theta - \phi)].$$

EXAMPLE 48-4.   Find the trigonometric form of the reciprocal of the complex number $z = r (\cos \theta + i \sin \theta)$.

Solution. We are to calculate the quotient $1/z$. Since 1 may be written as $1 = 1 (\cos 0° + i \sin 0°)$, it follows that

$$\frac{1}{z} = \frac{1}{r} [\cos (0° - \theta) + i \sin (0° - \theta)]$$

$$= \frac{1}{r} (\cos \theta - i \sin \theta).$$

Problems 48

1. Find the absolute value and argument of each of the following complex numbers and plot as a point in the plane.

   (a) $\sqrt{3} + i$ (c) -1 (e) $-1 - \sqrt{3}i$

   (b) $-i$ (d) $-2 + 2i$ (f) $1 - 2i$

2. Write each of the following numbers in non-trigonometric form $a + bi$ and plot as a point in the plane.

   (a) $2 \left(\cos \dfrac{5\pi}{6} + i \sin \dfrac{5\pi}{6} \right)$

   (b) $3 (\cos \pi + i \sin \pi)$

   (c) $2 \left(\cos \dfrac{\pi}{4} + i \sin \dfrac{\pi}{4} \right)$

   (d) $5 (\cos 1 + i \sin 1)$

   (e) $7 (\cos 200° + i \sin 200°)$

   (f) $4 (\cos 3 + i \sin 3)$

3. Show that $|uv| = |u| \cdot |v|$ and that $|u/v| = |u|/|v|$.

4. Show that $|z| = |-z| = |\bar{z}| = |iz| = |z (\cos \theta + i \sin \theta)|$.

5. Use the facts stated in the preceding problem to show that $|4 - 3z| = |4 - 3\bar{z}|$.

6. Let $u = a + bi$ and $v = c + di$. Show that $|u - v|$ is the distance between the points that represent u and v.

7. Describe in your own words the result stated in Equation 48-4.

8. Find the product uv and the quotient $\dfrac{u}{v}$ if $u = 12 \left(\cos \dfrac{\pi}{3} + i \sin \dfrac{\pi}{3} \right)$ and if:

(a) $v = 4 \left(\cos \dfrac{\pi}{4} + i \sin \dfrac{\pi}{4} \right)$

(b) $v = 3 \left(\cos \pi + i \sin \pi \right)$

(c) $v = .5 \left(\cos 20° + i \sin 20° \right)$

(d) $v = 1.5 \left(\cos 40° - i \sin 40° \right)$

9. Perform the following operations both algebraically and by first writing the numbers in trigonometric form.

(a) $(1 + i)(2 + 2i)(3 + 3i)$

(b) $\dfrac{-1 + i}{\sqrt{3} + i}$

(c) $(1 + i)(1 + i\sqrt{3}) \left(-\dfrac{1}{2} + \dfrac{1}{2} i \right) \left(-\dfrac{1}{2} + i \dfrac{\sqrt{3}}{2} \right)$

(d) $\dfrac{(\sqrt{3} + i)(-1 - i)}{(1 + i\sqrt{3})(2\sqrt{3} - 2i)}$

10. Prove that two complex numbers are equal if, and only if, (i) their absolute values are equal, and (ii) their arguments are equal or differ by a multiple of $360°$ or 2π radians.

11. Describe geometrically the location of all points z that satisfy the following conditions:

(a) $|z| = 1$

(b) $z + \bar{z} = 2$

(c) $|z| < 2$

(d) $z + \bar{z} > 1.$

49 ROOTS OF COMPLEX NUMBERS

In Example 48-3 we showed that if $z = r (\cos \theta + i \sin \theta)$, then $z^2 = r^2 (\cos 2\theta + i \sin 2\theta)$. Now $z^3 = z^2 \cdot z$, so another application of the rule for multiplying complex numbers in trigonometric form (Equation 48-2) shows that

$$z^3 = r^3 [\cos (2\theta + \theta) + i \sin (2\theta + \theta)] = r^3 (\cos 3\theta + i \sin 3\theta).$$

If we repeat the process once more we get

$$z^4 = z^3 \cdot z = r^4 (\cos 4\theta + i \sin 4\theta).$$

Indeed, for any positive integer n, it may be shown that

49-1 $z^n = r^n (\cos n\theta + i \sin n\theta).$

EXAMPLE 49-1. If θ is any angle and n is any positive integer, show
that

49-2 $(\cos \theta + i \sin \theta)^n = \cos n\theta + i \sin n\theta.$

Solution. We simply let z be the complex number $z = (\cos \theta + i \sin \theta)$.
Then Equation 49-1 becomes $(\cos \theta + i \sin \theta)^n = 1^n \cdot (\cos n\theta + i \sin n\theta)$, which is the equation to be verified. Equation 49-2 is known
as **DeMoivre's Theorem.**

Let n be a positive integer and u be a complex number. *A complex
number z is called an* **nth root of u** *if*

49-3 $z^n = u.$

The numbers 1, -1, i, and $-i$, for example, are 4th roots of the
number 1, since $(-1)^4 = (1)^4 = (i)^4 = (-i)^4 = 1$. We can easily
solve Equation 49-3 if u and z are expressed in trigonometric form.
Suppose that $u = s (\cos \phi + i \sin \phi)$ and that z is an nth root of u
expressed in the trigonometric form $z = r (\cos \theta + i \sin \theta)$. Let us
suppose that $u \neq 0$, and therefore $s > 0$. Then, using Equation
49-1, we may write Equation 49-3 in the form

$$r^n (\cos n\theta + i \sin n\theta) = s (\cos \phi + i \sin \phi).$$

Our problem is to find a positive number r and an angle θ for which
this last equation is valid. Two complex numbers can be equal only
if their absolute values are equal, and hence we must choose r so
that $r > 0$ and $r^n = s$. Therefore,

49-4 $r = \sqrt[n]{s}.$

Our equation then reduces to the two equations

$$\cos n\theta = \cos \phi \quad \text{and} \quad \sin n\theta = \sin \phi.$$

It is clear from these equations that the angles $n\theta$ and ϕ can differ
only by a multiple of $360°$ or 2π radians (see Exercise 10 of Problems
48). More precisely, $n\theta = \phi + k \cdot 360°$, where k is an integer—
positive, negative, or 0. Therefore

49-5 $\theta = \dfrac{\phi}{n} + k \dfrac{360°}{n}.$

We can also write this equation as

49-6
$$\theta = \frac{\phi}{n} + k\frac{2\pi}{n} \text{ radians.}$$

EXAMPLE 49-2.   Find the cube roots of the complex number $u = 8(\cos 60° + i \sin 60°)$.

Solution.   According to Equations 49-4 and 49-5, $z = r(\cos \theta + i \sin \theta)$ will be a cube root of u if $r = \sqrt[3]{8} = 2$ and θ is an angle of the form $(60/3)° + k(360/3)° = 20° + k\,120°$, where k is any integer.   The cube roots we are seeking can therefore be expressed as

$$z_k = 2[\cos(20° + k\,120°) + i \sin(20° + k\,120°)].$$

We now observe that even though there are an infinite number of possibilities for the integer k, there are really only three values of z_k. To illustrate this statement, we will list a few values of z_k for specific choices of the integer k:

$$z_0 = 2(\cos 20° + i \sin 20°),$$

$$z_1 = 2(\cos 140° + i \sin 140°),$$

$$z_2 = 2(\cos 260° + i \sin 260°),$$

$$z_3 = 2(\cos 380° + i \sin 380°),$$

$$z_4 = 2(\cos 500° + i \sin 500°).$$

But it is clear that $z_3 = z_0$ and $z_4 = z_1$, since $T(380°) = T(20°)$ and $T(500°) = T(140°)$ for any trigonometric function T.   You should be able to convince yourself that any choice of k will lead to one of the numbers z_0, z_1, or z_2.

The results of our work with the roots of complex numbers suggest the following theorem.

THEOREM 49-1.   *A non-zero complex number $u = s(\cos \phi + i \sin \phi)$ has, for any given positive integer n, exactly n distinct nth roots given by the formula*

49-7
$$z_k = \sqrt[n]{s}\left[\cos\left(\frac{\phi}{n} + k \cdot \frac{360°}{n}\right) + i \sin\left(\frac{\phi}{n} + k \cdot \frac{360°}{n}\right)\right],$$

$k = 0, 1, 2, \ldots, (n-1)$.   (An analogous formula applies when ϕ is measured in radians.)

EXAMPLE 49-3.   Find the 5th roots of 32.

Solution.   Using radian measure for the angles, we can write $32 =$ $32 (\cos 0 + i \sin 0)$.   Hence, the 5th roots of 32 are the five numbers given by the formula

$$z_k = \sqrt[5]{32} \left[\cos \left(0 + \frac{2k\pi}{5} \right) + i \sin \left(0 + \frac{2k\pi}{5} \right) \right]$$

$$= 2 \left(\cos \frac{2k\pi}{5} + i \sin \frac{2k\pi}{5} \right), \; (k = 0, 1, 2, 3, 4).$$

It is interesting to plot the 5th roots of 32 as points in the plane.   We see that all the 5th roots of 32 are on a circle with a radius of 2 and are equally spaced about the circumference with one of them on the *x*-axis.   The geometric picture of the 5th roots of 32 appears in Fig. 49-1.

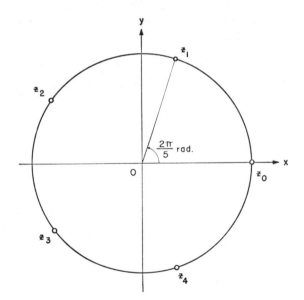

Figure 49-1

If $u \geq 0$, we reserve the symbol $\sqrt{u}$ to mean the non-negative number whose square is u.   This usage is standard; wherever you see the symbol $\sqrt{9}$, for example, it always means 3, not -3.   If u is not a positive number, the symbol $\sqrt{u}$ is ordinarily not used without some explanation of its meaning.   Since we shall have occasion to use this symbol later, we will agree that *if u is not a negative real* *number, then the symbol $\sqrt{u}$ will denote the solution to the equation $z^2 = u$, whose real part is not negative. If $u < 0$, then $\sqrt{u} = i\sqrt{|u|}$.* These statements do not represent fundamental mathematical truths. They are just a means of selecting which of the two numbers whose square is u we shall designate by the symbol $\sqrt{u}$. A different selection may be used in other books.

EXAMPLE 49-4. Find $\sqrt{2i}$ and $\sqrt{-4}$.

Solution. In Example 46-2 we found that the two numbers whose square is $2i$ were the numbers $1 + i$ and $-1 - i$. The real part of the first is the positive number 1, so according to our agreement, we write $\sqrt{2i} = 1 + i$. Since $-4 < 0$, we have agreed that $-4 = i\sqrt{|-4|} = i\sqrt{4} = 2i$.

EXAMPLE 49-5. Find $\sqrt{-1 + \sqrt{3}i}$.

Solution. To find $\sqrt{-1 + \sqrt{3}i}$ we must find that solution to the equation $z^2 = -1 + \sqrt{3}i$ whose real part is non-negative. In trigonometric form,

$$-1 + \sqrt{3}i = 2 (\cos 120° + i \sin 120°),$$

so

$$z_1 = \sqrt{2} (\cos 60° + i \sin 60°) = \frac{\sqrt{2}}{2} (1 + \sqrt{3}i) \quad \text{and}$$

$$z_2 = \sqrt{2} (\cos 240° + i \sin 240°) = \frac{-\sqrt{2}}{2} (1 + \sqrt{3}i).$$

Since the real part of z_1 is $\sqrt{2}/2 > 0$, we write

$$\sqrt{-1 + \sqrt{3}i} = \frac{\sqrt{2}}{2} (1 + \sqrt{3}i).$$

Problems 49

1. Use DeMoivre's Theorem to calculate the following:
   (a) $(\cos 45° + i \sin 45°)^8$ (d) $(3 + 3i)^6$
   (b) $(1 + i)^8$ (e) $(\cos 1 + i \sin 1)^{12}$
   (c) $(\sqrt{3} + i)^{12}$ (f) $(.8192 + .5736i)^9$

2. If u is a solution to the equation $z^8 - 1 = 0$, show that $\bar{u}$ is also a solution.

3. Find the 3 cube roots of u; write in non-trigonometric form $a + bi$, and plot as points in the plane.
(a) $u = 1$ (c) $u = -1$
(b) $u = i$ (d) $u = -i$

4. Describe how you can geometrically construct the 5th roots of u if:
(a) $u = 1$ (c) $u = -1$
(b) $u = i$ (d) $u = 1 + i$

5. Write the following radicals in the form $a + bi$:
(a) $\sqrt{-16}$ (c) $\sqrt{2 - 2i}$ (e) $\sqrt{i^3}$
(b) $\sqrt{4i}$ (d) $\sqrt{\sqrt{3} - i}$ (f) $\sqrt{.1736 + .9848i}$

6. Can the two square roots of a complex number z be written as $\sqrt{z}$ and $-\sqrt{z}$?

7. Use DeMoivre's Theorem to find a formula for $\cos 3\theta$.

8. Suppose that $z^6 = 1$, and that $z \neq 1$. Let $S = z^5 + z^4 + z^3 + z^2 + z + 1$. Show that $Sz = S$, and hence $S = 0$.

9. Let f be a function whose domain is the set of complex numbers. Find the zeros of f if:
(a) $f(z) = z^2 + 2i$ (b) $f(z) = 3z^4 + 1$ (c) $f(z) = iz^3 - 1$

10. Let n be a positive integer. Use DeMoivre's Theorem to show that if $z = r (\cos \theta + i \sin \theta)$, then $z^{-n} = r^{-n} [\cos (-n\theta) + i \sin (-n\theta)]$.

Review Problems, Chapter Five

You should be able to answer the following questions without referring back to the text.

1. Find the solution to the equation
$$\frac{iz}{(3 - i)} = \frac{(2 + 5i)z + 5}{(-4 + 3i)}.$$

2. If the sum of two complex numbers is real, are the two numbers complex conjugates?

3. Let f be the function that is defined by the equation $f(z) = z + \bar{z}$. What is the range of f?

4. Describe geometrically the result of multiplying a number by $\sqrt{i}$.

5. Which of the following equations are always true?
(a) $|z|^2 = |z^2|$ (c) $|3z| = 3|z|$
(b) $|u + v| = |u| + |v|$ (d) $\sqrt{|z|} = |\sqrt{z}|$

6. Let the function f be defined as follows: $f(z)$ is the real part of z.
(a) What is $f(3 + i)$?
(b) Does $f(u + v)$ equal $f(u) + f(v)$?
(c) Does $f(uv)$ equal $f(u) f(v)$?

7. Answer the preceding problem if:

(a) $f(z) = \bar{z}$

(b) $f(z) = \log |z|$

8. Make a careful sketch showing the point $u = \frac{40}{13} + \frac{96}{13}i$ and the three cube roots of u. Write the three cube roots of u in the form $a + bi$ by using your sketch to estimate the values of a and b.

9. Let ω denote any cube root of 1, except that $\omega \neq 1$. Show that the three cube roots of 1 are ω, ω^2, and ω^3.

10. Let f be defined by the equation $f(x) = x + i \log x$. What is the domain of f? What is the range of f? Prove that $|f(x)| \neq 0$ for all numbers x in the domain of f.

Miscellaneous Problems, Chapter Five

These problems are designed to test your ability to apply your knowledge of complex numbers to somewhat more difficult problems.

1. Describe geometrically the location of all points z that satisfy the following conditions:

(a) $|z - 2| = 3$

(b) $|z - \bar{z}| = 2$

(c) $1 < |z| \leq 2$

(d) $1 < |z - 3| < 4$

2. Let f be a function whose domain is the set of complex numbers. Describe geometrically the relation between the numbers z and $f(z)$ if:

(a) $f(z) = (\cos \alpha + i \sin \alpha)z$ (α a given real number)

(b) $f(z) = kz$ (k a given real number)

3. Let U and V denote the points representing $u = r (\cos \theta + i \sin \theta)$ and $v = s (\cos \phi + i \sin \phi)$, where θ and ϕ are acute angles. Let O denote the origin, A the point $(1,0)$, and P the point that represents the product uv. Show that triangle OVP is similar to triangle OAU.

4. Solve the equation $(z + \bar{z})z = 2 + 4i$.

5. Let u and v be complex numbers that are not real numbers. If both uv and u/v are real numbers, what can you conclude about u and v?

6. Let f be a function whose domain is the set of points in the complex plane defined by the inequality $|z| \leq 1$. Describe geometrically the range of f if:

(a) $f(z) = 2z$

(b) $f(z) = z^2$

7. Show that for any complex number $z \neq 1$,
$$1 + z + z^2 + z^3 + z^4 + z^5 = (1 - z^6)/(1 - z).$$
Use this relation and DeMoivre's Theorem to derive the formula
$$1 + \cos \theta + \cos 2\theta + \cos 3\theta + \cos 4\theta + \cos 5\theta = \frac{1}{2} + \frac{\sin 11\theta/2}{2 \sin \frac{1}{2}\theta}.$$

C H A P T E R   S I X

THE THEORY OF
EQUATIONS

Anyone who knows how to add, subtract, and multiply can show that when we substitute 2 for x in the expression $2x^3 - 3x + 7$, we get the number 17.   But it is more difficult to *start* with the number 17 and then solve the equation $2x^3 - 3x + 7 = 17$.   In this chapter we will touch on some of the high spots of the theory of such algebraic equations.

50 POLYNOMIALS

If n is a positive integer or 0, and if $a_0, a_1, \ldots, a_n$ are $n + 1$ numbers, where $a_n \neq 0$, then the expression

$$a_n x^n + a_{n-1} x^{n-1} + \ldots + a_1 x + a_0$$

218

is called a **polynomial of degree n in x.**   We shall use symbols such as $P(x)$, $Q(x)$, $R(x)$, and $D(x)$ to denote polynomials.   The numbers $a_0, a_1, \ldots, a_n$ are the **coefficients** of the polynomial.   Note that in a polynomial of degree n, the coefficient a_n is not 0, but some of the other coefficients may be.   Each expression such as $a_j x^j$ is called a **term** of the polynomial.   The number 0 is also regarded as a polynomial, but no degree is assigned to it.   Examples of polynomials are:

(i) $P(x) = 3x^4 - \pi x^2 - 2x + 1$.   The degree of this polynomial is $n = 4$, and its coefficients are the numbers $a_4 = 3$, $a_3 = 0$, $a_2 = -\pi$, $a_1 = -2$, and $a_0 = 1$.

(ii) $Q(x) = ix^2 - 3x + 17 - 2i$.   In this example, $n = 2$, $a_2 = i$, $a_1 = -3$, and $a_0 = 17 - 2i$.

(iii) $R(x) = 4$.   The degree of this polynomial is 0, and its only coefficient is $a_0 = 4$.

A polynomial in x consists of a sum of one or more terms; each term is either a number or consists of the product of a number and a positive integral power of x.   Expressions such as $3x^2 + 2\sqrt{x} - 5$, $2^x + i$, $2x + 3 - 1/x$, and $2x + \sin x + 3$ are *not* polynomials in x. If $P(x)$ is a polynomial, and if r is a given number, then we use the symbol $P(r)$ to denote the number that results from replacing x in $P(x)$ by r.   Thus, if $P(x) = x^2 - 3x + 1$, then $P(2) = 2^2 - 3(2) + 1 = -1$.   At times we shall confine our attention to polynomials whose coefficients are real numbers, or rational numbers, or integers; but unless otherwise indicated, the following theory is applicable when the coefficients are any complex numbers.

Two polynomials are **equal** if, and only if, the coefficients of the corresponding powers of x are equal.   Thus $ax^2 + bx + c = -x^2 + 2$, if, and only if, $a = -1$, $b = 0$, and $c = 2$.   If $P(x)$ and $Q(x)$ are equal polynomials, then the numbers $P(r)$ and $Q(r)$ are equal every time a number r is substituted for x.   The algebraic operations of addition, subtraction, and multiplication of polynomials should be familiar to you from elementary algebra.   Thus, for example,

$$(3x^2 - 2x + 1) + (x^3 - 5) = x^3 + 3x^2 - 2x - 4,$$

and

$$(3x^2 - 2x + 1)(x^3 - 5) = 3x^5 - 2x^4 + x^3 - 15x^2 + 10x - 5.$$

The process of division, however, demands a more extended discussion.   In Section 1, we defined the quotient a/b of two numbers

a and b as the number q that satisfies the equation $a = qb$. We then noticed that if the numbers a, b, and q were limited to the integers, a given pair of numbers need not have a quotient. If $a = 7$ and $b = 3$, for example, then there is no integer q such that $7 = 3q$. To cope with this situation, we then considered the rational numbers and found that there was a rational number that satisfies the equation $7 = 3q$. There is, however, another way to avoid the difficulty—namely, to devise a somewhat different definition of division. Suppose that we do not demand that $a = qb$, but that $a = qb + r$, where the integer r is in some sense the smallest possible choice. For example, we could write $7 = 2 \cdot 3 + 1$. The number q is then called the **quotient** and the number r is called the **remainder** in the division of a by b. The ordinary process of "long division" of a positive integer a by a positive integer b is simply a method of finding the numbers q and r such that $a = qb + r$ and $0 \leq r < b$.

EXAMPLE 50-1. If $a = 217$ and $b = 23$, find the quotient q and the remainder r when a is divided by b.

Solution. By long division,

$$
\begin{array}{r}
9 = q \\
23\overline{)217} \\
207 \\
\hline
10 = r.
\end{array}
$$

Thus, $217 = 9 \cdot 23 + 10$ and $0 \leq 10 < 23$.

A similar situation exists in regard to the division of polynomials. We state the result as a theorem, but omit the proof.

THEOREM 50-1.   *Let $P(x)$ and $D(x)$ be polynomials of degrees n and m respectively, where $m \leq n$. Then there are polynomials $Q(x)$ and $R(x)$, where $R(x)$ is either the number 0 or is of lower degree than $D(x)$, such that*

50-1 $P(x) = Q(x) D(x) + R(x).$

The dividend $P(x)$ and the divisor $D(x)$ determine the quotient $Q(x)$ and the remainder $R(x)$ uniquely.

Finding the polynomials $Q(x)$ and $R(x)$, which are the quotient and remainder when polynomials $P(x)$ and $D(x)$ are given, is merely a matter of "long division."

EXAMPLE 50-2.   Let $P(x) = 2x^4 - x^3 + 7x^2 - 2x - 2$ and $D(x) = 2x^2 - x + 1$.   Find $Q(x)$ and $R(x)$.

Solution.

$$D(x) = 2x^2 - x + 1 \overline{\left) \begin{array}{l} x^2 + 3 = Q(x) \\ 2x^4 - x^3 + 7x^2 - 2x - 2 = P(x) \end{array} \right.}$$

$$
\begin{array}{r}
x^2 + 3 = Q(x) \\
\hline
2x^4 - x^3 + 7x^2 - 2x - 2 = P(x) \\
2x^4 - x^3 + x^2 \\
\hline
6x^2 - 2x - 2 \\
6x^2 - 3x + 3 \\
\hline
x - 5 = R(x).
\end{array}
$$

Thus $Q(x) = x^2 + 3$ and $R(x) = x - 5$.

Example 50-2 illustrates the following useful fact. If $P(x) = a_n x^n + \ldots + a_0$ and $D(x) = b_m x^m + \ldots + b_0$ $(m \leq n)$, then the first term of the quotient polynomial $Q(x)$ is $\dfrac{a_n}{b_m} x^{n-m}$.

If $D(x)$ is of the form $x - d$, the process of long division can be shortened considerably by a method known as **synthetic division**. This method will be explained in Example 50-3.

EXAMPLE 50-3.   Divide $2x^4 + x^3 - 3x^2 + x - 10$ by $x - 2$.

Solution.

$$
\begin{array}{r}
2x^3 + 5x^2 + 7x + 15 = Q(x) \\
\hline
x - 2 \overline{\smash{\big)}\, 2x^4 + x^3 - 3x^2 + x - 10} \\
2x^4 - 4x^3 \\
\hline
5x^3 - 3x^2 \\
5x^3 - 10x^2 \\
\hline
7x^2 + x \\
7x^2 - 14x \\
\hline
15x - 10 \\
15x - 30 \\
\hline
20 = R.
\end{array}
$$

The remainder R will always be simply a number, maybe 0, since the degree of the divisor polynomial is 1.   We have put the number R and the coefficients of the quotient $Q(x)$ in bold-faced type where they first appear in the division.   The problem of division amounts to finding these bold-faced numbers.   When we inspect our division we see that *each coefficient of the quotient results from multiplying the coefficient that precedes it by* (-2) *and then subtracting the result from the corresponding coefficient of the dividend.* For example, the coefficient 5 is $1 - (-2)2$ $= 5$. Since the first coefficient of the quotient is the first coefficient of the dividend, we can start with this information and determine all the coefficients (and the remainder) successively. Instead of multiplying by (-2) and then subtracting, we multiply by $+2$ and add. The result in schematic form is

$$
\begin{array}{c c c c c}
2 & 1 & -3 & 1 & -10 \\
& 4 & 10 & 14 & 30 \\
\hline
2 \big| 2 & 5 & 7 & 15 & \big| 20
\end{array}
$$

The first row in the array consists of the coefficients of the dividend. We write the number 2 at the lower left because we are dividing by $(x - 2)$; if we were dividing by $x + 2$, the number would be -2. The arrows, usually omitted, indicate that the number at the "tail," when multiplied by 2, gives the number at the head. The number 20 at the lower right is the remainder.

EXAMPLE 50-4. Use synthetic division to find $Q(x)$ and R if $P(x) = 2x^5 - 30x^3 + x - 1$ and $D(x) = x + 4$.

Solution. The coefficients of the terms in x^4 and x^2 of $P(x)$ are 0; that is, $P(x) = 2x^5 + 0x^4 - 30x^3 + 0x^2 + x - 1$. Then the starting point of our synthetic division is the array

$$
\begin{array}{c c c c c c}
2 & 0 & -30 & 0 & 1 & -1 \\
\\
-4 \,\big| & & & & & \big| \\
\end{array}
$$

The coefficients of $Q(x)$ and R will appear in the last line. To carry out the synthetic division, we bring down the first coefficient, 2, and then follow the procedure outlined above.

$$
\begin{array}{r r r r r r}
2 & 0 & -30 & 0 & 1 & -1 \\
& -8 & 32 & -8 & 32 & -132 \\
\hline
-4 \big| \; 2 & -8 & 2 & -8 & 33 & \big| -133
\end{array}
$$

We therefore have $Q(x) = 2x^4 - 8x^3 + 2x^2 - 8x + 33$, and $R = -133$.

Problems 50

1. Write each of the following expressions in the form

$$a_n x^n + a_{n-1} x^{n-1} + \ldots + a_1 x + a_0.$$

(a) $(x - 4)(x + 6) + x(x^3 - 1)$
(b) $(x^2 - 4)(3 - x) - 4(x - 2)$
(c) $(x + 4)(x^2 - 2)(x^3 + 1)$
(d) $(3 - x)(2 - 4x + 3x^2) - (x^3 - 1)$

2. Let $A(x) = 3x^2 - 4x + 1$, $B(x) = 2x^3 - 5$, and $C(x) = x + 3$.   Find:
  (a) $A(x) B(x) + A(x) C(x)$
  (b) $[A(x)]^2 - [B(x)]^2$
  (c) $xA(x) + 5B(x) - 5C(x)$
  (d) $B(x) + 2[C(x) - 3]^3$

3. If $P(x)$ is a polynomial of degree n, and $Q(x)$ is a polynomial of degree m, what is the degree of:
  (a) $P(x) Q(x)$
  (b) $P(x) + Q(x)$
  (c) $[P(x)]^k$
  (d) $P(ax + b)$

4. Let $P(x) = 3x^3 + x^2 - 2x + 1$.   Find:
  (a) $P(2)$
  (b) $P(-x)$
  (c) $P(x) + P(-x)$
  (d) $P(x) - P(-x)$
  (e) $P(x + h) - P(x)$
  (f) $[P(x + h) - P(x)]/h$

5. If $A(x) = x^2 + 2x - 4$, $B(x) = x^3 + 24$, $P(x) = -x^2 + 2x - 8$, and $Q(x) = x$, show that $P(x) A(x) + Q(x) B(x) = 32$.

6. Find positive integers q and r such that $a = qb + r$, $0 \le r < b$, if:
  (a) $a = 13$, $b = 3$
  (b) $a = 5216$, $b = 46$
  (c) $a = 331$, $b = 19$
  (d) $a = 3716$, $b = 2617$

7. Find the quotient $Q(x)$ and remainder $R(x)$ such that $P(x) = Q(x) D(x) + R(x)$ if:
  (a) $P(x) = x^4 + x^2 - x + 1$, $D(x) = x^2 + x + 1$
  (b) $P(x) = 3x^3 - x + 1$, $D(x) = 2x^2 - 1$
  (c) $P(x) = x^4 + x^2 + 1$, $D(x) = x^4 - x^2 - 1$

8. Use synthetic division to find the quotient $Q(x)$ and the remainder R such that $P(x) = Q(x) D(x) + R$ if:
  (a) $P(x) = x^3 - x^2 + x - 1$, $D(x) = x - 1$
  (b) $P(x) = x^5 - 4x^3 + 5x^2 - 5$, $D(x) = x + 1$
  (c) $P(x) = x^5 + 1$, $D(x) = x + 1$
  (d) $P(x) = x^3 - x + x^4 - x^2$, $D(x) = x + 3$
  (e) $P(x) = 3x^4 - 14x^3 - 7x^2 + 21x - 55$, $D(x) = x - 5$
  (f) $P(x) = 3x^4 + 22x^3 - 19x^2 - 22x + 16$, $D(x) = x + 8$

9. Show that the quotient obtained by dividing $x^{100} - \pi^{100}$ by $x - \pi$ is $x^{99} + x^{98}\pi + x^{97}\pi^2 + \ldots + x\pi^{98} + \pi^{99}$.

10. Explain how the method of synthetic division can be used if $D(x)$ is of the form $ax + b$.   Illustrate the method by dividing $3x^3 - x + 1$ by $2x - 4$.

51   POLYNOMIALS OF THE FIRST DEGREE

A polynomial of the first degree has the form $P(x) = ax + b$, where $a \ne 0$.   One of the main problems we will encounter in our study of polynomials will be to find values of x for which a polynomial is zero. These numbers are called the **zeros** of the polynomial. It is easy to find the zeros of polynomials of degree 1;

$$ax + b = 0 \text{ if, and only if, } x = -\frac{b}{a}.$$

Anticipating some of our future discussion, we now state a theorem that is extremely simple, but which possesses an important generalization in regard to polynomials of higher degree.

THEOREM 51-1. *If $P(x) = ax + b$ and r is the number such that $P(r) = 0$, then $P(x) = a(x - r)$.*

Proof. Since $r = -b/a$, we have

$$a(x - r) = a\left[x - \left(-\frac{b}{a}\right)\right] = ax + b = P(x).$$

Many algebraic equations may be reduced to the form $ax + b = 0$; let's look at some examples.

EXAMPLE 51-1. Solve for x, $3x/2 - \frac{2}{3} = 2x + 1$.

Solution. The equation may be written as $3x/2 - 2x = 1 + \frac{2}{3}$. Then $-x/2 = \frac{5}{3}$, and so $x = -\frac{10}{3}$.

EXAMPLE 51-2. Solve for x, $\dfrac{5}{x - 1} + \dfrac{1}{4 - 3x} = \dfrac{3}{6x - 8}$.

Solution. This equation may be written as

$$\frac{5}{x - 1} + \frac{1}{4 - 3x} + \frac{3}{2(4 - 3x)} = 0.$$

Multiplying both sides of this last equation by $2(x - 1)(4 - 3x)$ yields the equation

$$10(4 - 3x) + 2(x - 1) + 3(x - 1) = 0.$$

Hence,

$$-5x + 7 = 0,$$

and

$$x = \tfrac{7}{5}.$$

EXAMPLE 51-3. Seven engineering firms agree to contribute equally to the cost of a joint technical library. If three more firms join the plan, the cost to each member of the group would be reduced by $600. Find the cost of the library.

Solution. Let x be the cost, in dollars, to each member of the seven-member group. Then $7x = 10(x - 600)$, so $6000 = 3x$ and hence $x = 2000$. Therefore, the cost of the library is $14,000.

In Section 16 we learned that a real linear function f is defined by an equation $f(x) = mx + b$. Thus the expression that defines a linear function is a polynomial of the first degree if $m \neq 0$. First-degree polynomials are also known as **linear polynomials,** and an equation $mx + b = 0$ is called a **linear equation.** We saw in Section 16 that the graph of any real linear function is a line; that is, the graph of an equation $y = mx + b$, where m and b are real numbers, is a line. The question of whether or not every line must be the graph of such an equation is answered by the following theorem.

THEOREM 51-2. *Any line not parallel to the y-axis is the graph of an equation $y = mx + b$. A line parallel to the y-axis is the graph of an equation $x = a$.*

Proof. First, let us consider the case where a line is parallel to the y-axis. A line parallel to the y-axis must intersect the x-axis at some point $(a,0)$. Then the x-coordinate of every point on the line must be $x = a$, which is the equation of the line.

If a line is not parallel to the y-axis, then it must intersect that axis and every line parallel to that axis. Suppose such a line intersects the y-axis at the point $(0,b)$ and the line $x = 1$ at the point $(1,c)$, and let $m = c - b$. A given line therefore determines the numbers m and b, and we shall show that the equation of the line is $y = mx + b$. We know that the graph of the equation $y = mx + b$ is a line. Furthermore, it is easy to establish that the graph of this equation contains the points $(0,b)$ and $(1,c)$. Since there is only one line containing these points, it follows that the graph of the equation $y = mx + b$ must be the line we started with.

The following theorem completes our discussion of lines.

THEOREM 51-3. *If A, B, and C are three real numbers such that A and B are not both 0, then the points whose coordinates (x,y) satisfy the equation*

$Ax + By + C = 0$ *form a line. This line is the graph of the equation* $Ax + By + C = 0$.

Proof. (i) Suppose $B \neq 0$ and (x, y) is a pair of numbers such that $Ax + By + C = 0$. Then $y = (-A/B)x - C/B$. Thus every pair of coordinates that satisfies the given equation satisfies the equation $y = mx + b$, where $m = -A/B$ and $b = -C/B$. We know this latter equation is the equation of a line, so the points whose coordinates satisfy the given equation lie on a line.

(ii) If $B = 0$, then $A \neq 0$, since we have assumed that A and B are not both 0. The equation $Ax + By + C = 0$ then reduces to the equation $x = -C/A$, which we know is the equation of a line parallel to the y-axis.

Problems 51

1. Solve the following equations for x. State any conditions that are necessary for your solution to be valid; e.g., $b \neq 0$ in 1(c).

   (a) $2x - 4(3 - 2x) = 5$

   (b) $\dfrac{x - 1}{3} + \dfrac{x - 3}{2} = \dfrac{2 + x}{10} - 4$

   (c) $2bx = 3 + d$

   (d) $b^2 + bx = a^2 - ax$

   (e) $xy^2 - 2xy + 3y + 1 = 0$

   (f) $S = \dfrac{x - xr^n}{1 - r}$

   (g) $xy + ix - y = 1$

   (h) $\dfrac{x}{y + 1} - \dfrac{2x}{y - 1} = 0$

2. A rectangular plot of ground is twice as long as it is wide. When each side is increased by $2\frac{1}{2}$ rods, 31 rods of fencing are required to enclose it. Find the dimensions of the original plot.

3. One metal stamping machine can complete one lot of finished material in 8 min, while another requires 10 min. How long does it take to complete 900 lots of material if both machines are running?

4. A vat contains homogenized milk whose butterfat content is 5% by volume. How much of this milk should be withdrawn and replaced by skim milk (0% butterfat) to reduce the butterfat content of the mixture to 3.5%?

5. How many ounces of a 30% acetic acid solution should a photographer add to 15 oz of a 5% acetic acid solution in order to obtain a 12% solution?

6. At what time between 9 and 10 o'clock will the minute hand of a watch be directly over the hour hand?

7. Solve for x.   (These equations are linear in $\log x$ or 10^x.)

(a) $3 \log x - 2 = 6$

(b) $4(\log x - 1) = 2(2 - \log x)$

(d) $\dfrac{10^z - 1}{2} = \dfrac{10^{z-1}}{2}$

(c) $\dfrac{10^z}{3} = 7 - 2(10^z + 1)$

8. One alloy contains 20% nickel and another contains 55% nickel.   How much of each alloy should be melted together to produce 20 lb of an alloy that contains 30% nickel?

9. Sketch the graphs of the following equations:

(a) $x = 3$

(b) $2x - 3y = 1$

(c) $x + 2y - 4 = 0$

(d) $5x + 2 = 3(y - 4)$

10. Show that the graphs of the equations $x - 2y + 3 = 0$ and $4y - 2x - 6 = 0$ are the same line.

11. Suppose sugar is 10¢ a lb and shortening is 40¢ a lb.   A mixture contains x lb of sugar and y lb of shortening and is worth 50¢.   Graph the set of points (x, y) that represent the possible values of x and y.

12. Graph the equation $|x| + |y| = 1$.

52   POLYNOMIALS OF THE SECOND DEGREE

A polynomial of the second degree is called a **quadratic polynomial** and has the form $P(x) = ax^2 + bx + c$, where $a \neq 0$.   In the preceding section we noted that every polynomial of the first degree has exactly one zero, and it is easy to find.   We will now find the zeros of a quadratic polynomial.

EXAMPLE 52-1.   Find the zeros of the polynomial $P(x) = x^2 + x - 6$.

Solution.   Since $x^2 + x - 6 = (x + 3)(x - 2)$, our problem is to find those numbers x for which $(x + 3)(x - 2) = 0$.   Now the product of two numbers is 0 if, and only if, at least one of the numbers is 0.   Therefore, x is a zero of $P(x)$ if x is either 2 or -3.

Finding the zeros of a quadratic polynomial by factoring, as we did in Example 52-1, works well if we can easily recognize the factors. If we cannot recognize the factors, the following device, known as **completing the square,** will always work.   To illustrate this method, consider finding the zeros of a general quadratic polynomial; that is, consider solving the quadratic equation

52-1 $$ax^2 + bx + c = 0.$$

We first subtract c from both sides of the equation, and then divide both sides by a (which is not 0 by hypothesis) to obtain

52-2 $$x^2 + \frac{b}{a} x = -\frac{c}{a}.$$

Now we add the quantity $\dfrac{b^2}{4a^2}$ to both sides of Equation 52-2 to get

52-3 $$x^2 + \frac{b}{a} x + \frac{b^2}{4a^2} = \frac{b^2 - 4ac}{4a^2}.$$

It is now apparent that the left side of Equation 52-3 is simply the expression $(x + b/2a)^2$. We added the particular quantity $b^2/4a^2$ to both sides in order to "complete" the left-hand side in such a way as to make it a perfect square. Thus we have

$$\left(x + \frac{b}{2a}\right)^2 = \frac{b^2 - 4ac}{4a^2}.$$

It follows from this last equation that either

$$x + \frac{b}{2a} = \frac{\sqrt{b^2 - 4ac}}{2a} \quad \text{or} \quad x + \frac{b}{2a} = -\frac{\sqrt{b^2 - 4ac}}{2a}.$$

These last two equations lead to a result which is so important that we list it as a theorem.

THEOREM 52-1.   *The polynomial $P(x) = ax^2 + bx + c$ has two zeros (which may be equal) given by the formulas*

$$r_1 = \frac{-b + \sqrt{b^2 - 4ac}}{2a} \quad \text{and} \quad r_2 = \frac{-b - \sqrt{b^2 - 4ac}}{2a}.$$

These formulas are called the **Quadratic Formulas,** and you should memorize them.

EXAMPLE 52-2.   Find the zeros of the polynomial $P(x) = 2x^2 - 2x + 1$.

Solution.   The quadratic formulas yield

$$r_1 = \frac{2 + \sqrt{4 - 8}}{4} = \frac{2 + 2i}{4} = \frac{1 + i}{2} \quad \text{and}$$

$$r_2 = \frac{2 - \sqrt{4 - 8}}{4} = \frac{1 - i}{2}.$$

Two interesting facts emerge from Example 52-2.

(i) Although the coefficients of $P(x)$ are real numbers, indeed integers, the zeros of $P(x)$ are not real.

(ii) The relation between the numbers r_1 and r_2 is $r_1 = \bar{r}_2$.

The fact that a quadratic polynomial with real coefficients may have zeros that are not real should not surprise you if you examine the Quadratic Formulas. Finding the zeros involves taking the square root of the number $b^2 - 4ac$, and if this quantity is negative, the zeros will not be real. The number $b^2 - 4ac$ is called the **discriminant** of the quadratic polynomial $ax^2 + bx + c$. Table 52-4 summarizes the relationship between the sign of the discriminant and the character of the zeros of a quadratic polynomial with real coefficients. You can easily verify these facts by referring to the Quadratic Formulas.

$$P(x) = ax^2 + bx + c; \; a, \, b, \text{ and } c \text{ real}$$

52-4

$b^2 - 4ac$	zeros of $P(x)$
positive	real, unequal
zero	real, equal
negative	complex conjugates

EXAMPLE 52-3.   Solve the equation $x^2 + 2ix - 2 = 0$.

Solution.   According to the Quadratic Formulas,

$$r_1 = \frac{-2i + \sqrt{-4 + 8}}{2} = \frac{-2i + 2}{2} = 1 - i \quad \text{and}$$

$$r_2 = \frac{-2i - \sqrt{-4 + 8}}{2} = \frac{-2i + 2}{2} = -1 - i.$$

Note that $b^2 - 4ac > 0$, but r_1 and r_2 are not real numbers. Why doesn't this fact contradict Table 52-4?

The method of completing the square has many uses in addition to solving quadratic equations, so it is a procedure worth remembering. In order to improve our understanding of this method, let us solve a quadratic equation by completing the square rather than by using the Quadratic Formulas.

EXAMPLE 52-4.   Solve the equation $2x^2 + 8x + 4 = 0$ by completing the square.

Solution. To solve this equation by completing the square, we go through the steps we followed in deriving the Quadratic Formulas, replacing the letters *a*, *b*, and *c* by the numbers 2, 8, and 4. Thus, we have

$$x^2 + 4x = -2,$$
$$x^2 + 4x + 4 = 2,$$
$$(x + 2)^2 = 2.$$

Therefore,

$$x + 2 = \sqrt{2}, \quad \text{or} \quad x + 2 = -\sqrt{2},$$

and hence,

$$x = -2 + \sqrt{2}, \quad \text{or} \quad x = -2 - \sqrt{2}.$$

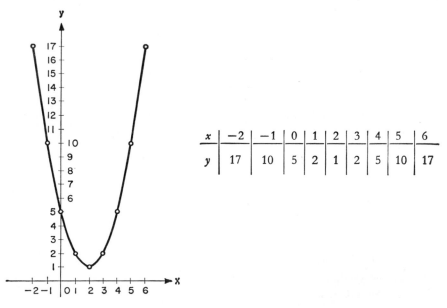

x	-2	-1	0	1	2	3	4	5	6
y	17	10	5	2	1	2	5	10	17

Figure 52-1

The graph of a polynomial $P(x)$ with real coefficients is the graph of the equation $y = P(x)$. The graph of every quadratic polynomial is similar in appearance either to the graph in Fig. 52-1 or to the graph in Fig. 52-2.

EXAMPLE 52-5.   Graph the polynomial $x^2 - 4x + 5$.

Solution.   In order to sketch the graph of the equation $y = x^2 - 4x + 5$, we construct a table that shows corresponding values of x and y. If we plot the points whose coordinates (x,y) are given in this table and join them by a smooth curve, we obtain the graph shown in Fig. 52-1. The graph does not intersect the x-axis. We could have predicted that it would not because the discriminant of the polynomial $x^2 - 4x + 5$ is -4, which means that this polynomial does not have any real zeros.

In Section 4 we devoted some time to the solution of inequalities that involve quadratic polynomials (see Example 4-4). The next example illustrates another method by which we can solve such inequalities.

EXAMPLE 52-6.   Solve the inequality $1 - 2x - x^2 > 0$.

Solution.   We first sketch the graph of the equation $y = -x^2 - 2x + 1$ (Fig. 52-2). Our problem is to determine those values of x for which $y > 0$. It is clear from Fig. 52-2 that $y > 0$ for those numbers x that lie *between* the two points where the graph crosses the x-axis. In

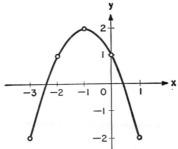

Figure 52-2

other words, the solution to the inequality is given by the inequalities $r_1 < x < r_2$, where r_1 and r_2 are the zeros of the polynomial $-x^2 - 2x + 1$. By using the Quadratic Formulas, we find that the zeros of this polynomial are $-1 - \sqrt{2}$ and $-1 + \sqrt{2}$. Thus, a number x such that $1 - 2x - x^2 > 0$ must satisfy the inequalities

$$-1 - \sqrt{2} < x < -1 + \sqrt{2}.$$

Problems 52

1. Solve the following equations by factoring:
   (a) $2x^2 + 3x = 0$ (c) $y^2 - 2y - 3 = y - 3$
   (b) $z^2 - z - 2 = 0$ (d) $2m^2 + 11m - 6 = 0$

2. Solve the following equations by completing the square:
   (a) $x^2 + 2x - 1 = 0$ (b) $3t^2 - 2t + 1 = 0$

3. Use the Quadratic Formulas to solve the following equations:
   (a) $x^2 - 7x - 7 = 0$ (d) $4y^2 + 4 = 7y$
   (b) $x^2 + x + 1 = 0$ (e) $x^2 + 2\sqrt{3}x - 1 = 0$
   (c) $8z(z + 1) = 1$ (f) $\sqrt{5}x^2 + 4x + \sqrt{5} = 0$

4. (a) If $ax^2 + 2bx + c = 0$, solve for x.
   (b) If $Lm^2 + Rm + 1/C = 0$, solve for m.
   (c) If $s = v_0t - \frac{1}{2}gt^2$, solve for t.
   (d) If $ay^2 + by + c = by^2 + cy + a$, solve for y.

5. Calculate the discriminant to determine the character of the **zeros of** $P(x)$.
   (a) $P(x) = 32x^2 - 20x - 3$
   (b) $P(x) = 36x^2 - 60x + 25$
   (c) $P(x) = 2x^2 - 7x + 7$
   (d) $P(x) = x^2 + 2\sqrt{.3294}x + \log 2.135$

6. Solve the following equations for x:
   (a) $2x^2 + ix - 1 = 0$ (c) $x^2 - 2ix - (1 + 2i) = 0$
   (b) $3x^2 - i\sqrt{2}x - \frac{1}{4} = 0$ (d) $x^2 - 2x + (1 - 8i) = 0$

7. Determine how many times the graph of the function f crosses the x-axis if:
   (a) $f(x) = x^2 + x - 1$ (b) $f(x) = x^2 + x + 1$

8. Solve the following equations for x:
   (a) $x^2 - xy + y^2 = 0$ (b) $2x^2 - x + xy - y = 0$

9. Sketch the graphs of the following equations:
   (a) $y = 1 - x^2$ (c) $y = 2x^2 - 4x + 1$
   (b) $y = x^2 - x$ (d) $y = x + 1 - x^2$

10. Solve the following inequalities:
    (a) $x^2 - 2x - 1 < 0$ (c) $4 + 3x < x^2$
    (b) $x^2 - 3x - 5 > 0$ (d) $x(2 - x) < 2$

11. For each of the following equations, determine the values of k for which the solutions are real numbers.
    (a) $x^2 + kx + 5 = 0$ (c) $kx^2 - 2x + 7 = 0$
    (b) $x^2 = 2kx - 4$ (d) $kx^2 - 2x + 3k = 0$

12. A circular field is surrounded by a circular track 20 ft wide. The area of the track is .1 of the area of the field. Find the radius of the field.

13. A plane takes $\frac{1}{2}$ hr to fly 150 miles with the wind and 65 miles back against the wind. The speed of the wind is 30 mph. What is the plane's airspeed?

14. The outside dimensions of a rectangular picture frame are 2 ft by 3 ft. The area of the frame is equal to the area of the picture inside the frame. What is the width of the frame?

53 EXPRESSIONS IN QUADRATIC FORM

We may sometimes use the methods described in Section 52 to solve equations that do not involve quadratic polynomials in x.

EXAMPLE 53-1.   Find the zeros of the polynomial $P(x) = x^4 - x^2 - 6.$

Solution. If we let $x^2 = y$, the problem is reduced to solving the equation $y^2 - y - 6 = 0$. When we factor the polynomial on the left, we have $(y - 3)(y + 2) = 0$ and hence $y = 3$ or $y = -2$. From the original substitution $x^2 = y$, we see that $x^2 = 3$ or $x^2 = -2$. Thus, the zeros of $P(x)$ are $\sqrt{3}$, $-\sqrt{3}$, $i\sqrt{2}$, and $-i\sqrt{2}$.

Example 53-1 illustrates the fact that many equations that can be written in the form $ax^2 + bx + c = 0$, even if a substitution is necessary, may be solved by the technique we use for solving quadratic equations.

EXAMPLE 53-2.   Find those zeros of the function f, defined by the equation $f(t) = \sin^2 t - 3 \cos t - 2$, which lie between 0 and π.

Solution. If we use the identity $\sin^2 t = 1 - \cos^2 t$, the problem is reduced to finding the solution to the equation $\cos^2 t + 3 \cos t + 1 = 0$. This equation has the form of a quadratic equation, as the substitution $x = \cos t$ will readily show. The Quadratic Formulas yield the solutions

$$\cos t = \frac{-3 + \sqrt{5}}{2} \quad \text{or} \quad \cos t = \frac{-3 - \sqrt{5}}{2}.$$

Since $\dfrac{-3 - \sqrt{5}}{2} < -1$ and $|\cos t| \le 1$, the only zeros of f are found from the other solution. If we take 2.24 as the approximate value of $\sqrt{5}$, we get $\cos t = -.38$. The only number t between 0 and π such that $\cos t = -.38$ is (Table II) $\pi - 1.18 = 1.96$.

EXAMPLE 53-3. Solve the equation $2x^{2/3} + 5x^{1/3} - 3 = 0$.

Solution. Let $y = x^{1/3}$. Then $y^2 = x^{2/3}$ and the equation to be solved becomes $2y^2 + 5y - 3 = (2y - 1)(y + 3) = 0$. Therefore, $y = x^{1/3} = \frac{1}{2}$ or $y = x^{1/3} = -3$. Since $x = y^3$, $x = \frac{1}{8}$ or $x = -27$.

Many equations involving radicals may be solved by reducing them to either a linear or quadratic equation. In such a reduction the process of squaring both sides of the equation is usually involved. This process can lead to a new equation with some solutions that are not solutions of the original equation. Such solutions are called **extraneous solutions.** To illustrate how these extraneous solutions can appear, consider the simple linear equation $2x = x + 1$. Now if we square both sides and simplify, we get the equation $3x^2 - 2x - 1 = (3x + 1)(x - 1) = 0$. The only solution to the original equation is $x = 1$; the new equation has two solutions, $x = 1$ and $x = -\frac{1}{3}$. When we squared both sides of the original equation, we really argued as follows: *If x is a number such that $2x = x + 1$, then x is a number such that $3x^2 - 2x - 1 = 0$.* Thus, every solution of the first equation is a solution of the second, but not every solution of the second equation is necessarily a solution of the first.

Because algebraic operations can yield extraneous solutions, **you should check every solution you find by substituting it in the original equation to be solved.**

EXAMPLE 53-4. Solve the equation

$$\text{53-1} \qquad \sqrt{x + 7} = \sqrt{2x + 9}.$$

Solution. If we square both sides of Equation 53-1, we obtain the equation $x + 7 = 2x + 9$. The solution to this equation is $x = -2$. If we replace x with -2 in Equation 53-1, we get $\sqrt{-2 + 7} = \sqrt{-4 + 9}$; that is, $\sqrt{5} = \sqrt{5}$. Thus -2 is a solution to Equation 53-1.

EXAMPLE 53-5. Solve the equation

$$\text{53-2} \qquad \sqrt{x + 5} = x - 1.$$

Solution. Squaring both sides of Equation 53-2, we get

$$x + 5 = x^2 - 2x + 1.$$

This equation may be simplified to

$$x^2 - 3x - 4 = (x - 4)(x + 1) = 0.$$

It then follows that $x = 4$ and $x = -1$ are possible solutions to Equation 53-2. If we replace x with -1 in Equation 53-2, we see that $\sqrt{4} \neq -2$, so that -1 is not a solution of the equation to be solved; $x = -1$ is an extraneous solution. You can easily verify that $x = 4$ is a solution of Equation 53-2.

The fact that extraneous solutions sometimes appear when we solve an equation such as Equation 53-2 may bother you a little, but it does not present any serious difficulties. A more serious situation involves "losing" a solution in the process of trying to solve an equation. For example, if we try to solve the equation $x^2 = x$ by improperly dividing both sides of the equation by x to obtain the solution $x = 1$, we "lose" the solution $x = 0$. We need not memorize an elaborate set of rules in order to deal with the introduction of extraneous solutions, or the possible loss of solutions. All we have to do is carefully check the logical steps in our work. Solving equations consists of a series of steps in which one equation, say Equation A, is replaced by another, say Equation B. In each step we must ask ourselves two questions.

(i) "If x is a solution to Equation A, is x necessarily a solution to Equation B?"

(ii) "If x is a solution to Equation B, is x necessarily a solution to Equation A?"

If the answer to either question is "No," then we have either introduced an extraneous solution or we have lost a solution.

Problems 53

1. Solve the following equations for x:
   (a) $x^4 - x^2 - 2 = 0$
   (c) $x^4 - 2x^2 + 2 = 0$
   (b) $x^2 - 5 + 6/x^2 = 0$
   (d) $x^4 + 2ix^2 - 2 = 0$

2. Solve the following equations for x:
   (a) $x^{2/5} - x^{1/5} - 2 = 0$
   (c) $3x^{2/3} - 4 = 4x^{1/3}$
   (b) $x^{1/3} - 1 = 12x^{-1/3}$
   (d) $5x + 3\sqrt{x} = 2$

3. Find the smallest positive zero of the function f if:
- (a) $f(t) = \sin^2 t - \sin t - \cos^2 t$
- (b) $f(t) = (\log t)^2 - \log t - \log 100$
- (c) $f(t) = \cos 2t + \cos t$

4. Solve the following equations for x:
- (a) $\sqrt{x + 7} = \sqrt{3x + 1}$
- (b) $\sqrt{x - 1} = \sqrt{x} - 1$
- (c) $\sqrt{x + 1} - \sqrt{x} = 2$
- (d) $\sqrt{4x^2 + 6x + 6} - 2\sqrt{x^2 + x - 1} = 2$

5. What is wrong with dividing both sides of the equation $x^2 = x$ by x?

6. Are there any numbers t for which $4(\sin^2 t - \cos t) + 11 = 0$?   Explain.

7. Solve for x: $x^6 - 7x^3 - 8 = 0$.

8. The area of a given circle can be doubled by increasing its radius by 1 unit.   Find the radius of the circle.

9. Find two real numbers whose difference is 1 such that the sum of their reciprocals is also 1.

10. The base of a rectangle is 2 ft longer than the height.   If the base were to be increased by 6 ft, the length of the diagonal would be doubled. Find the dimensions of the rectangle.

54   FACTORING POLYNOMIALS OF THE SECOND DEGREE

Factoring a polynomial and finding its zeros are closely related problems.   In Section 51, for example, we stated the simple theorem that if the polynomial $P(x) = ax + b$ has the number r as a zero, then $P(x) = a(x - r)$.   We also know that it is easy to find the zeros of any polynomial that we can factor.   In this section we shall show how our knowledge of the zeros of a quadratic polynomial enables us to factor the polynomial.

Before we discuss the factoring problem, we will establish two facts that are interesting in themselves.   If r_1 and r_2 are the zeros of the quadratic polynomial $P(x) = ax^2 + bx + c$, then

54-1
$$r_1 + r_2 = -\frac{b}{a} \quad \text{and} \quad r_1 r_2 = \frac{c}{a}.$$

These equations stem directly from the Quadratic Formulas 52-4, for

$$r_1 + r_2 = \frac{-b + \sqrt{b^2 - 4ac}}{2a} + \frac{-b - \sqrt{b^2 - 4ac}}{2a} = -\frac{b}{a}$$

and

$$r_1 r_2 = \left(\frac{-b + \sqrt{b^2 - 4ac}}{2a} \right) \left(\frac{-b - \sqrt{b^2 - 4ac}}{2a} \right)$$

$$= \frac{b^2 - (b^2 - 4ac)}{4a^2} = \frac{c}{a}.$$

It is now an easy matter to show that every second-degree polynomial may be written as the product of first-degree polynomials.

THEOREM 54-1.   *If $P(x) = ax^2 + bx + c$ is a polynomial of the second degree with zeros r_1 and r_2, then*

54-2 $$P(x) = a(x - r_1)(x - r_2).$$

Proof.   Using Equations 54-1 we have

$$a(x - r_1)(x - r_2) = a[x^2 - (r_1 + r_2)x + r_1 r_2]$$

$$= a[x^2 + bx/a + c/a]$$

$$= ax^2 + bx + c = P(x).$$

EXAMPLE 54-1.   Factor the polynomial $P(x) = 2x^2 + 8x + 4$.

Solution.   In Example 52-4 we found that the zeros of this polynomial are $r_1 = -2 + \sqrt{2}$ and $r_2 = -2 - \sqrt{2}$.   It follows from Theorem 54-1 that

$$2x^2 + 8x + 4 = 2[x - (-2 + \sqrt{2})][x - (-2 - \sqrt{2})]$$

$$= 2(x + 2 - \sqrt{2})(x + 2 + \sqrt{2}).$$

EXAMPLE 54-2.   Factor the polynomial $P(x) = 2x^2 - 2x + 1$.

Solution.   The zeros of $P(x)$ are $r_1 = (1 + i)/2$ and $r_2 = (1 - i)/2$ (see Example 52-2).   Therefore,

$$P(x) = 2\left[x - \frac{1 + i}{2} \right]\left[x - \frac{1 - i}{2} \right]$$

$$= \tfrac{1}{2}(2x - 1 - i)(2x - 1 + i).$$

Note that even though the coefficients of the original polynomial are real numbers, the coefficients of its factors are not.

EXAMPLE 54-3.   Factor the polynomial $P(x) = x^2 + 2ix - 2$.

Solution.   From Example 52-3 we have $r_1 = 1 - i$ and $r_2 = -1 - i$. Thus

$$x^2 + 2ix - 2 = [x - (1 - i)][x - (-1 - i)]$$
$$= (x - 1 + i)(x + 1 + i).$$

Problems 54

1. The sum of the zeros of a quadratic polynomial $P(x)$ is 5 and their product is -1.
   (a) Write $P(x)$ in the form $x^2 + bx + c$.
   (b) Find the zeros of $P(x)$.
   (c) Write $P(x)$ in factored form.

2. Use Equations 54-1 to find k if:
   (a) $P(x) = 3x^2 - x + (k - 1)$ and 1 is a zero of $P(x)$.
   (b) $P(x) = 2x^2 - 5x + k$ and the zeros of $P(x)$ are reciprocals of each other.
   (c) $P(x) = 5x^2 + 18x + k$ and the quotient of the zeros of $P(x)$ is 5.

3. Prove that one solution to the equation $ax^2 + bx + c = 0$ is the negative of the other solution if, and only if, $b = 0$.

4. Find a quadratic polynomial such that the sum of its zeros is twice their product.

5. Factor the following quadratic polynomials:
   (a) $x^2 - 7x - 1$
   (b) $2x^2 - 4x - 3$
   (c) $x^2 + x + 1$
   (d) $x^2 + x - i - 1$
   (e) $\frac{2}{3}x^2 - \frac{1}{4}x + 6$
   (f) $5ix^2 - x + i$

6. Find a quadratic polynomial of the form $x^2 + bx + c$ that has the following numbers as zeros:
   (a) $-1, -\frac{1}{3}$
   (b) $1 + \sqrt{5}, 1 - \sqrt{5}$
   (c) $2 - i, 2 + i$
   (d) $\sqrt{a}, \sqrt{b}$
   (e) $\sqrt{2} - i, -\sqrt{2} + i$
   (f) $i, 1 + i$
   (g) $bi, -bi$
   (h) $i, 1 - \sqrt{i}$

7. Factor the following expressions into a product of linear polynomials in x:
   (a) $x^2 - xy + y^2$
   (b) $x^2 + 3xy - y^2$
   (c) $kx^2 - (k^2 - 1)x - k$
   (d) $18x^2 - 9xyz - 35y^2z^2$

55   THE REMAINDER AND FACTOR THEOREMS

In Section 50 (see Theorem 50-1) we discussed the problem of dividing a polynomial $P(x) = a_nx^n + a_{n-1}x^{n-1} + \ldots + a_0$ by a polynomial $D(x) = d_m x^m + d_{m-1} x^{m-1} + \ldots + d_0$, where the degree m of $D(x)$ is not greater than the degree n of $P(x)$. We mentioned that the process of long division produces two polynomials $Q(x)$ and $R(x)$, where $R(x)$ is either the number 0 or a polynomial of lower degree than $D(x)$, such that

55-1 $$P(x) = Q(x) D(x) + R(x).$$

Now suppose that $P(x) = a_n x^n + \ldots + a_0$, where $n > 0$, and $D(x) = x - r$, where r is a given number. The polynomial $R(x)$ in Equation 55-1 is either the number 0 or a polynomial of lower degree than $D(x)$. Since $D(x)$ is a first-degree polynomial, $R(x)$ is 0 or its degree is 0. In either case $R(x)$ is merely a number. These facts are summarized in the following theorem.

THEOREM 55-1. *If* $P(x) = a_n x^n + \ldots + a_0$ *is a given polynomial and* r *is a given number, then there is a polynomial* $Q(x)$ *and a number* R *(which may be 0) such that*

55-2 $$P(x) = Q(x)(x - r) + R.$$

It is apparent that the first term of $Q(x)$ is $a_n x^{n-1}$, and therefore $Q(x)$ has the form $a_n x^{n-1} + \ldots + q_0$. For our purposes it is unnecessary to find the general expressions for the coefficients of the terms of $Q(x)$ other than the first; they can be easily computed in any specific example.

EXAMPLE 55-1. Let $P(x) = 3x^3 - 2x^2 + x - 2$ and $r = 2$. Find $Q(x)$ and R.

Solution. We can find $Q(x)$ and R by dividing $P(x)$ by $(x - 2)$. We can use synthetic division here to shorten our labor.

$$
\begin{array}{r|rrrr}
 & 3 & -2 & 1 & -2 \\
 &   & 6 & 8 & 18 \\
\hline
2 & 3 & 4 & 9 & 16 \\
\end{array}
$$

We therefore see that $Q(x) = 3x^2 + 4x + 9$ and $R = 16$, so

$$3x^3 - 2x^2 + x - 2 = (3x^2 + 4x + 9)(x - 2) + 16.$$

A number of important theorems are immediate consequences of Theorem 55-1.

THEOREM 55-2 **(The Remainder Theorem).** *If R is the remainder when $P(x)$ is divided by $x - r$, then $R = P(r)$.*

Proof: Equation 55-2 is valid if x is replaced by any number, so we may let $x = r$ to obtain

$$P(r) = Q(r)(r - r) + R = 0 + R = R.$$

EXAMPLE 55-2. If $P(x) = 3x^3 - 2x^2 + x - 2$, find $P(2)$ by using the Remainder Theorem.

Solution. If we divide $P(x)$ by $x - 2$, then $R = 16$ (Example 55-1). Therefore, according to the Remainder Theorem, $P(2) = 16$. To check this result we note that $P(2) = 3(2)^3 - 2(2)^2 + (2) - 2 = 24 - 8 + 2 - 2 = 16$.

From the Remainder Theorem and Equation 55-2 we see that if $P(x)$ is any polynomial of degree greater than zero and r is any number, then there is a polynomial $Q(x)$ such that

55-3 $$P(x) = (x - r)Q(x) + P(r).$$

The polynomial $D(x)$ is a **factor** of the polynomial $P(x)$ if there exists a polynomial $Q(x)$ such that $P(x) = Q(x)D(x)$; that is, if after dividing $P(x)$ by $D(x)$ the remainder is zero. It is clear from Equation 55-3 that $x - r$ is a factor of $P(x)$ if, and only if, $P(r) = 0$. This result is known as the *Factor Theorem and its converse.*

THEOREM 55-3 **(The Factor Theorem).** *If $P(x) = a_n x^n + \ldots + a_0$ is a polynomial of degree $n > 0$ and if r is a zero of $P(x)$, then $x - r$ is a factor of $P(x)$.*

THEOREM 55-4 **(Converse of the Factor Theorem).** *If $P(x)$ is a polynomial and $x - r$ is a factor of $P(x)$, then r is a zero of $P(x)$.*

The Factor Theorem tells us that if we can find a zero of $P(x)$, then we can factor $P(x)$ into a product of a polynomial of lower degree than the degree of $P(x)$ and a linear factor. According to the Converse of the Factor Theorem, if we know a linear factor of $P(x)$, then we know a zero of $P(x)$.

Example 55-3.   Let $P(x) = x^3 - 8$.   Factor $P(x)$.

Solution.   The number 2 is clearly a zero of $P(x)$.   According to the Factor Theorem, $x - 2$ will be a factor, and the other factor, found by dividing $P(x)$ by $x - 2$, will be a quadratic polynomial.   Using long division we get

$$x^3 - 8 = (x - 2)(x^2 + 2x + 4).$$

We can use the methods we covered in Section 54 to factor the quadratic polynomial $x^2 + 2x + 4$.

Problems 55

1. Find $Q(x)$ and R such that $P(x) = Q(x)(x - r) + R$ if:
   (a) $P(x) = x^5 + x + 1, r = -3$ (c) $P(x) = x^3 + 5, r = \sqrt{5}$
   (b) $P(x) = x^6 - x^2 - 6, r = 2$ (d) $P(x) = x^3 + x, r = -2$

2. Use the Remainder Theorem to find $P(r)$ if:
   (a) $P(x) = x^4 - x^2 + x + 1, r = 1$
   (b) $P(x) = 3x^3 - 2x^2 + x - 5, r = -2$
   (c) $P(x) = x^5 + 3x^4 - x + 2, r = 3$
   (d) $P(x) = x^3 - 3x^2 - 1, r = \frac{5}{2}$

3. Find the remainder if:
   (a) $x^8 + 3$ is divided by $x - 10$
   (b) $x^7 + \sqrt{2}$ is divided by $x + \sqrt{2}$

4. Find a polynomial of the form $x^n + a_{n-1}x^{n-1} + \ldots + a_1x + a_0$ that has the following numbers as its only zeros.
   (a) $1, i, -i$ (c) $i, -1 + i, 1 + i$
   (b) $1 + \sqrt{2}, 1 - \sqrt{2}, 1 + i, 1 - i$ (d) $\sqrt{3}, 2\sqrt{2}, \sqrt{5}$

5. The graph of a polynomial $P(x) = x^4 + a_3x^3 + a_2x^2 + a_1x + a_0$ crosses the x-axis at the points whose x-coordinates are $1, -1, 2, -2$.   Find $P(0)$.   Sketch the graph of $P(x)$.

6. Use the Factor Theorem to show that:
   (a) $x - a$ is a factor of $x^n - a^n$, where n is any positive integer
   (b) $x + 2y^2$ is a factor of $x^5 + 32y^{10}$

7. Factor $P(x)$ into a product of linear polynomials.
   (a) $P(x) = x^4 - 16$ (c) $P(x) = 12x^3 - 17x^2 - 6x + 8$
   (b) $P(x) = x^3 + x^2 - x - 1$ (one zero is $\frac{2}{3}$)

8. Determine k such that:
   (a) $x - 1$ is a factor of $2x^3 + x^2 - 2kx + 1$
   (b) $x + 3$ is a factor of $x^3 + k^2x^2 - 2kx - 9$
   (c) $x - 2$ is a factor of $2x^4 - (kx)^2 + 3kx - 1$

56   FACTORING A GENERAL POLYNOMIAL

The Factor Theorem states that if r is a zero of the polynomial $P(x) = a_n x^n + \ldots + a_0$, then there is a polynomial $Q(x) = a_n x^{n-1} + \ldots + q_0$ such that

56-1 $$P(x) = (x - r)Q(x).$$

Obviously the theorem is not applicable unless we know something about the zeros of $P(x)$. We know how to find the zeros of first- and second-degree polynomials, but so far we have said nothing about polynomials of higher degree. In fact, we have not even said that polynomials of higher degree necessarily have any zeros. For example, it is not immediately evident that there is a number r that satisfies the equation

$$37x^7 - (5 + 2i)x^3 + 2x^2 + \pi = 0.$$

The following theorem does not help us to find the zeros of a polynomial, but it does tell us that they do exist. We must accept this theorem on faith because proving it is not a simple matter. We give this theorem its traditional name, but you should not infer that it is necessarily the most basic theorem in the entire field of algebra.

THEOREM 56-1 **(The Fundamental Theorem of Algebra).** *If $P(x)$ is a polynomial of degree greater than zero, then there is at least one number r (which is not necessarily a real number) for which $P(r) = 0$.*

Suppose that $P(x) = a_n x^n + \ldots + a_0$ is a polynomial of degree $n > 0$. According to the Fundamental Theorem of Algebra, there is a zero, call it r_1, of $P(x)$. Hence, according to Equation 56-1, there is a polynomial $Q_1(x) = a_n x^{n-1} + \ldots + q_1$ such that

56-2 $$P(x) = (x - r_1)Q_1(x).$$

Now if $n - 1 > 0$, we can apply the Fundamental Theorem to the polynomial $Q_1(x)$ to see that there is a number r_2 such that $Q_1(r_2) = 0$. Then according to the Factor Theorem, there is a polynomial $Q_2(x) = a_n x^{n-2} + \ldots + q_2$ such that

56-3 $$Q_1(x) = (x - r_2)Q_2(x).$$

From Equations 56-2 and 56-3 we have

56-4 $$P(x) = (x - r_1)(x - r_2)Q_2(x).$$

If the degree of $Q_2(x)$ (which is $n - 2$) is greater than zero, then there is a polynomial $Q_3(x) = a_n x^{n-3} + \ldots + q_3$ and a number r_3 such that

56-5 $$P(x) = (x - r_1)(x - r_2)(x - r_3)Q_3(x).$$

Clearly we can continue this process until the degree of the quotient polynomial is zero—that is, for n steps. The last quotient polynomial is $Q_n(x) = a_n x^{n-n} = a_n$, and we see that

56-6 $$P(x) = a_n(x - r_1)(x - r_2) \ldots (x - r_n).$$

We can state the result of our reasoning as a theorem.

THEOREM 56-2.   *If $P(x)$ is a polynomial of degree $n > 0$, then there are n numbers, $r_1, r_2, \ldots,$ and r_n (which need not all be different) such that Equation 56-6 is valid. In other words, any polynomial of degree n can be written as a product of n linear factors.*

We have already covered two special cases of this theorem (when $n = 1$ and $n = 2$) in Theorems 51-1 and 54-1 respectively.

From Equation 56-6 it is clear that $P(x) = 0$ if, and only if, x is one of the numbers $r_1, \ldots, r_n$. These numbers may not all be different, but there can't be more than n different numbers for which $P(x) = 0$.

THEOREM 56-3.   *A polynomial of degree n has at most n zeros.*

EXAMPLE 56-1.   Suppose that there are 11 distinct numbers, $r_1, r_2, \ldots, r_{11}$, for which the polynomial $P(x) = a_{10}x^{10} + a_9 x^9 + \ldots + a_0$ is zero. What can we conclude about $P(x)$?

Solution. $P(x)$ is either a polynomial of degree $n \leq 10$, or $P(x)$ is the zero polynomial; that is, $P(x) = 0$. But $P(x)$ cannot be a polynomial of degree $n \leq 10$ because it has 11 zeros, and this fact contradicts Theorem 56-3. Thus $P(x) = 0$; that is, $a_0 = a_1 = \ldots = a_{10} = 0$.

This result is important, for on the basis of it we can conclude that $P(r) = 0$ for *every* number r by showing that $P(r) = 0$ for *only 11* choices of r.

If a number r appears twice in the sequence $r_1, r_2, \ldots, r_n$ of zeros of a polynomial $P(x)$, then it is called a **double zero** of $P(x)$. A number appearing three times in the sequence is called a **triple zero**. In general, if a number r appears m times in the sequence of zeros of a polynomial $P(x)$, then r is a **zero of multiplicity** m. If we should agree to count every zero as many times as its multiplicity, then Theorem 56-3 could be replaced by the statement that *a polynomial of degree n has exactly n zeros.*

EXAMPLE 56-2. Let $P(x) = 2x^3 - x^2 - 1$. If $r_1 = 1$ is a zero of $P(x)$, write $P(x)$ as the product of linear factors.

Solution. Since r_1 is a zero of $P(x)$, we know from the Factor Theorem that $x - 1$ divides $P(x)$. Performing the division synthetically we have

$$
\begin{array}{r|rrrr}
 & 2 & -1 & 0 & -1 \\
 &   & 2 & 1 & 1 \\
\hline
1 & 2 & 1 & 1 & 0 \\
\end{array}
$$

Thus, $P(x) = (2x^2 + x + 1)(x - 1)$. We then find the other zeros of $P(x)$ by solving the equation $2x^2 + x + 1 = 0$. If we use the Quadratic Formulas we get

$$
r_2 = \frac{-1 + i\sqrt{7}}{4} \quad \text{and} \quad r_3 = \frac{-1 - i\sqrt{7}}{4}.
$$

Thus,

$$
P(x) = 2(x - 1)\left(x - \frac{-1 + i\sqrt{7}}{4}\right)\left(x - \frac{-1 - i\sqrt{7}}{4}\right).
$$

EXAMPLE 56-3. Find the zeros of the polynomial $P(x) = x^3 - 2x^2 + 4x - 8$.

Solution. By trial and error we find that $P(2) = 0$. Then, by division, we find that $P(x) = (x - 2)(x^2 + 4)$. Hence, the remaining zeros of $P(x)$ are the solutions to the equation $x^2 + 4 = 0$, which are $2i$ and $-2i$. The zeros of $P(x)$ are therefore the numbers 2, $2i$, and $-2i$. Theorem 56-3 tells us that these are all the zeros there are.

Problems 56

1. Let $P(x) = a_n x^n + \ldots + a_0$. Is it true that the graph of $y = P(x)$ must cross the x-axis n times? Can it cross the x-axis more than n times?

2. Let $A(x)$ and $B(x)$ both be polynomials of degree n. What can you conclude if you find that $A(x) = B(x)$ for more than n different substitutions for x?

3. For what numbers a and b is $x - 9 = a(x - 1) + b(x + 3)$?

4. Let f be the function that is defined by the equation
$$f(x) = 3 \sin^3 x + 6 \sin^2 x - \sin x + 2.$$
Does the Fundamental Theorem of Algebra state that f must have at least one zero? How many zeros does the function g have if $g(x) = 2 \sin x - 1$?

5. Prove that there does not exist a polynomial $P(x)$ such that $\sin x = P(x)$.

6. Write $P(x)$ as a product of linear factors. In each case it is easy to guess one or more zeros of $P(x)$.
   (a) $P(x) = x^3 - 2x + 1$
   (b) $P(x) = 2x^3 + x^2 + 1$
   (c) $P(x) = x^4 + 2x^3 - x - 2$
   (d) $P(x) = x^5 - 3x^4 + 4x^3 - 4x^2 + 3x - 1$
   (e) $P(x) = x^5 - 10x^2 + 15x - 6$
   (f) $P(x) = x^5 - 1$

7. Let r_1, r_2, r_3 be three given numbers, no two of which are equal, and let $a_1, a_2,$ and a_3 be three other given numbers. Let
$$P(x) = \frac{a_1(x - r_2)(x - r_3)}{(r_1 - r_2)(r_1 - r_3)} + \frac{a_2(x - r_1)(x - r_3)}{(r_2 - r_1)(r_2 - r_3)} + \frac{a_3(x - r_1)(x - r_2)}{(r_3 - r_1)(r_3 - r_2)}.$$
Show that $P(x)$ is the only quadratic polynomial such that $P(r_1) = a_1,$ $P(r_2) = a_2, P(r_3) = a_3$.

8. Find the quadratic polynomial $P(x)$ such that $P(-1) = 2, P(0) = 1,$ and $P(1) = 3$ (see Problem 7). Write $P(x)$ in the form $ax^2 + bx + c$.

9. Find the quadratic polynomial whose graph passes through the points $(0,0)$, $(1,3)$, and $(2,1)$ (see Problem 7).

10. Find all the zeros of $P(x) = 2x^3 + 5x^2 + 2k^2x + 24k$ if $x = 2$ is one zero of $P(x)$.

11. Let r be a zero of $P(x) = x^3 + bx^2 + cx + d$. Show that the two remaining zeros of $P(x)$ are zeros of the polynomial $x^2 + (b + r)x - d/r$.

57 ZEROS OF POLYNOMIALS WITH REAL COEFFICIENTS

In this section we shall confine our attention to polynomials that have real numbers as coefficients. Since we must use some simple facts regarding the conjugate of a complex number, it will be profit-able for you to review the remarks concerning complex conjugates given in Section 47 before proceeding.

THEOREM 57-1. *Let $P(x) = a_n x^n + \ldots + a_0$ be a polynomial of degree $n > 0$ with real coefficients. Then if r is a zero of $P(x)$, the conjugate $\bar{r}$ of r is also a zero of $P(x)$.*

Proof. To say that r is a zero of $P(x)$ means that

57-1 $$P(r) = a_n r^n + \ldots + a_0 = 0.$$

If we take the conjugate of both sides of this equation, we obtain the equation

57-2 $$\overline{P(r)} = \overline{a_n r^n + \ldots + a_0} = \bar{0} = 0.$$

Theorem **47-1** states that the conjugate of the sum of two complex numbers is the same as the sum of the conjugates of the numbers. We can easily extend this fact to the sum of any number of terms, so Equation 57-2 can be written as

57-3 $$\overline{a_n r^n} + \overline{a_{n-1} r^{n-1}} + \ldots + \overline{a_0} = 0.$$

Theorem 47-1 also states that we can reverse the order of multiplica-tion and of taking conjugates, which means that

$$\overline{a_n r^n} = \bar{a}_n \bar{r}^n, \quad \overline{a_{n-1} r^{n-1}} = \bar{a}_{n-1} \bar{r}^{n-1}, \quad \text{and so on.}$$

Now Theorem 47-2 states that the conjugate of a real number is the number itself, and since the numbers a_k are real numbers in this case, Equation 57-3 can be written as

$$a_n \bar{r}^n + a_{n-1} \bar{r}^{n-1} + \ldots + a_0 = 0.$$

But this equation merely states that $P(\bar{r}) = 0$; that is, $\bar{r}$ is a zero of $P(x)$.

EXAMPLE 57-1. Illustrate Theorem 57-1 by letting $P(x) = x^3 - x^2 + 2$.

Solution. You can easily check to see that -1, $1 + i$, and $1 - i$ are zeros of $P(x)$. Then $\bar{r}_1 = \overline{(-1)} = -1 = r_1$ is "also" a zero of $P(x)$. Likewise, $\bar{r}_2 = \overline{(1 + i)} = 1 - i = r_3$ is a zero, and so is $\bar{r}_3 = \overline{(1 - i)} = 1 + i = r_2$.

EXAMPLE 57-2.   Two zeros of $P(x) = x^4 - 4x^3 + 14x^2 - 4x + 13$ are $r_1 = 2 + 3i$ and $r_2 = i$.   Find the other two.

Solution.   According to Theorem 57-1 we can let $r_3 = \bar{r}_1 = 2 - 3i$ and $r_4 = \bar{r}_2 = -i$.

If $P(x) = a_n x^n + \ldots + a_0$, we saw in Section 56 that $P(x)$ can be written as

57-4 $$P(x) = a_n(x - r_1)(x - r_2) \ldots (x - r_n),$$

where $r_1, r_2, \ldots, r_n$ are the zeros of $P(x)$.   Some of the numbers $r_1, \ldots, r_n$ may be real, and some may not.   They need not all be different, but every zero of $P(x)$ must appear somewhere in this set of numbers.   If the coefficients of $P(x)$ are real, Theorem 57-1 tells us that if $r = a + bi$ is a zero (where a and b are real and $b \neq 0$), then so is $\bar{r} = a - bi$.   Therefore if $(x - r)$ appears in the factorization of $P(x)$, so must $(x - \bar{r})$.   Now

$$(x - r)(x - \bar{r}) = x^2 - (r + \bar{r})x + r\bar{r} = x^2 - 2ax + a^2 + b^2,$$

so the latter quantity is a factor of $P(x)$.   Further, since a and b are real numbers, this quantity has real coefficients.   This observation enables us to see how a polynomial with real coefficients can be written as the product of polynomials with real coefficients.

THEOREM 57-2.   *If $P(x) = a_n x^n + \ldots + a_0$ is a polynomial of degree $n > 0$ with real coefficients, then it can be factored as a_n times the product of polynomials with real coefficients, which are either of the form $x - r$ or $x^2 + px + q$.*

Proof.   If r is a real zero of $P(x)$, then $(x - r)$ is a factor of $P(x)$. If a zero r is not real, we just saw that $(x - r)(x - \bar{r})$, which is of the form $x^2 + px + q$, is a factor.   The remainder of the proof follows the line of argument we used to prove Theorem 56-1.

EXAMPLE 57-3.   Factor the polynomial $P(x) = x^3 - x^2 + 2$ into linear and quadratic factors with real coefficients.

Solution.   The zeros of this polynomial (see Example 57-1) are -1, $1 + i$, and $1 - i$.   Therefore,

$$P(x) = (x + 1)[x - (1 + i)][x - (1 - i)]1$$
$$= (x + 1)(x^2 - 2x + 2).$$

EXAMPLE 57-4.   Write the polynomial of Example 57-2 as a product of real polynomials of the first or second degree.

Solution.   In Example 57-2 we found that the zeros of $P(x)$ are i, $-i$, $2 + 3i$, and $2 - 3i$.   Now

$$(x - i)(x + i) = x^2 + 1,$$

and

$$[x - (2 + 3i)][x - (2 - 3i)] = x^2 - 4x + 13,$$

so we may write

$$x^4 - 4x^3 + 14x^2 - 4x + 13 = (x^2 + 1)(x^2 - 4x + 13).$$

EXAMPLE 57-5.   Write the polynomial $x^4 + 1$ as the product of real polynomials of the first or second degree.

Solution.   First, we solve the equation $x^4 + 1 = 0$, that is, we find the fourth roots of -1.   Since $-1 = \cos \pi + i \sin \pi$, the methods of Section 49 give us the four roots

$$\cos \left(\frac{\pi}{4} + \frac{k\pi}{2} \right) + i \sin \left(\frac{\pi}{4} + \frac{k\pi}{2} \right),$$

where k can take any of the values 0, 1, 2, or 3.   When we substitute these values of k into the formula, we find that the four zeros of our polynomial $x^4 + 1$ are the numbers

$$\frac{1}{\sqrt{2}} + \frac{i}{\sqrt{2}}, \qquad\qquad -\frac{1}{\sqrt{2}} - \frac{i}{\sqrt{2}},$$

$$\frac{1}{\sqrt{2}} - \frac{i}{\sqrt{2}}, \quad \text{and} \quad -\frac{1}{\sqrt{2}} + \frac{i}{\sqrt{2}}.$$

Hence,

$$x^4 + 1 = \left[x - \left(\frac{1}{\sqrt{2}} + \frac{i}{\sqrt{2}} \right) \right]\left[x - \left(\frac{1}{\sqrt{2}} - \frac{i}{\sqrt{2}} \right) \right]$$

$$\left[x - \left(-\frac{1}{\sqrt{2}} + \frac{i}{\sqrt{2}} \right) \right]\left[x - \left(-\frac{1}{\sqrt{2}} - \frac{i}{\sqrt{2}} \right) \right].$$

After some multiplication, this last expression becomes

$$x^4 + 1 = (x^2 - \sqrt{2}x + 1)(x^2 + \sqrt{2}x + 1).$$

Problems 57

1. Find the lowest degree polynomial with real coefficients and with 1 as the coefficient of the term of highest degree if two of the zeros of the polynomial are the numbers given.
   (a) $-1, i$ (c) $1 - i, 1 - 2i$
   (b) $3, 1 + i$ (d) $i, i\sqrt{2}$

2. Find all the zeros of $P(x)$ if one zero is the number in the parentheses at the right.
   (a) $P(x) = 2x^3 - x^2 + 2x - 1$; (i)
   (b) $P(x) = x^4 - 3x^3 + 3x^2 - 2$; $(1 + i)$
   (c) $P(x) = 3x^4 - 16x^3 + 24x^2 + 44x - 39$; $(3 + 2i)$
   (d) $P(x) = x^4 - 2x^3 + 4x^2 + 4x - 12$; $(1 - \sqrt{5}i)$
   (e) $P(x) = x^3 + (2 - i)x^2 - (5 + 2i)x + 5i$; (i)

3. Let $a + bi$ be a zero of $P(x) = x^3 + px^2 + qx + r$, where p, q, and r are real numbers. Show by actual substitution that $a - bi$ is also a zero of $P(x)$.

4. Using the methods described in Section 49 calculate the five 5th roots of 1 to solve the equation $x^5 - 1 = 0$. Verify that each of the roots is the complex conjugate of a root.

5. Prove that every cubic polynomial with real coefficients has at least one real zero.

6. Write $P(x)$ as a product of first- and second-degree polynomials with real coefficients.
   (a) $P(x) = x^3 - 1$
   (b) $P(x) = x^4 + 16$
   (c) $P(x) = x^4 - 3x^3 + 3x^2 - 2$ (Problem 2(b))
   (d) $P(x) = 3x^4 - 16x^3 + 24x^2 + 44x - 39$ (Problem 2(c))

58   THE RATIONAL ZEROS OF POLYNOMIALS WHOSE COEFFICIENTS ARE INTEGERS

In this section we will consider polynomials $P(x) = a_nx^n + \ldots + a_0$ whose coefficients, $a_0, \ldots, a_n$, are *integers*. Such polynomials, of course, have zeros but they may, or may not, have zeros that are rational numbers. In this section we will learn how to determine whether or not a polynomial with integral coefficients does have rational zeros and if it does, how to find them.

Before taking up the question of polynomials with integral coefficients, we should emphasize one point about integers.

Remark. Let b and c be integers with no common factors. Let a be an integer and n be a positive integer. If c is a factor of ab^n, then c is a factor of a.

Although we will not give a formal proof of this statement, you can probably convince yourself of its validity by considering a few examples such as the following. Suppose that $c = 6$, $b = 35$, and $n = 4$. Then c and b have no common factors. If a is an integer such that 6 is a factor of $35^4 a$, there must be an integer d such that $2 \cdot 3 \cdot d = 5^4 7^4 a$. Clearly, then, the number a must contain the numbers 2 and 3 as factors, so 6 is a factor of a.

Recall that a rational number is a number that can be represented as the quotient of two integers. This fraction can always be reduced to lowest terms; that is, a rational number r can always be represented as a quotient b/c, where b and c are integers with no common factors. We then say that b/c is the **reduced form of r.**

We now turn to the problem of finding the rational zeros of a polynomial with integral coefficients. The basic theorem follows.

THEOREM 58-1.   *If r is a rational zero of the polynomial $P(x) = a_n x^n + \ldots + a_0$, where the coefficients $a_0, \ldots, a_n$ are integers, and if b/c is the reduced form of r, then b is a factor of a_0 and c is a factor of a_n.*

Proof.   Since $r = b/c$ is a zero of $P(x)$,

58-1 $$a_n \left(\frac{b}{c}\right)^n + a_{n-1} \left(\frac{b}{c}\right)^{n-1} + \ldots + a_1 \left(\frac{b}{c}\right) + a_0 = 0.$$

We can multiply both sides of this equation by c^n to obtain the equation

58-2 $$a_n b^n + a_{n-1} b^{n-1} c + \ldots + a_1 b c^{n-1} + a_0 c^n = 0.$$

Now we can write Equation 58-2 as

58-3 $$a_n b^n = (-a_{n-1} b^{n-1} - \ldots - a_0 c^{n-1})c.$$

From Equation 58-3 we see that c is a factor of $a_n b^n$. Since b/c is the reduced form of r, the integers b and c have no common factors. It follows immediately from the "Remark" we made about integers that c is a factor of a_n.

We can also write Equation 58-2 as

58-4 $$a_0 c^n = (-a_n b^{n-1} - \ldots - a_1 c^{n-1})b.$$

This equation shows that b is a factor of $a_0 c^n$. Now we can again utilize the "Remark" about integers (the roles of b and c are interchanged) to see that b is a factor of a_0.

It is important to note that Theorem 58-1 does *not* state that $P(x)$ has any rational zeros at all. It merely says that if it does, they must be of a certain form.

EXAMPLE 58-1. Find the rational zeros (if any) of the polynomial $P(x) = 2x^3 + 3x^2 + 2x + 3$.

Solution. If $P(x)$ has a rational zero of reduced form b/c, then b must be a factor of 3 and c must be a factor of 2. The factors of 3 are 1, 3, -1, and -3, and the factors of 2 are 1, -1, 2, and -2. Hence, the only possible rational zeros will be found among the numbers 1, -1, 3, -3, $\frac{1}{2}$, $-\frac{1}{2}$, $\frac{3}{2}$, $-\frac{3}{2}$. Obviously not all these eight numbers are zeros of $P(x)$, since $P(x)$ has at most three zeros, and perhaps none of these eight numbers is a zero. To see which of them (if any) are zeros, we must calculate $P(1)$, $P(-1)$, and so on. We can calculate these numbers directly or we can use synthetic division, in which case the numbers will appear as remainders. Either method will reveal that $P(-\frac{3}{2}) = 0$, and that none of the other seven possible rational zeros is a zero.

EXAMPLE 58-2. Show that the polynomial $P(x) = x^3 + 3x - 5$ has no rational zeros.

Solution. If $r = b/c$ is a rational zero of $P(x)$, then b must be a factor of 5 and c must be a factor of 1. The possible choices for b are 1, -1, 5, and -5; for c, only 1 or -1. Therefore, the possible choices for r are the integers 1, -1, 5, -5. But when we check these numbers, we find that none is a zero. Hence, $P(x)$ has no rational zeros. Of course, $P(x)$ has zeros, but they are not rational and may not be real. Incidentally, we can show that $P(x)$ must in fact have one irrational real zero (see Exercise 5 of Problems 57).

EXAMPLE 58-3. Find all the zeros of the polynomial of Example 58-1.

Solution. In Example 58-1 we saw that $-\frac{3}{2}$ is a zero of $P(x)$, so $x + \frac{3}{2}$ is a factor of $P(x)$. We find by dividing that $P(x) = 2(x^2 + 1)(x + \frac{3}{2})$. The other two zeros of $P(x)$ are the zeros of the quadratic polynomial $x^2 + 1$; namely, i and $-i$.

Although Theorem 58-1 pertains specifically to polynomials whose coefficients are integers, it may also be used to investigate the rational zeros of polynomials with rational coefficients. If we multiply a polynomial $P(x)$ by a non-zero number k, it is clear that $kP(x)$ is again a polynomial. In factored form

58-5 $$kP(x) = ka_n(x - r_1) \ldots (x - r_n).$$

From Equation 58-5 it is obvious that the zeros of $kP(x)$ are the same as the zeros of $P(x)$. Now if the coefficients of $P(x)$ are rational, a proper choice of k (the product of all the denominators of the coefficients of $P(x)$, for example) will insure that $P(x)$ has integral coefficients. We can therefore study the rational zeros of $P(x)$ by investigating the rational zeros of $kP(x)$.

EXAMPLE 58-4.   Find all the rational zeros of $P(x) = \frac{2}{3}x^3 - \frac{1}{2}x^2 + \frac{2}{3}x - \frac{1}{2}$.

Solution.   If we multiply $P(x)$ by 6, we get the equation

$$6P(x) = 4x^3 - 3x^2 + 4x - 3.$$

The only possible rational zeros of this polynomial are 1, -1, 3, -3, $\frac{1}{2}$, $-\frac{1}{2}$, $\frac{3}{2}$, $-\frac{3}{2}$, $\frac{1}{4}$, $-\frac{1}{4}$, $\frac{3}{4}$, and $-\frac{3}{4}$. We find by checking that $\frac{3}{4}$ is the only rational zero of $6P(x)$; hence, $\frac{3}{4}$ is the only rational zero of $P(x)$.

Problems 58

1. If $P(x) = x^n + a_{n-1}x^{n-1} + \ldots + a_1x + a_0$, where the a's are integers, show that the only possible rational zeros of $P(x)$ are integers.

2. Find all the rational zeros of $P(x)$ or show that none exist.
   (a) $P(x) = x^4 + x^2 + 2x + 6$
   (b) $P(x) = 9x^4 - 9x^3 + 5x^2 + 4x - 4$
   (c) $P(x) = 12x^4 + 4x^3 - 3x^2 - x$
   (d) $P(x) = 2x^6 + 3x^3 + x$

3. Find all the zeros of $P(x)$.
   (a) $P(x) = x^3 - 3x - 2$
   (b) $P(x) = x^3 - 4x^2 - 5x + 14$
   (c) $P(x) = x^4 - 6x^3 - 3x^2 - 24x - 28$
   (d) $P(x) = 2x^4 + 3x^3 + 2x^2 - 1$
   (e) $P(x) = 48x^4 - 52x^3 + 13x - 3$
   (f) $P(x) = 12x^4 + 7x^3 + 7x - 12$

4. Prove that $\sqrt{2}$ is irrational by considering the equation $x^2 - 2 = 0$.

5. Prove that the following numbers are irrational:

(a) $\sqrt[3]{5}$

(c) $\sqrt{3}/\sqrt{2}$

(b) $\sqrt{40}$

(d) $\sqrt{3} + \sqrt{2}$

6. Find all the rational zeros of $P(x)$ or show that none exist.

(a) $P(x) = x^3 + \frac{3}{2}x^2 - \frac{2}{3}x + 1$

(b) $P(x) = \frac{2}{3}x^3 + \frac{17}{6}x^2 - \frac{55}{6}x + 5$

59   FINDING REAL ZEROS OF POLYNOMIALS WITH REAL COEFFICIENTS

Suppose that $P(x) = a_n x^n + \ldots + a_0$ is a polynomial with real coefficients $a_0, \ldots, a_n$. The Fundamental Theorem of Algebra states that $P(x)$ has at least one zero, and we have seen that it can have as many as n different zeros. There are many ingenious and complicated methods for finding the zeros of such a polynomial. It is an important problem, but we will restrict ourselves only to some simple observations about it. Our results will apply only to finding the real zeros of $P(x)$.

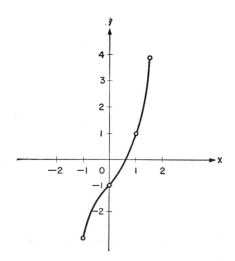

The method of successive approximations, which we consider here, can best be described in terms of a graph. If we graph the equation $y = P(x)$, the real zeros of $P(x)$ are the x-coordinates of

Figure 59-1

the points at which the curve meets (crosses or touches) the x-axis. This fact suggests a method of finding the real zeros of a polynomial— namely, graph the equation $y = P(x)$, and find the points where the curve meets the x-axis. As an example, let us consider the graph of the equation $y = x^3 + x - 1$ (Fig. 59-1). It is apparent that the part of the curve in which we are interested lies between $x = 0$ and $x = 1$, so we'll make an enlarged graph of this portion of the curve (Fig.

59-2).   From Fig. 59-2 we see that $P(x) = x^3 + x - 1$ has a zero about equal to .7.

To draw graphs such as the one in Fig. 59-1 we plot a number of points and then join them "by eye."   This is all we can do, considering our present knowledge of the graphs of functions; but of course there is always the possibility that if we had calculated a few more points, our curve would have had a radically different appearance. As you study more mathematics, you will learn how to sketch fairly accurate graphs, like those in Figs. 59-1 and 59-2, even though plotting relatively few points.

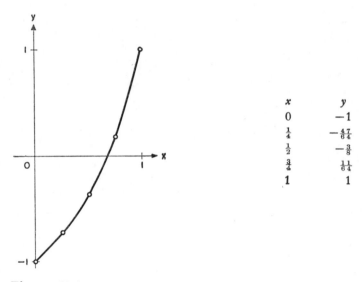

x	y
0	-1
$\frac{1}{4}$	$-\frac{47}{64}$
$\frac{1}{2}$	$-\frac{3}{8}$
$\frac{3}{4}$	$\frac{11}{64}$
1	1

Figure 59-2

We shall state (without proof) one theorem of advanced mathematics that is important for us here and which you will probably regard as obvious.

THEOREM 59-1.   *Let $P(x)$ be a polynomial with real coefficients and suppose that a and b are two numbers such that $a < b$.   If the numbers $P(a)$ and $P(b)$ have opposite signs, then there is a number c, where $a < c < b$ such that $P(c) = 0$.*

This theorem states that the part of the graph of the equation $y = P(x)$ that joins the points $(a,P(a))$ and $(b,P(b))$ must cross the

x-axis at least once if these points are on opposite sides of that axis. Note that Theorem 59-1 does *not* say how many zeros lie between the numbers a and b, it merely says that there must be at least one. And it does *not* say that there cannot be a zero between the numbers a and b even though the numbers $P(a)$ and $P(b)$ do have the same sign.

It is apparent from the table of values that accompanies the graph in Fig. 59-2 that the polynomial has a zero between $\frac{1}{2}$ and $\frac{3}{4}$, since $P(\frac{1}{2}) < 0$ and $P(\frac{3}{4}) > 0$. We can improve our rough estimate of .7 as a zero of this polynomial by using Theorem 59-1 to locate the zero between successive tenths. If we do a little calculating, we see that $P(.6) = -.184$ and $P(.7) = .043$. Hence, a zero of $P(x)$ lies between .6 and .7. To guess just where it lies between these two numbers, we may utilize the following scheme. We plot the points $(.6, -.184)$ and $(.7, .043)$ and join them by a straight line. Although this line is not the graph of the equation $y = P(x)$, we can consider it an approximation to the graph. So we take the next approximation to the zero of $P(x)$ as the x-co-ordinate of the point where the

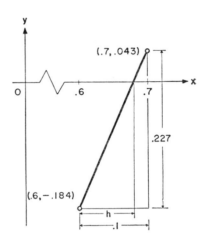

Figure 59-3

line crosses the x-axis. This crossing occurs at about the point $x = .68$ (Fig. 59-3). Actually, $P(.68) = -.0056$ and $P(.69) = .0285$, so the zero is between .68 and .69. Instead of reading off the value .68 from the figure, we could have used the similar triangles of Fig. 59-3 to calculate $h/.1 = .184/.227 = .8$. Therefore, $h = .08$, and the zero is about $.6 + h = .68$. Obviously, we could use this procedure over and over to locate the zero as accurately as we wished. It is a simple process, but somewhat laborious, even with the help of a desk calculator.

EXAMPLE 59-1.   Bracket the real zeros of the polynomial $x^4 - 2x^3 - 3x^2 + 4x + 2$ between consecutive integers.

Solution. A little calculating (we might use the Remainder Theorem and synthetic division) gives us the following table.

x	-2	-1	0	1	2	3
$P(x)$	14	-2	2	2	-2	14

From the table we see that $P(x)$ has zeros between -2 and -1, between -1 and 0, between 1 and 2, and between 2 and 3. Since $P(x)$ is a polynomial of degree 4, it has at most four zeros. Thus, there is exactly one zero between each of the pairs of integers listed.

The method of solution that we employed here is not restricted to polynomials. We can often approximate the zeros of a function f by using the graph of the equation $y = f(x)$, even though $f(x)$ is not a polynomial. In particular, we will discuss in Chapter Ten graphical methods that can be used to solve the equation $f(x) = 0$, when f involves trigonometric functions.

Problems 59

1. Bracket the real zeros of $P(x)$ between consecutive integers.
   (a) $P(x) = x^4 - x^2 - 4x + 4$
   (b) $P(x) = x^5 + 5x^4 - 3x^3 - 29x^2 + 2x + 23$
   (c) $P(x) = x^4 - 20x^2 - 21x - 22$
   (d) $P(x) = x^4 - 11x - 50$

2. Show that the polynomial $P(x) = x^3 - 3x^2 - 4x + 13$ has two real zeros between 2 and 3 even though $P(2)$ and $P(3)$ have the same algebraic sign.

3. Find the real zero of $P(x)$ that lies between 1 and 2 correct to one decimal place.
   (a) $P(x) = 3x^3 - x^2 - 8x - 2$
   (b) $P(x) = 2x^3 - 5x^2 - x + 5$

4. Find the real zero of $P(x)$ that lies between 0 and 1 correct to two decimal places.
   (a) $P(x) = x^3 + 2x^2 - 1$
   (b) $P(x) = x^3 + 2x^2 - x - 1$

5. We can find the approximate value of $\sqrt[n]{k}$ by using the methods we employed in this section to find the zeros of $x^n - k$. Find the values of the following numbers correct to two decimal places:
   (a) $\sqrt{7}$ (c) $\sqrt[3]{7}$
   (b) $\sqrt{14}$ (d) $\sqrt[4]{10}$

6. Show that the equation $\log x - x + 3 = 0$ has a solution that lies between 3 and 4. Does it have any other solutions?

7. There is a zero of the function f, defined by $f(x) = \sin x - \log x$, which lies between 2 and 3. Find the zero correct to two decimal places.

8. Find, correct to two decimal places, the solution to $x \sin x - \cos x = 0$ that lies between 0 and $\pi/2$.

9. The dimensions of a rectangular box are 1 ft, 2 ft, and 4 ft. In order to double the volume of the box, each edge is to be increased by the same amount. How much should each edge be increased?

10. An open box containing 20 cu in. is to be made from a sheet of tin 6 in. by 10 in. by cutting equal squares out of the corners and turning up the edges. How large a square should be cut out?

Review Problems, Chapter Six

You should be able to answer the following questions without referring back to the text.

1. If $A(x)$ and $B(x)$ are polynomials such that $A(x)B(x) = 1$, what can you conclude about $A(x)$ and $B(x)$?

2. Let k be a positive integer. Determine the values of k for which:
   (a) $x + a$ is a factor of $x^k + a^k$
   (b) $x - a$ is a factor of $x^k + a^k$

3. For what value of c will $2x^2 - x + c$ and $4x^2 + 4x + 1$ have a common factor?

4. Solve for x:
   (a) $\dfrac{1 - c}{cx} = \dfrac{3cr + 1}{1 - x} + \dfrac{cr - 1}{x - x^2}$ (c) $\sqrt{x - 2} = 3 + \sqrt{2x + 5}$

   (b) $\dfrac{1}{kx^2 + k} = \dfrac{k}{2k^2x + 1}$

5. If an airplane has enough fuel to fly for 16 hr at 400 mph, how far can it travel from its base if it flies directly into a 50 mph wind and returns with a 50 mph tail wind?

6. Solve for x: $(1 - a^2)(x + a) - 2a(1 - x^2) = 0$.

7. Find the value of k such that k is the remainder after the polynomial $x^3 - kx^2 - 14x + 15k$ is divided by $x - 5$.

8. Let $P(x) = 3x^2 - 2x + 1$ and let $P'(x) = 6x - 2$. Given any number r, we can find a polynomial such that $P(x) = (x - r)Q(x) + R$. Use synthetic division to divide $P(x)$ by $x - r$ to calculate $Q(x)$ and R. Show that $Q(r) = P'(r)$.

9. If 2 is a zero of the polynomial $x^3 + ax + b$, what quadratic equation must the other two zeros satisfy?

10. Solve for x: $(x + 2a)^3 + (x - a)^3 = (2x + a)^3$.

11. The zeros of $x^2 + bx + c$ are $-c \pm \sqrt{bc}$. Find b and c if $c \neq 0$.

12. Let $P(x) = 2x^3 + x^2 + ax + b$. If a and b are real numbers and one zero of $P(x)$ is $1 + i$, find all the zeros of $P(x)$.

13. Find the relation between a, b, and c if one zero of the quadratic polynomial $ax^2 + bx + c$ is n times the other.

14. The square of twice a number is larger than the square of the sum of the number and 1. Which numbers possess this property?

15. Let r_1 and r_2 be the zeros of the polynomial $ax^2 + bx + c$. Find:

(a) $\dfrac{1}{r_1} + \dfrac{1}{r_2}$ (c) $r_1^3 + r_2^3$

(b) $r_1^2 + r_2^2$ (d) $|r_1 - r_2|$

Miscellaneous Problems, Chapter Six

The following exercises are designed to test your ability to apply your knowledge of the theory of equations to somewhat more difficult problems.

1. Solve for x: $4^{3x} - 2^{3x+1} + 1 = 0$.

2. Let $Q(x) = (x + 1)(x^2 + 1)(x^4 + 1)(x^8 + 1)(x^{16} + 1)$. Show that $(x - 1)Q(x) = x^{32} - 1$. (*Hint:* After multiplying both sides of the original equation by $x - 1$, combine the first two factors of the product first.)

3. If r_1 and r_2 are solutions of the equation $x^2 - x + 1 = 0$, find the value of $r_1^3 + 3r_1^3r_2^3 + r_2^3$.

4. Let $P(x)$ be a polynomial of degree n with real coefficients. Prove that no straight line can intersect the graph of $P(x)$ more than n times.

5. For what values of k will the difference between the zeros of $5x^2 + 4x + k$ be equal to the sum of the squares of the zeros?

6. Solve the inequality $\dfrac{x + 5}{5x} > \dfrac{x}{3}$.

7. Solve the following equations for x:

(a) $x - 7\sqrt{x} + 15 = 0$ (c) $(x^2 + x - 1)^2 + x^2 + x - 2 = 0$
(b) $\sqrt[4]{x} + \sqrt{x} = 20$

8. For what real values of k are the zeros of $x^2 - 2kx - k + 1$ real numbers?

9. Find a quadratic polynomial whose zeros are the cubes of the zeros of $x^2 + bx + c$.

10. A rectangular strip of carpet 3 ft wide is laid diagonally across the floor of a room 9 ft by 12 ft so that each of the four corners of the strip touches a wall. How long is the strip?

11. Let $P(x) = x^n + \ldots + a_1x + a_0$ be a polynomial with integral co-efficients such that $P(0)$ and $P(1)$ are odd integers. Show that $P(x)$ does not have any rational zeros.

12. If $P(x)$ is a polynomial and a is a number, then according to Theorems 55-1 and 55-2 we can write
$$P(x) = (x - a)Q(x) + P(a).$$
Now suppose we are looking for a number r, which is a zero of $P(x)$. Then,
$$P(r) = 0 = (r - a)Q(r) + P(a).$$
Thus,
$$r - a = -\frac{P(a)}{Q(r)}.$$
If a is almost equal to r, then we might expect the number $Q(a)$ to be a good approximation of $Q(r)$. Thus, we could write
$$r_1 - a = -\frac{P(a)}{Q(a)};$$
that is,
$$r_1 = a - \frac{P(a)}{Q(a)}.$$
We might expect r_1 to be a closer approximation of r than a is. For example, a quick sketch of the graph of $P(x) = x^3 + x - 1$ shows that $P(x)$ has a zero at about .7. Use $a = .7$ and the formula for r_1 to find a closer approximation of this zero.

13. If $y = ax^2 + bx + c$, then by completing the square we may write $y = a\left(x + \frac{b}{a}\right)^2 + c - \frac{b^2}{4a}$. From this equation deduce that if a, b, and c are real numbers, then $y \leq c - \frac{b^2}{4a}$ if $a < 0$ and $y \geq c - \frac{b^2}{4a}$ if $a > 0$.

14. Let $y = ax^2 + bx + c$, where a, b, c are real numbers and $a < 0$. Use the results you obtained in the preceding problem to show that the maximum value of y occurs when $x = -b/2a$. What is this maximum value? Discuss the case when $a > 0$ and interpret all your results geometrically.

15. A man has 100 ft of wire and wishes to fence in a rectangular area by driving 2 stakes in a line parallel to a stone wall and putting his wire along 3 sides of the enclosure so that the wall forms the fourth side. Where should he drive his stakes in order to enclose the maximum area? (*Hint:* Use the result obtained in the preceding problem.)

CHAPTER SEVEN

SYSTEMS OF EQUATIONS

Suppose we know that the area of a rectangle is 24 square inches and its perimeter is 20 inches. How can we determine its dimensions? In this problem we are given *two* relations, and we wish to find *two* quantities, length and width. One way to solve this problem is to denote the length of one side of the rectangle by x and the length of the other side by y and use the information we have to write the following two equations that connect x and y:

$$xy = 24$$

$$2x + 2y = 20.$$

The solutions to this *system of equations* are $x = 6$, $y = 4$, or $x = 4$, $y = 6$, so the dimensions of the rectangle are 4 inches by 6 inches.

This type of problem, in which we have a number of unknown quantities and a given set of relations among these unknowns, occurs frequently in the applications of mathematics. In this chapter we will discuss methods by which we can find the unknowns in problems of this type, concentrating on cases in which the number of unknowns is the same as the number of equations.

60   EQUIVALENT SYSTEMS

A **solution** to a system of equations consists of a set of numbers $x, y, z, \ldots$ that satisfy all the equations of the system. For example, you can readily verify by substitution that the pair of numbers $x = 1$ and $y = -1$ is a solution to the system.

60-1
$$x - 2y = 3$$
$$2x^2 + 3y^2 = 5.$$

We now turn to the question of how this solution can be found and whether or not there are other solutions to this system.

The most direct way to treat a system such as the one in Equations 60-1 is to solve one of the equations for one unknown in terms of the other and then to substitute this result in the remaining equation to get one equation in one unknown. We then solve the equation in one unknown, and this solution leads to a solution of the original system. The equation $x - 2y = 3$ yields $x = 2y + 3$, and when we substitute this expression for x in the second equation, we get the equation $2(2y + 3)^2 + 3y^2 = 5$. When we simplify this quadratic equation we get:

$$11y^2 + 24y + 13 = 0$$
$$(y + 1)(11y + 13) = 0.$$

It follows that $y = -1$ or $y = -\frac{13}{11}$. We then find values of x from the equation $x = 2y + 3$. Corresponding to $y = -1$, we have $x = 2(-1) + 3 = 1$; and corresponding to $y = -\frac{13}{11}$, we find $x = \frac{7}{11}$. We must write the solutions in such a way that the proper values of x and y are associated. The solutions to System 60-1 could be written as $(1, -1)$ and $(\frac{7}{11}, -\frac{13}{11})$, the first number of the pair being the value of x and the second number, the value of y. The solutions could also be put in the form of a table:

x	1	$\frac{7}{11}$
y	-1	$-\frac{13}{11}$

EXAMPLE 60-1.   Solve the system of equations

60-2

$$4y \cos x = 3$$

$$y = 3 \cos x.$$

Solution.   If we substitute $3 \cos x$ for y in the first equation, we get the equation $4 \cos^2 x = 1$, which means that $\cos x = +\frac{1}{2}$ or $\cos x = -\frac{1}{2}$. If the value of x is such that $\cos x = \frac{1}{2}$, then $y = \frac{3}{2}$; if the value of x is such that $\cos x = -\frac{1}{2}$, then $y = -\frac{3}{2}$. Recall that $\cos x$ is positive for values of x that satisfy the inequalities $-\pi/2 < x < \pi/2$, and the only numbers in this range such that $\cos x = \frac{1}{2}$ are $x = \pi/3$ and $x = -\pi/3$. We can add any multiple of 2π to either the number $\pi/3$ or $-\pi/3$ to obtain another solution to the equation $\cos x = \frac{1}{2}$. In the same way we find that $2\pi/3 + k \cdot 2\pi$ and $4\pi/3 + k \cdot 2\pi$, where k is an integer, are the solutions to the equation $\cos x = -\frac{1}{2}$. A partial table of solutions for System 60-2 follows.

x	$\frac{\pi}{3}$	$\frac{5\pi}{3}$	$\frac{7\pi}{3}$	$-\frac{\pi}{3}$	$-\frac{5\pi}{3}$	$-\frac{7\pi}{3}$	$\frac{2\pi}{3}$	$\frac{4\pi}{3}$
y	$\frac{3}{2}$	$\frac{3}{2}$	$\frac{3}{2}$	$\frac{3}{2}$	$-\frac{3}{2}$	$\frac{3}{2}$	$-\frac{3}{2}$	$-\frac{3}{2}$

In theory, we may apply the procedure we have just outlined to a system of n equations in n unknowns, where n is any positive integer (for example, to a system of five equations in five unknowns). The first equation (or any one for that matter) is used to express one of the unknowns in terms of the other unknowns. This expression is then substituted in the remaining equations, and a new system results that has one less equation and one less unknown. The process is repeated until just one equation in one unknown remains. This last equation is then solved, and its solution leads to the values of the other unknowns.

DEFINITION 60-1.   *Two systems of equations are* **equivalent** *if every solution to either one is also a solution to the other.*

The systems

$$\begin{cases} 7x + 3y = 4 \\ x + y = 0 \end{cases} \quad \text{and} \quad \begin{cases} x = 1 \\ x + y = 0, \end{cases}$$

for example, are equivalent, since the only solution to each system is the pair of numbers $(1, -1)$.

When confronted with a system of equations, we shall try to replace it with an equivalent system that is easier to solve. *We can transform a system of equations into an equivalent system by performing the following operations.*

Operation 60-1. *We can interchange the position of any two equations.*

Operation 60-2. *We can replace any equation with a non-zero multiple of itself.* (A *multiple of an equation* is the equation that results when we multiply both sides of the equation by the same number.)

Operation 60 3. *We can replace any equation with the equation that results when that equation is added to any other equation in the system.* (*Adding two equations* means, of course, adding the corresponding sides of the equations.) For example, we may replace the second equation of a system of four equations with the sum of the second and third equations.

Operations 60-2 and 60-3 are frequently combined as follows.

Operation 60-4. *We can replace any equation with the sum of a non-zero multiple of itself and a multiple of any other equation of the system.* For example, we may replace the third equation of a system of three equations with the equation that results when 2 times the third equation is added to -5 times the first equation.

EXAMPLE 60-2. Replace the following system with an equivalent system.

60-3
$$x^2 + xy + y^2 = 2$$
$$x^2 + y^2 = 4.$$

Solution 1. We can replace the first equation with the equation that results when the second equation is multiplied by -1 and then added to the first (Operation 60-4). This operation yields the following system:

60-4
$$xy = -2$$
$$x^2 + y^2 = 4.$$

Note that this operation could be described as "subtracting the second equation from the first."

Solution 2. If we replace the first equation with the equation that results from subtracting the second equation from twice the first we get another system equivalent to System 60-3:

60-5
$$x^2 + 2xy + y^2 = 0$$
$$x^2 + y^2 = 4.$$

Of course, there are many other systems that are equivalent to System 60-3. We are interested in finding a system that is easy to solve. For example, the solutions to System 60-4 can be found by solving the first equation of the system for y to obtain $y = -2/x$, then substituting in the second equation to get

$$x^2 + \frac{4}{x^2} = 4,$$

$$x^4 - 4x^2 + 4 = 0,$$

$$(x^2 - 2)^2 = 0,$$

$$x^2 = 2,$$

$$x = \sqrt{2} \text{ or } x = -\sqrt{2}.$$

If $x = \sqrt{2}$, $y = -2/\sqrt{2} = -\sqrt{2}$. If $x = -\sqrt{2}$, $y = -2/-\sqrt{2} = \sqrt{2}$. Thus, Systems 60-3, 60-4, and 60-5 each have the solutions $(\sqrt{2}, -\sqrt{2})$ and $(-\sqrt{2}, \sqrt{2})$.

Problems 60

1. Determine whether or not the given numbers are a solution to the given system of equations.

(a) $(3, -2)$; $2x - y = 8$
$\qquad x^2 - y^3 = 17$

(b) $(4, -1)$; $\sqrt{x} - y = 3$
$\qquad xy^2 = 4$

(c) $(10, 3)$; $x - 3y = 1$
$\qquad y \log x = 3$

(d) $(\pi/2, \pi/3)$ $2 \sin x \cos y = 1$
$\qquad \sin^2 x + \cos^2 y = 1$

(e) $(-\tfrac{1}{2}, \tfrac{3}{2})$ $4^x + 4^y = 4$
$\qquad 4xy = -3$

(f) $(30, \tfrac{1}{2})$ $xy = 15$
$\qquad \sin x + y = 1$

2. Solve one equation for one unknown and substitute in the other equation to find the solutions to the following systems.

(a) $xy = 1$
     $x + 2y = 3$

(b) $3y + x = 1$
     $iy - 6x = 4$

(c) $y^2 - 2 \log x + 1 = 0$
     $y - \log x = 0$

(d) $x - 4 \sin y = 0$
     $x \sin y = 3$

(e) $x - y = 2$
     $x^2 + y + 2y^2 = 1$

(f) $x^3 - y^2 = 4x$
     $y^2 = x(x - 4)$

3. Determine which of the following systems are equivalent to the system
$$x^2 + y^2 = 4$$
$$xy = 1.$$

(a) $2xy = 2$
     $x^2 + y^2 = 4$

(b) $(x + y)^2 = 6$
     $xy = 1$

(c) $(x - y)^2 = 2$
     $xy = 1$

(d) $(x + y)^2 = 6$
     $(x - y)^2 = 2$

4. Replace each of the following systems with an equivalent system you consider simpler.

(a) $x^2 - 2y^2 = 1$
     $x^2 - 3y^2 = -2$

(b) $x^2 + xy - y^2 = 1$
     $(x + iy)^2 = 1$

(c) $x^2y + xy^2 = -1$
     $x^3 + y^3 = 1$

(d) $x - 2y - 4 = 0$
     $2x + y - 5 = 0$
     $4y - 2x + 8 = 0$

5. The sum of the circumferences of two circles is 24π ft, and their combined area is 84π sq ft. Find the radii of the two circles.

6. Find the values of m and k such that $(x - 1)$ and $(x + 3)$ are factors of the polynomial $x^4 - 3x^2 + mx - k$.

61   SYSTEMS OF LINEAR EQUATIONS. TRIANGULAR FORM

A **linear equation** in n unknowns $x_1, x_2, \ldots, x_n$ has the form

$$a_1x_1 + a_2x_2 + \ldots + a_nx_n = b,$$

where $a_1, a_2, \ldots, a_n$, and b are given numbers. For example, $3x - 4y = 5$ and $6x - 7y + iz - 3 = 0$ are linear equations. We shall devote the next few sections to a study of systems of linear equations.

A very simple system of linear equations is a system in **triangular form.** A system of linear equations in n unknowns $x_1, x_2, \ldots, x_n$ is in triangular form if the first equation involves only x_1; the second equation involves x_2 and perhaps x_1, but not $x_3, x_4, \ldots$, and x_n; the third equation involves x_3 and perhaps x_1 and x_2, but not $x_4, \ldots,$ and x_n; and so on. The following system, for example, is in triangular form:

61-1
$$2x \qquad\qquad = 4$$
$$3x - 2y \qquad = 8$$
$$x + \ y - 4z = 1.$$

From the first equation of this system it is apparent that $x = 2$. Once we know that $x = 2$, it is clear from the second equation that $y = -1$, and then we can solve the third equation to find $z = 0$.

It is easy to solve a system of equations in triangular form so we adopt the following method of solving a system of linear equations. *By using Operations 60-1, 60-2, 60-3, and 60-4 we try to replace a given system of linear equations with an equivalent system in triangular form.* "Most" systems can be reduced to triangular form in this way, and, as we shall see later, our efforts will not be wasted if we attempt the reduction on a system that is not equivalent to a system in triangular form. We can best describe the procedure by applying it to some typical examples.

EXAMPLE 61-1. Solve the system of equations

61-2
$$2x + 3y = 4$$
$$6x - 2y = -10.$$

Solution. We first multiply the second equation by $\frac{1}{2}$ to get a new second equation $3x - y = -5$. Then we replace the first equation with $(2x + 3y) + 3(3x - y) = 4 + 3(-5)$. Thus, we obtain the equivalent system

61-3
$$11x \qquad = -11$$
$$3x - y = -5.$$

System 61-3 is in triangular form, and it is easy to see that its solution is $x = -1$ and $y = 2$. We can describe the steps we used in this example less formally. First, for simplicity, we "divided out" the common factor 2 in the second equation. Then we "combined" the two equations in such a way as to produce a new first equation that did not contain y.

EXAMPLE 61-2.   Solve the system

$$3x - 2y = 7$$
$$2x - iy = 6i.$$

Solution.   By replacing the first equation with the sum of -2 times the second and i times the first, we get the equivalent system

$$(-4 + 3i)x \qquad = -5i$$
$$2x - iy = 6i.$$

Therefore,

$$x = \frac{-5i}{-4 + 3i} = \frac{5i(4 + 3i)}{25} = -\frac{3}{5} + \frac{4}{5}i,$$

and

$$y = \frac{2x - 6i}{i} = -\frac{22}{5} + \frac{6}{5}i.$$

EXAMPLE 61-3.   Solve the system of equations

$$\tfrac{1}{2}x - \tfrac{2}{3}y + z = \tfrac{8}{3}$$

61-4

$$2x - y + z = 6$$
$$3x + 2y \qquad = 4.$$

Solution.   (*Note:* It takes longer to describe the solution process than it does to carry it out.   You are warned, however, against trying to carry out too many steps at once—it is all too easy to make little errors when solving linear systems.)   To simplify things, we multiply the first equation by 6, and change the order of the equations to

$$3x + 2y \qquad = 4$$

61-5

$$3x - 4y + 6z = 16$$
$$2x - y + z = 6.$$

Now we multiply the third equation by 6 and subtract it from the second to remove z from the second equation.

$$3x + 2y \qquad = 4$$

61-6

$$-9x + 2y \qquad = -20$$
$$2x - y + z = 6.$$

Next get an equivalent system in triangular form by subtracting the second of Equations 61-6 from the first:

61-7

$$12x \qquad\qquad = 24$$
$$-9x + 2y \qquad = -20$$
$$2x - \ y + z = 6.$$

System 61-7 easily yields the solution $x = 2$, $y = -1$, and $z = 1$. Needless to say, it is wise to check the final results in the original system.

EXAMPLE 61-4.   Solve the system

61-8

$$x - 6y + 2z = 5$$
$$2x - 3y + \ z = 4$$
$$3x + 4y - \ z = -2.$$

Solution.   When we add the third equation to the second, and twice the third equation to the first, we get the equivalent system

61-9

$$7x + 2y \qquad = 1$$
$$5x + \ y \qquad = 2$$
$$3x + 4y - z = -2.$$

Next we subtract twice the second of Equations 61-9 from the first to get

61-10

$$-3x \qquad\qquad = -3$$
$$5x + \ y \qquad = 2$$
$$3x + 4y - z = -2.$$

The solution then comes easily; $x = 1, y = -3$, and $z = -7$.   Notice that the last equation was used to eliminate one of the unknowns from all the other equations, then the next to the last equation was used to eliminate another unknown from the equation above it.   Although this procedure stops after two steps in our example, it is clear that it is a direct method that can be used to reduce a system consisting of more linear equations in more unknowns to triangular form.

Note that all the operations involved in solving a system of linear equations are the simplest possible—multiplication, division, addition, and subtraction.   But there are a lot of operations involved. Because these systems have great practical importance, many schemes have been, and are still being, devised to solve them in the most efficient way possible.   Some of these methods are especially suited for the modern electronic computers.   Each method has its advantages and its drawbacks.   All involve large amounts of computation. As general methods go, the practice of reducing the system to triangular form is probably as efficient as any, and in the next section we introduce some notation that simplifies this method.

Problems 61

1. Solve the following systems by first finding an equivalent triangular system:

(a) $2x + 4y = 0$
    $3x - 2y = 8$
(b) $x - 5y = -3$
    $2x + y = -6$

(c) $\frac{1}{3}x + y = 2$
    $x - \frac{1}{4}y = -1$
(d) $\frac{1}{2}x - \frac{1}{3}y = \frac{1}{5}$
    $x - .1y = 7.3$

2. Solve the following systems by first finding an equivalent triangular system:

(a) $ix - 2y = 3$
    $3x + 2iy = 4$
(b) $(1 + i)x - 3y = i$
    $x + (1 - i)y = 3$

(c) $x + 2y = i(x - 1)$
    $x - 2y = i(x + 1)$
(d) $3x - iy = (4 + i)(y - 2)$
    $ix - 4y = (x - 6y)/i$

3. Solve the following systems by first finding an equivalent triangular system:

(a) $x + 2y \qquad = 1$
    $x - 2y \qquad = 3$
    $2x + 4y - 2z = 5$

(b) $x + 3y - 4z = -13$
    $2x - y + 2z = 4$
    $4x - 6y + z = -1$

(c) $3x - 4y + 2w = 1$
    $2x - y + w = 2$
    $x + 5y - z = 6$
    $y - 3z + w = -1$
(d) $\quad\quad x_1 - x_4 = -1$
    $x_1 + x_3 + x_4 = 1$
    $x_1 + x_2 + x_4 = -2$
    $2x_1 + 3x_3 + 5x_4 = -2$

4. Solve each of the following systems by first making a substitution that yields a linear system; e.g., let $u = 1/x$ and $v = 1/y$ in (a):

(a) $3/x + 4/y = 6$
    $1/x - 5/y = 1$
(b) $2x^2 + 3y^2 = 1$
    $x^2 + 2y^2 = 3$

(c) $5 \log x - \log y = 3$
    $\log x + 3 \log y = 7$
(d) $4 \sin x - \sin y = 1$
    $2 \sin x + 3 \sin y = 4$

5. Use a system of two equations in two unknowns to find what quantities of coffee worth 75¢ a lb and $1.15 a lb are needed to produce a blend worth 85¢ a lb.

6. The sum of the digits of a two-digit integer is 13. The number formed by reversing the digits is 9 greater than the original number. Find the number.

62 MATRICES

The process of solving a system of linear equations by reducing it to triangular form requires the writing of a number of equivalent systems. We can cut down the amount of labor involved in this process by using a notation in which the x's, y's, and the like, need not be copied down every time we write out a new equivalent system.

To illustrate this notation, consider the system

62-1
$$\frac{1}{2}x - 3y + z = 5$$
$$x + 4y - 3z = 2$$
$$2x \qquad + \frac{1}{4}z = -1.$$

The coefficients can be exhibited as an array of numbers:

62-2
$$\begin{bmatrix} \frac{1}{2} & -3 & 1 \\ 1 & 4 & -3 \\ 2 & 0 & \frac{1}{4} \end{bmatrix}.$$

The numbers on the right-hand sides of Equations 62-1 can be displayed as the array:

62-3
$$\begin{bmatrix} 5 \\ 2 \\ -1 \end{bmatrix}.$$

An array of numbers such as 62-2 is called a **matrix.** In particular, 62-2 is the **coefficient matrix** of System 62-1. We combine the two arrays 62-2 and 62-3 to get the **augmented matrix** of System 62-1,

$$\begin{bmatrix} \frac{1}{2} & -3 & 1 & \bigg| & 5 \\ 1 & 4 & -3 & \bigg| & 2 \\ 2 & 0 & \frac{1}{4} & \bigg| & -1 \end{bmatrix}.$$

It is easy to construct the augmented matrix that corresponds to a given system of linear equations.   We must arrange the system so that each column of the matrix represents the coefficients of the same letter, of course, and we must decide which column corresponds to which letter.   But once we have disposed of these points, we have a unique matrix that represents the system.   Conversely, given the augmented matrix it is easy to find the system of equations that gives rise to it.   For us, the concept of a matrix is nothing more than a device to save us the trouble of writing out the x's, y's, z's, and the like, of a system of linear equations.

We can translate the operations that we used to obtain equivalent systems of equations from a given system into operations to be performed on the rows of numbers in the augmented matrix of the system.   *These operations always produce a matrix of an equivalent system of equations.*   They can be summarized as follows:

Operation 62-1.   *We can interchange any two rows in a matrix.*

Operation 62-2.   *We can multiply any row by a non-zero number.*

Operation 62-3.   *We can replace any row by the sum of a non-zero multiple of itself and a multiple of any other row.*

EXAMPLE 62-1.   Solve System 61-2 by matrix operations.

Solution.   The system is

$$2x + 3y = 4$$
$$6x - 2y = -10,$$

so the corresponding matrix is

$$\begin{bmatrix} 2 & 3 & | & 4 \\ 6 & -2 & | & -10 \end{bmatrix}.$$

We multiply the second row by $\frac{1}{2}$ to obtain the matrix

$$\begin{bmatrix} 2 & 3 & | & 4 \\ 3 & -1 & | & -5 \end{bmatrix}.$$

We now add 3 times the second row to the first to obtain the matrix

$$\begin{bmatrix} 11 & 0 & | & -11 \\ 3 & -1 & | & -5 \end{bmatrix}.$$

This matrix represents the system

$$11x \quad\ \ = -11$$
$$3x - y = \quad -5,$$

for which the solution $x = -1$ and $y = 2$ is easily found.

EXAMPLE 62-2.   Use matrix operations to solve System 61-8.

Solution.   The matrix that corresponds to System 61-8 is

$$\begin{bmatrix} 1 & -6 & 2 & 5 \\ 2 & -3 & 1 & 4 \\ 3 & 4 & -1 & -2 \end{bmatrix}.$$

If we add the last row to the second row, and add twice the last row to the first, we obtain the matrix

$$\begin{bmatrix} 7 & 2 & 0 & 1 \\ 5 & 1 & 0 & 2 \\ 3 & 4 & -1 & -2 \end{bmatrix}.$$

Now subtracting twice the second row from the first produces the matrix

$$\begin{bmatrix} -3 & 0 & 0 & -3 \\ 5 & 1 & 0 & 2 \\ 3 & 4 & -1 & -2 \end{bmatrix}.$$

This is the matrix of System 61-10, from which we easily obtained the solution to the original system.

EXAMPLE 62-3.   Solve the system of equations

62-4

$$2x - y + z - w = -1$$
$$x + 3y - 2z \quad\ \ = -5$$
$$3x - 2y + 4w \quad = 1$$
$$-x + y - 3z - w = -6.$$

Solution.   The matrix of this system is

62-5

$$\begin{bmatrix} 2 & -1 & 1 & -1 & -1 \\ 1 & 3 & -2 & 0 & -5 \\ 3 & -2 & 0 & 4 & 1 \\ -1 & 1 & -3 & -1 & -6 \end{bmatrix}.$$

First we multiply the last row by 4 and add to the third, then we subtract the last row from the first to produce the matrix

62-6

$$\begin{bmatrix} 3 & -2 & 4 & 0 & 5 \\ 1 & 3 & -2 & 0 & -5 \\ -1 & 2 & -12 & 0 & -23 \\ -1 & 1 & -3 & -1 & -6 \end{bmatrix}.$$

The fourth column is now in satisfactory form, so we concentrate on the first three rows and work to obtain zeros in the third position in the first two rows. We multiply the second row by 6. Then we subtract the third row from this new second row. Now we multiply the first row by 3 and add the third row. These operations yield the matrix

62-7

$$\begin{bmatrix} 8 & -4 & 0 & 0 & -8 \\ 7 & 16 & 0 & 0 & -7 \\ -1 & 2 & -12 & 0 & -23 \\ -1 & 1 & -3 & -1 & -6 \end{bmatrix}.$$

Now we add the second row to 4 times the first and obtain the matrix

62-8

$$\begin{bmatrix} 39 & 0 & 0 & 0 & -39 \\ 7 & 16 & 0 & 0 & -7 \\ -1 & 2 & -12 & 0 & -23 \\ -1 & 1 & -3 & -1 & -6 \end{bmatrix}.$$

This matrix is the matrix of the system of equations in triangular form

62-9

$$\begin{aligned} 39x &= -39 \\ 7x + 16y &= -7 \\ -x + 2y - 12z &= -23 \\ -x + y - 3z - w &= -6. \end{aligned}$$

From System 62-9, we readily find the solution to be $x = -1$, $y = 0$, $z = 2$, and $w = 1$.

A little practice with matrix operations will enable you to pick up a fair degree of speed in solving systems of linear equations. There is nothing fixed about the sequence of operations that are performed. The above systems could have been reduced to triangular form in a slightly different manner without affecting the solution. The exact procedure to follow is a matter of individual choice.

Problems 62

1. Form an augmented matrix associated with each of the following systems:

(a) $x - 2y = 3$
$\quad\ \ y - 3z = 4$
$\quad x + 3 \ \ = 2z$

(b)
$\qquad\qquad\qquad x_1 - x_5 = 1$
$\qquad\qquad x_2 + x_3 + x_4 = 6$
$\qquad\qquad 3x_3 - x_4 + x_5 = 7$
$\qquad\qquad\qquad x_2 + x_5 = 3$
$\qquad x_1 + \ x_3 + x_4 + 6 = x_5$

2. Use matrix notation to solve the following systems:

(a) $2x + 3y = 1$
$\quad\ \ x + 2y = 5$

(b) $2x - 3y = 14$
$\quad\ 5x - \frac{1}{4}y = 6$

(c) $\quad t - v = 1$
$\quad 2v - t = 4$

(d) $x - iy = 2$
$\quad ix + 2y = 3i$

3. Finish solving System 62-1.

4. Use matrix notation to solve the following systems:

(a) $2r + 3s - t = 3$
$\qquad\quad s + t = r$
$\qquad s - r - t = 1$

(b) $\qquad x - y = z$
$\quad\ 2x - 3z = -5$
$\quad x + 2y + z = 3$

(c) $\quad 2x + 4y - z + 3w = 14$
$\quad -2x + 2y + 3z - 2w = -13$
$\quad 2x - 2y + 2z + w = 5$
$\quad 3x - 4y - 2z + w = 11$

(d) $4x - 4y + z + u - v = 2$
$\quad 3y + 4z + 2u - v + 5 = 0$
$\quad 4x - y + z - v = 2$
$\quad 2x - 2y - z + 2u = 3$
$\quad 4y + 3z - u + 2v + 1 = 0$

5. Let A, B, and C denote the degree measure of three angles of a triangle. One angle is 20° less than the sum of the other two, and 10° more than the positive difference of the other two. Find the measures of the angles.

6. Three pipe lines supply an oil reservoir. The reservoir can be filled by pipes A and B running for 6 hr, or by pipes B and C running for 8 hr, or by pipes A and C running for 10 hr. How long does it take to fill the tank if (a) all three pipes run? (b) pipe A is used alone?

7. Let $P(x) = x^3 + ax^2 + bx + c$. If we know that $P(1) = 4, P(-1) = -2$, and $P(2) = 4$, find the values of a, b, and c.

8. You are told that a bag of 30 coins contains nickels, dimes, and quarters amounting to $3, and that there are twice as many nickels as there are dimes. Should you believe it?

63   DEPENDENT AND INCONSISTENT SYSTEMS

For each system of linear equations that we have seen thus far, there has been exactly one set consisting of numbers that satisfy all the equations—that is, there has been just one solution to the system. We will call a system of linear equations with just one solution a **determinative** system.   Not all systems are determinative.   A system may have no solution, in which case we say that the system is **inconsistent.**   An inconsistent system of equations imposes contradictory conditions on the unknowns.   On the other hand, a system may have infinitely many solutions, in which case the system is called **dependent.**   The equations of a dependent system impose too few conditions on the unknowns to determine them uniquely.   The method of solving systems of linear equations by trying to reduce them to triangular form is still applicable to inconsistent and dependent systems.   In fact, this method will enable us to tell when these conditions occur.   The following examples illustrate how we can detect these situations.

EXAMPLE 63-1.   Solve the system of equations

63-1
$$2x - y + z = 1$$
$$x + 2y - z = 3$$
$$x + 7y - 4z = 2.$$

Solution.   Using matrix notation, the various steps in reducing the system to triangular form appear as

$$\begin{bmatrix} 2 & -1 & 1 & | & 1 \\ 1 & 2 & -1 & | & 3 \\ 1 & 7 & -4 & | & 2 \end{bmatrix} \rightarrow \begin{bmatrix} 9 & 3 & 0 & | & 6 \\ 3 & 1 & 0 & | & 10 \\ 1 & 7 & -4 & | & 2 \end{bmatrix} \rightarrow \begin{bmatrix} 0 & 0 & 0 & | & -24 \\ 3 & 1 & 0 & | & 10 \\ 1 & 7 & -4 & | & 2 \end{bmatrix}.$$

The third matrix results from subtracting 3 times the second row from the first row of the second matrix.   This operation removes the 3 in the first row, but also removes the 9.   The final matrix can be considered as the matrix of the system

$$0 \qquad\qquad = 24$$
$$3x + y \qquad = 10$$
$$x + 7y - 4z = 2.$$

We must now interpret the presence of the false statement $0 = 24$.

Logically, our argument runs as follows.   *If* there is a solution to System 63-1, *then* $0 = 24$.   Since $0 \neq 24$, we conclude that there simply cannot be a solution to System 63-1.   The system is therefore inconsistent.

EXAMPLE 63-2.   Solve the system of equations

63-2
$$2x - y + z = 1$$
$$x + 2y - z = 3$$
$$x + 7y - 4z = 8.$$

Solution. (Note that this system is very similar to the system in Example 63-1.)   In this case, the matrix reduction is as follows:

$$\begin{bmatrix} 2 & -1 & 1 & | & 1 \\ 1 & 2 & -1 & | & 3 \\ 1 & 7 & -4 & | & 8 \end{bmatrix} \rightarrow \begin{bmatrix} 9 & 3 & 0 & | & 12 \\ 3 & 1 & 0 & | & 4 \\ 1 & 7 & -4 & | & 8 \end{bmatrix} \rightarrow \begin{bmatrix} 0 & 0 & 0 & | & 0 \\ 3 & 1 & 0 & | & 4 \\ 1 & 7 & -4 & | & 8 \end{bmatrix}.$$

The last matrix is the matrix of the system

63-3
$$0 \qquad\qquad = 0$$
$$3x + y \qquad = 4$$
$$x + 7y - 4z = 8.$$

Unlike Example 63-1 (which yielded 0 = 24), the first equation here is of absolutely no help.   There is nothing false about the statement that 0 = 0, but it doesn't tell us anything we didn't already know. Now there are many solutions to System 63-3.   For instance, we could choose $x = 1$; then $y = 1$, and $z = 0$.   Or if $x = 0$, then $y = 4$ and $z = 5$.   Indeed, if t is any number, then a solution to System 63-3 (and hence to System 63-2) is $x = t$, $y = 4 - 3t$, and $z = 5 - 5t$. System 63-2 is dependent.

If a system consists of two linear equations in two unknowns, and all the given numbers are real, there is a simple way of interpreting geometrically the meaning of inconsistency and dependence.   Recall (see Section 51) that a linear equation

63-4
$$ax + by = c,$$

where a, b, and c are real numbers, is the equation of a line.   The pair of equations

63-5
$$ax + by = c$$
$$dx + ey = f$$

therefore represents two straight lines.   Now there are three possibilities concerning the intersection of these two lines.

Case I. The two lines of Equations 63-5 may intersect in a single point (x_0, y_0).

In this case the point (x_0, y_0) is the one and only point that lies on both lines. Hence, the coordinates of this point are the only numbers that satisfy both equations, and so there is only one solution to System 63-5. In geometrical terms, finding the solution to a determinative system of two linear equations means finding the coordinates of the point of intersection of the two lines represented by the equations.

Case II. The two lines of System 63-5 may be parallel and non-intersecting.

In this case there are no points that lie on both lines. Therefore, there are no points whose coordinates satisfy both equations. Thus, there is no solution to System 63-5. The system is therefore inconsistent.

Case III. Both equations of System 63-5 may represent the same line.

In this case every point that is on one line is on the other. In other words, every pair of numbers (x, y) that satisfies one equation, satisfies the other, and the System 63-5 is dependent.

The results of this analysis may be put in tabular form.

Type of System	*Description of Graph*
Determinative	Two intersecting lines
Inconsistent	Two parallel lines
Dependent	One line

Problems 63

1. Find a solution to System 63-2 such that:

   (a) $x = -1$ (c) $x = 1 + i$

   (b) $y = 3$ (d) $x = \sqrt{3} + i$

2. The augmented matrix of a given system of equations is

$$\begin{bmatrix} 24 & 0 & 0 & | & 0 \\ 1 & 2 & 0 & | & 2 \\ 3 & 4 & 1 & | & 5 \end{bmatrix}.$$

Is the system determinative?

3. Determine whether the following systems are determinative, inconsistent, or dependent.

(a) $2x - 4y = 5$
$8y - 4x = -10$

(c) $z - 4y = 4$
$3x - 2y - z = 5$
$2x - z = 2$

(b) $2x - 3y + z = 1$
$x - 4y - z = 1$
$x + 2y + 3z = 4$

(d) $5x + 6y = z$
$7x + 6y - 2z + 8 = 0$
$3x + 2y - z + 5 = 0$

4. Determine whether the following systems are determinative, inconsistent, or dependent.

(a) $2x - 6y + 2z + 10w = -7$
$2x + 4y - z - 5w = 6$
$x - 3y + z + 5w = -3$
$2x + 2y - z + 3w = 4$

(b) $x + w = 3$
$y + z = -1$
$x + z = 1$
$y + w = 1$

5. In each case find the point of intersection of the pair of given lines or show that the lines do not intersect.

(a) $2x - 3y = 1$
$x + 3y = -1$

(b) $x - y = 3$
$x + \dfrac{1}{2} = \dfrac{x}{2} - 1$

(c) $y = \dfrac{3x}{4} + 1$
$3x - 4y = 2$

(d) $2x - 3y = 3$
$x - 4y = -4$

6. Find the value of k such that the following system is not determinative.
$$kx + y - z = 1$$
$$x - 2y + z = 4$$
$$3x - 3y + z = 1$$

7. The sum of the digits of a three-digit number is 14 and the middle digit is the sum of the other two digits. If the last two digits are interchanged, the number obtained is 27 less than the original number. Find the number. Can you solve the problem if all the information is the same except that the number obtained when the last two digits are interchanged is 72 less than the original number?

8. Four high schools, South, East, North, and West, have a total enrollment of 1000 students. South reports that 10% of the students make A's, 25% B's, and 50% C's; East reports 15% A's, 25% B's, and 55% C's; North reports 25% A's, 15% B's, and 35% C's; West reports 15% A's, 20% B's, and 40% C's. Is this information consistent with the fact that of the total student enrollment in all four schools 15% receive A's, 25% B's, and 50% C's?

64 SYSTEMS INVOLVING QUADRATIC EQUATIONS

There are times when it is necessary to solve a system of equations in which products of the unknowns appear in one or more of the equations.   Systems 60-1 and 60-3 are of this type.   The solution of the most general system of two quadratic equations in two unknowns is rather complicated and we will not discuss it here.   In this section we will consider some isolated types of systems involving quadratic equations that occur most often in practice.

If the system consists of one linear and one quadratic equation, we can solve it by the method of substitution suggested in Section 60.

EXAMPLE 64-1.   Solve the system

64-1
$$2x + y = 1$$
$$3x^2 - xy - y^2 = -2.$$

Solution.   The first equation yields $y = 1 - 2x$, and when we substitute this result in the second equation we get

$$3x^2 - x(1 - 2x) - (1 - 2x)^2 = -2,$$

so that $x^2 + 3x + 1 = 0$,

$$x = \frac{-3 + \sqrt{5}}{2} \quad \text{or} \quad x = \frac{-3 - \sqrt{5}}{2}.$$

We then obtain corresponding values of y from the relation $y = 1 - 2x$. In this way we see that the solutions to System 64-1 are

$$\left(\frac{-3 + \sqrt{5}}{2}, 4 - \sqrt{5}\right) \quad \text{and} \quad \left(\frac{-3 - \sqrt{5}}{2}, 4 + \sqrt{5}\right).$$

The substitution method may also be used when neither of the equations is linear, as illustrated by the next example.

EXAMPLE 64-2.   A publisher wishes to print a book with 1-inch margins at the top, bottom, inside, and outside of each page.   Each page is to have an area of 42 square inches, and the printed area is to be 20 square inches.   What must be the dimensions of the page?

Solution. Suppose that one edge of the page is x inches long and that the other edge is y inches long. Then, since the area of the page is to be 42 square inches, we have

64-2
$$xy = 42.$$

Now the dimensions of the printed area are $(x - 2)$ and $(y - 2)$, so we also have

64-3
$$(x - 2)(y - 2) = 20.$$

Equations 64-2 and 64-3 taken together yield a system of two quadratic equations:

64-4
$$xy = 42$$
$$xy - 2x - 2y = 16.$$

If we solve the first of these equations for y and substitute the result in the second, we get the equation

$$42 - 2x - \frac{84}{x} = 16.$$

This equation reduces to

$$x^2 - 13x + 42 = 0 \quad \text{or} \quad (x - 6)(x - 7) = 0.$$

Hence, $x = 6$ and $y = 42/6 = 7$, or $x = 7$ and $y = 6$. These solutions both say the same thing. The dimensions of the page should be 6 inches by 7 inches.

Another non-linear system that is easy to solve consists of two equations of the form $ax^2 + by^2 = c$. The equations of such a system become linear if we substitute u for x^2 and v for y^2.

EXAMPLE 64-3. Solve the system

64-5
$$3x^2 + 4y^2 = 8$$
$$x^2 - y^2 = 5.$$

Solution. Substituting u for x^2 and v for y^2 leads to the system of linear equations

$$3u + 4v = 8$$
$$u - v = 5.$$

The solution to this linear system is $u = 4$ and $v = -1$. Therefore, the solution to System 64-5 is given by the following table.

x	2	2	-2	-2
y	i	$-i$	i	$-i$

Other systems that involve quadratic equations may be solved by replacing the given system with an equivalent system that is easier to solve.

EXAMPLE 64-4. Solve the system

64-6
$$2x^2 + xy - y^2 = 2$$
$$6x^2 - xy - 4y^2 = 4.$$

Solution. If we subtract twice the first equation from the second equation, we obtain the equivalent system

$$2x^2 + xy - y^2 = 2$$
$$2x^2 - 3xy - 2y^2 = 0.$$

After the second equation is factored, the above system becomes

$$2x^2 + xy - y^2 = 2$$
$$(2x + y)(x - 2y) = 0.$$

Clearly this latter system is equivalent to the following *two* systems:

64-7
$$2x^2 + xy - y^2 = 2$$
$$2x + y = 0.$$

64-8
$$2x^2 + xy - y^2 = 2$$
$$x - 2y = 0.$$

We can now solve both of these systems by substitution. Substituting $y = -2x$ in the first equation of System 64-7 yields the solution $x = i/\sqrt{2}$ and $x = -i/\sqrt{2}$, so the solution to System 64-7 is $(i/\sqrt{2}, -i\sqrt{2})$ and $(-i/\sqrt{2}, i\sqrt{2})$. Similarly, the solution to System 64-8 is $(2\sqrt{2}/3, \sqrt{2}/3)$ and $(-2\sqrt{2}/3, -\sqrt{2}/3)$. Thus, the solution to System 64-6 consists of the four number pairs: $(i/\sqrt{2}, -i\sqrt{2})$, $(-i/\sqrt{2}, i\sqrt{2})$, $(2\sqrt{2}/3, \sqrt{2}/3)$, and $(-2\sqrt{2}/3, -\sqrt{2}/3)$.

The methods we have discussed in this section are by no means exhaustive. It can be shown that any two equations of the form

$$ax^2 + bxy + cy^2 + dx + ey = f$$

may be solved algebraically.

Problems 64

1. Solve the following systems:

(a) $\quad 2x - y = -3$	(c) $\quad\quad y^2 = 4x$
$\quad x^2 + xy - y^2 = -1$	$\quad 3x - 5y = 13$
(b) $\quad xy + 6 = 0$	(d) $\quad\quad y = mx + c$
$\quad x + y + 1 = 0$	$\quad \dfrac{x^2}{a^2} + \dfrac{y^2}{b^2} = 1$

2. Solve the following systems:

(a) $2x^2 - y^2 = 22$	(c) $a^2x^2 + b^2y^2 = a^2b^2$
$x^2 - 3y^2 = 21$	$b^2x^2 + a^2y^2 = a^2b^2$
(b) $4x^2 + 9y^2 = 36$	(d) $ax^2 + by^2 = r$
$3x^2 - 5y^2 = 27$	$cx^2 + dy^2 = s$

3. Solve the following systems:

(a) $2x^2 - 3xy - 2y^2 = 0$	(c) $\quad xy + 4y^2 = 0$
$x^2 + xy - y^2 = 45$	$x^2 + 2xy - 4y^2 = 0$
(b) $x^2 + 2xy - y^2 = 4$	(d) $\quad x^2 - 4xy - 3y^2 + 14 = 0$
$x^2 - 3xy + y^2 = -4$	$6x^2 + 5xy + 2y^2 = 9$

4. Find the lengths of the sides of a right triangle if the hypotenuse is 34 in. and the area is 240 sq in.

5. A box with a volume of 80 cu in. is to be constructed by cutting 2-in. squares from the corners of a rectangular piece of cardboard and then bending up the sides and tying a piece of string around them to hold them up. If the piece of string required is 27 in. long (including 1 in. for making the knot), what should be the dimensions of the original piece of cardboard?

6. Solve the system

$$x^3 + y^3 = 16$$
$$x + y = 4.$$

7. The area of the base of a rectangular box is a sq ft, the area of one side is b sq ft, and the area of the end is c sq ft.   What is the volume of the box?

65   THE DETERMINANT OF A SQUARE MATRIX

We have found that matrix notation is useful because it saves us the trouble of copying down x's, y's, z's, and plus signs while solving a system of linear equations.   Actually, we have barely scratched the surface of the important and useful theory of matrices. In this section and the next we shall present, largely without proofs, a few of the results of matrix theory that you are likely to encounter again.

For us, a matrix is simply an array of numbers written in rows and columns. If the number of rows of a matrix is the same as the number of columns, then the matrix is a **square matrix**. The **order** of a square matrix is the number of rows (or columns) of the matrix. The matrix

$$\begin{bmatrix} 1 & 2 & 3 \\ 4 & 5 & 6 \\ 7 & 8 & 9 \end{bmatrix},$$

for example, is a square matrix of order 3. In particular, the square matrix

$$\begin{bmatrix} a & b \\ c & d \end{bmatrix}$$

is the **coefficient matrix** of the system of linear equations

65-1
$$ax + by = r$$
$$cx + dy = s.$$

With each square matrix we associate a number, called the **determinant** of the matrix. This number tells us something about the solutions to a system of equations for which the given matrix is the coefficient matrix. First we shall discuss matrices of order 2. In the following section we shall consider matrices of higher order.

DEFINITION 65-1. *The **determinant** of the square matrix* $\begin{bmatrix} a & b \\ c & d \end{bmatrix}$ *is the number $ad - bc$, and we denote this number by* $\begin{vmatrix} a & b \\ c & d \end{vmatrix}$.

Thus,
$$\begin{vmatrix} a & b \\ c & d \end{vmatrix} = ad - bc.$$

EXAMPLE 65-1. Find the determinant of the matrix $\begin{bmatrix} 1 & 2 \\ 2 & 3 \end{bmatrix}$.

Solution. According to Definition 65-1,

$$\begin{vmatrix} 1 & 2 \\ 2 & 3 \end{vmatrix} = 1 \cdot 3 - 2 \cdot 2 = -1.$$

Now let's look at System 65-1. It would be ridiculous to consider a system in which all the coefficients a, b, c, and d are zero, so we will assume that at least one of them is not zero. Then, by interchanging the equations or by interchanging x and y and relettering if necessary, we can always arrange the system so that $d \neq 0$. So let us assume that $d \neq 0$ and solve System 65-1 by matrix reduction:

$$\begin{bmatrix} a & b & | & r \\ c & d & | & s \end{bmatrix} \rightarrow \begin{bmatrix} ad - bc & 0 & | & rd - bs \\ c & d & | & s \end{bmatrix}.$$

(We multiplied the first row of the first matrix by d and subtracted b times the second row to get the second matrix.)

System 65-1 is therefore equivalent to the system

65-2
$$(ad - bc)\, x \qquad = rd - bs$$
$$cx \qquad + dy = s.$$

We can now easily obtain the following facts about System 65-1 from the equivalent System 65-2.

(i) If $ad - bc = 0$ and $rd - bs \neq 0$, the system is inconsistent.
(ii) If $ad - bc = 0$ and $rd - bs = 0$, the system is dependent.
(iii) If $ad - bc \neq 0$, the system is determinative.

We therefore have the following theorem.

THEOREM 65-1. *A system of two linear equations in two unknowns is determinative if, and only if, the determinant of the coefficient matrix is not zero.*

If the numbers r and s are both 0, then System 65-1 is said to be **homogeneous,** and reduces to the system

65-3
$$ax + by = 0$$
$$cx + dy = 0.$$

Obviously, one solution to System 65-3 is the pair $x = 0$, $y = 0$. A question that arises very often in the applications of mathematics is, "Under what circumstances does a homogeneous system possess solutions other than the 'trivial' solution $x = 0$, $y = 0$?" Theorem 65-1 gives us a partial answer. If the determinant $\begin{vmatrix} a & b \\ c & d \end{vmatrix} \neq 0$, System

65-3 is determinative; that is, it has exactly one solution. And since the pair $x = 0$, $y = 0$ is a solution, we see that there can be no others. Thus, System 65-3 can have a "non-trivial" solution only if the determinant of the coefficient matrix is zero. The complete answer to our question is contained in the next theorem.

THEOREM 65-2. *The homogeneous System 65-3 has a solution in addition to the trivial solution $x = 0$, $y = 0$, if, and only if, the determinant of the coefficient matrix is zero.*

Proof. We must show that if $ad - bc = 0$, then System 65-3 has a solution (x,y) in addition to $(0,0)$. If all the coefficients a, b, c, and d are 0, then any pair of numbers (x,y) satisfies System 65-3. So let us suppose that at least one of the coefficients, say d, is not 0. Then the pair $(d,-c)$ is not the pair $(0,0)$, and $(d,-c)$ satisfies the second equation of System 65-3, as we can see by substitution. If we substitute d for x and $-c$ for y in the left-hand side of the first of Equations 65-3, we obtain $ad - bc$, the determinant of the coefficient matrix. This number is 0 by hypothesis, so we see that the pair $(d,-c)$ satisfies both equations of System 65-3.

Now let us suppose that System 65-1 is determinative. From Equations 65-2 we see that

65-4
$$x = \frac{rd - bs}{ad - bc} = \frac{\begin{vmatrix} r & b \\ s & d \end{vmatrix}}{\begin{vmatrix} a & b \\ c & d \end{vmatrix}}.$$

Note that we can obtain the determinant in the numerator from the determinant of the coefficient matrix by replacing the coefficients of the x terms with the letters on the right-hand sides of Equations 65-1. You can easily verify that y can be written in determinant form as

65-5
$$y = \frac{\begin{vmatrix} a & r \\ c & s \end{vmatrix}}{\begin{vmatrix} a & b \\ c & d \end{vmatrix}}.$$

Here we obtain the determinant in the numerator from the determinant of the coefficient matrix by replacing the coefficients of the y terms with the letters on the right-hand sides of Equations 65-1.

EXAMPLE 65-2.   Write the solution to the system

$$2x + \pi y = \sqrt{17}$$

$$ix - 23y = 89$$

as the quotients of determinants.

Solution.   The determinant of the coefficient matrix of this system is $-46 - \pi i$, which is not 0.   Hence, we may use Equations 65-4 and 65-5 to write

$$x = \begin{vmatrix} \sqrt{17} & \pi \\ 89 & -23 \end{vmatrix} \bigg/ \begin{vmatrix} 2 & \pi \\ i & -23 \end{vmatrix} \quad \text{and} \quad y = \begin{vmatrix} 2 & \sqrt{17} \\ i & 89 \end{vmatrix} \bigg/ \begin{vmatrix} 2 & \pi \\ i & -23 \end{vmatrix}.$$

The following theorem lists a number of useful facts concerning the determinant of a matrix of order 2.

THEOREM 65-3.   *For a matrix of order 2.*

(i) *Interchanging the rows and columns of a matrix does not affect the value of its determinant; that is,*

$$\begin{vmatrix} a & b \\ c & d \end{vmatrix} = \begin{vmatrix} a & c \\ b & d \end{vmatrix}.$$

(ii) *Interchanging two rows (or columns) of a matrix changes the algebraic sign of the determinant; that is,*

$$\begin{vmatrix} c & d \\ a & b \end{vmatrix} = -\begin{vmatrix} a & b \\ c & d \end{vmatrix} \quad \text{and} \quad \begin{vmatrix} b & a \\ d & c \end{vmatrix} = -\begin{vmatrix} a & b \\ c & d \end{vmatrix}.$$

(iii) *If any row (or column) of a matrix is multiplied by a number k, the determinant also is multiplied by the number k; for example,*

$$\begin{vmatrix} ka & kb \\ c & d \end{vmatrix} = k\begin{vmatrix} a & b \\ c & d \end{vmatrix} \quad \text{and} \quad \begin{vmatrix} ka & b \\ kc & d \end{vmatrix} = k\begin{vmatrix} a & b \\ c & d \end{vmatrix}.$$

(iv) *If a multiple of any row (or column) is added to any other row (or column) the value of the determinant is unchanged; for example,*

$$\begin{vmatrix} a + kc & b + kd \\ c & d \end{vmatrix} = \begin{vmatrix} a & b \\ c & d \end{vmatrix} \quad \text{and} \quad \begin{vmatrix} a + kb & b \\ c + kd & d \end{vmatrix} = \begin{vmatrix} a & b \\ c & d \end{vmatrix}.$$

You can easily verify the equations listed in the theorem by using Definition 65-1.   For example,

$$\begin{vmatrix} ka & kb \\ c & d \end{vmatrix} = kad - kbc = k(ad - bc) = k\begin{vmatrix} a & b \\ c & d \end{vmatrix}.$$

Problems 65

1. Find the determinants of the following matrices:

   (a) $\begin{bmatrix} 2 & -1 \\ 3 & 1 \end{bmatrix}$ 　　　　　　　　(c) $\begin{bmatrix} 1+i & i \\ 2 & -i \end{bmatrix}$

   (b) $\begin{bmatrix} 2 & 1 \\ -1 & i \end{bmatrix}$ 　　　　　　　　(d) $\begin{bmatrix} 1-i & 2-i \\ 2+i & 1+i \end{bmatrix}$

2. Solve for x:

   (a) $\begin{vmatrix} 2 & 1 \\ -1 & x \end{vmatrix} = 0$ 　　　　　　(c) $\begin{vmatrix} x & -2 \\ x-4 & x^2-2 \end{vmatrix} = 0$

   (b) $\begin{vmatrix} x & 3 \\ 2 & x-1 \end{vmatrix} = 5$ 　　　　　(d) $\begin{vmatrix} x^2+1 & x \\ x+3 & x+1 \end{vmatrix} = 0$

3. For what numbers x is the following inequality true?
$$\begin{vmatrix} x & 1 \\ 5 & 2 \end{vmatrix} < \begin{vmatrix} 2 & x \\ 3 & 5 \end{vmatrix}$$

4. Prove that System 65-3 is dependent if the determinant of the coefficient matrix is zero.

5. Prove that if the determinant of the coefficient matrix of System 65-3 is zero, then for any number k, the pair $(kd, -kc)$ is a solution to the system.

6. Find three solutions to the system
$$2x - 4y = 0$$
$$-\tfrac{1}{2}x + y = 0.$$

7. Write the solution to each system in determinant form.

   (a) $3x - 5y = 7$ 　　　　　　　(c) $a_1x + b_1y + c_1 = 0$
   　　$y - 4x = -2$ 　　　　　　　　　$a_2x + b_2y + c_2 = 0$

   (b) $ix - \pi y = 4$ 　　　　　　　(d) $x \log a = 4y - 7$
   　　$x - 3y = \sqrt{5}$ 　　　　　　　$y \log b = 9x + 5$

8. Prove part (iv) of Theorem 65-3.

9. Prove that the determinant of a matrix of order 2 that has two identical columns (or two identical rows) is zero.

10. Prove:

    (a) $\begin{vmatrix} a+u & b \\ c+v & d \end{vmatrix} = \begin{vmatrix} a & b \\ c & d \end{vmatrix} + \begin{vmatrix} u & b \\ v & d \end{vmatrix}$

    (b) $\begin{vmatrix} a+u & b+v \\ c & d \end{vmatrix} = \begin{vmatrix} a & b \\ c & d \end{vmatrix} + \begin{vmatrix} u & v \\ c & d \end{vmatrix}$

66   THE DETERMINANT OF A SQUARE MATRIX OF ORDER GREATER THAN 2

The numbers a and d are called the **diagonal numbers** of the matrix $\begin{bmatrix} a & b \\ c & d \end{bmatrix}$. If $b = 0$, the determinant of the matrix is $ad - bc = ad - 0 \cdot c = ad$, the product of the diagonal numbers. Any square matrix can be reduced to a form in which all the numbers above the diagonal numbers are zero by using Operations 62-1, 62-2, and 62-3, and Theorem 65-3 tells us how these operations affect the determinant of a matrix. One method of calculating the determinant of a matrix of order 2 therefore consists of the following steps.

(i) Reduce the matrix to a form in which $b = 0$, taking into account the effect of our matrix operations on the value of the determinant.

(ii) Compute the product of the diagonal numbers of the resulting matrix.

The table below shows how operations on matrices affect the corresponding determinants. You can verify the facts contained in the table by referring to Theorem 65-3.

Item	*Matrix operations*	*Determinants of corresponding matrices*
Operation 62-1 Interchanging rows	$\begin{bmatrix} a & b \\ c & d \end{bmatrix} \rightarrow \begin{bmatrix} c & d \\ a & b \end{bmatrix}$	$\begin{vmatrix} a & b \\ c & d \end{vmatrix} = - \begin{vmatrix} c & d \\ a & b \end{vmatrix}$
Operation 62-2 Multiplying a row by a non-0 number k	$\begin{bmatrix} a & b \\ c & d \end{bmatrix} \rightarrow \begin{bmatrix} ka & kb \\ c & d \end{bmatrix}$	$\begin{vmatrix} a & b \\ c & d \end{vmatrix} = \frac{1}{k} \begin{vmatrix} ka & kb \\ c & d \end{vmatrix}$
Operation 62-3 Adding a multiple of one row to another row	$\begin{bmatrix} a & b \\ c & d \end{bmatrix} \rightarrow \begin{bmatrix} a + kc & b + kd \\ c & d \end{bmatrix}$	$\begin{vmatrix} a & b \\ c & d \end{vmatrix} = \begin{vmatrix} a + kc & b + kd \\ c & d \end{vmatrix}$

EXAMPLE 66-1.   Find the number $\begin{vmatrix} 1 & 2 \\ 3 & 4 \end{vmatrix}$ by following steps (i) and (ii).

Solution.   We can reduce the matrix $\begin{bmatrix} 1 & 2 \\ 3 & 4 \end{bmatrix}$ to triangular form by performing the following sequence of steps (the numbers under the arrows indicate which operation we carried out):

$$\begin{bmatrix} 1 & 2 \\ 3 & 4 \end{bmatrix} \underset{(62\text{-}2)}{\to} \begin{bmatrix} 2 & 4 \\ 3 & 4 \end{bmatrix} \underset{(62\text{-}3)}{\to} \begin{bmatrix} -1 & 0 \\ 3 & 4 \end{bmatrix}.$$

We find the corresponding relations among the determinants from the table on p. 288:

$$\begin{vmatrix} 1 & 2 \\ 3 & 4 \end{vmatrix} = \tfrac{1}{2}\begin{vmatrix} 2 & 4 \\ 3 & 4 \end{vmatrix} = \tfrac{1}{2}\begin{vmatrix} -1 & 0 \\ 3 & 4 \end{vmatrix} = \tfrac{1}{2}(-1)\cdot 4 = -2.$$

This answer agrees with the result we get by evaluating the determinant directly from Definition 65-1.

It would have been simpler to calculate the determinant in Example 66-1 directly. But we chose the more complicated procedure outlined in the example because this procedure also can be used to calculate determinants of order greater than 2. There is no simple way to calculate such determinants. The following theorem, which we won't prove, tells us something about determinants of any order.

THEOREM 66-1. *With a square matrix of any order we can associate a number, called the* **determinant of the matrix,** *such that,*

(i) *statements* (i), (ii), (iii), *and* (iv) *in Theorem 65-3 are valid, and*
(ii) *the determinant of a matrix in which all the numbers above the diagonal numbers are 0 is the product of the diagonal numbers.*

As you read the solution to the following example, note which of the Operations, 62-1, 62-2, or 62-3, we used to proceed from one array of numbers to the next, and use the table on p. 288 to see how the application of these operations changes the numbers that multiply the determinants.

EXAMPLE 66-2. Evaluate the determinant $\begin{vmatrix} 1 & 1 & 2 \\ 1 & 1 & -1 \\ 3 & 4 & 2 \end{vmatrix}$.

Solution. According to Theorem 66-1,

$$\begin{vmatrix} 1 & 1 & 2 \\ 1 & 1 & -1 \\ 3 & 4 & 2 \end{vmatrix} = -\begin{vmatrix} 1 & 1 & 2 \\ 3 & 4 & 2 \\ 1 & 1 & -1 \end{vmatrix} = -\begin{vmatrix} 3 & 3 & 0 \\ 5 & 6 & 0 \\ 1 & 1 & -1 \end{vmatrix} = -\tfrac{1}{2}\begin{vmatrix} 6 & 6 & 0 \\ 5 & 6 & 0 \\ 1 & 1 & -1 \end{vmatrix}$$

$$= -\tfrac{1}{2}\begin{vmatrix} 1 & 0 & 0 \\ 5 & 6 & 0 \\ 1 & 1 & -1 \end{vmatrix} = -\tfrac{1}{2}\cdot 1 \cdot 6 \cdot (-1) = 3.$$

Theorems corresponding to Theorems 65-1 and 65-2 are also valid for systems of linear equations in more than two unknowns, but we will not prove them here.

THEOREM 66-2. *A system of n linear equations in n unknowns is determinative if, and only if, the determinant of the coefficient matrix is not zero.*

THEOREM 66-3. *A system of n linear and homogeneous equations in n unknowns, x_1, x_2, . . . , x_n, has solutions in addition to the trivial solution $x_1 = x_2 = \ldots = x_n = 0$ if, and only if, the determinant of the coefficient matrix is 0.*

You might verify that the system

$$2x - y + z = 0$$
$$x - 2y + 3z = 0$$
$$3x \qquad - z = 0$$

has the solution $x = 1$, $y = 5$, $z = 3$ in addition to the solution $x = 0, y = 0, z = 0$, and that the determinant of the coefficients is 0. Can you find all the solutions to this system?

By a somewhat lengthy process, we can show that if the system

$$a_1x + b_1y + c_1z = d_1$$
$$a_2x + b_2y + c_2z = d_2$$
$$a_3x + b_3y + c_3z = d_3$$

is determinative, then the solution for x can be represented as

$$x = \frac{\begin{vmatrix} d_1 & b_1 & c_1 \\ d_2 & b_2 & c_2 \\ d_3 & b_3 & c_3 \end{vmatrix}}{\begin{vmatrix} a_1 & b_1 & c_1 \\ a_2 & b_2 & c_2 \\ a_3 & b_3 & c_3 \end{vmatrix}}.$$

The solutions for y and z are written in a similar way, and these results can be generalized to apply to systems of n linear equations in n unknowns.

Problems 66

1. Compute the determinant of each matrix by the method illustrated in Example 66-1.

   (a) $\begin{bmatrix} 1 & -1 \\ 2 & 1 \end{bmatrix}$ (c) $\begin{bmatrix} \sin x & \cos x \\ -\cos x & \sin x \end{bmatrix}$

   (b) $\begin{bmatrix} 3 & 4 \\ 1 & -2 \end{bmatrix}$ (d) $\begin{bmatrix} \tan x & -1 \\ 1 & \tan x \end{bmatrix}$

2. Evaluate the following determinants:

   (a) $\begin{vmatrix} 1 & 0 & 0 \\ 2 & 4 & 0 \\ 6 & -1 & 3 \end{vmatrix}$ (c) $\begin{vmatrix} 1 & 1 & 1 \\ 0 & 1 & 0 \\ 1 & 0 & 0 \end{vmatrix}$

   (b) $\begin{vmatrix} 1 & 2 & 0 \\ 3 & 0 & 0 \\ -1 & 5 & 2 \end{vmatrix}$ (d) $\begin{vmatrix} 0 & 3 & 0 & 0 \\ 0 & 0 & 2 & 0 \\ 3 & 0 & 0 & 0 \\ 5 & 1 & 2 & -1 \end{vmatrix}$

3. Evaluate the following determinants:

   (a) $\begin{vmatrix} 2 & 1 & 0 \\ -1 & 1 & 2 \\ 3 & 6 & -2 \end{vmatrix}$ (c) $\begin{vmatrix} -1 & 1 & 1 \\ 1 & -1 & 1 \\ 1 & 1 & -1 \end{vmatrix}$

   (b) $\begin{vmatrix} 5 & 2 & 1 \\ 0 & -1 & 3 \\ 0 & 2 & -4 \end{vmatrix}$ (d) $\begin{vmatrix} 1 & 2 & 3 \\ 2 & 0 & 4 \\ 0 & 3 & 0 \end{vmatrix}$

4. Evaluate the following determinants:

   (a) $\begin{vmatrix} 1 & 2 & 1 & 2 \\ -1 & 2 & 1 & 2 \\ -1 & -2 & 1 & 2 \\ -1 & -2 & -1 & 2 \end{vmatrix}$ (b) $\begin{vmatrix} 2 & 0 & 1 & 3 \\ 0 & 0 & 5 & 1 \\ -1 & 0 & -1 & 0 \\ 0 & 4 & 0 & 6 \end{vmatrix}$

5. Prove that the determinant of a square matrix that has two identical columns is zero.

6. Write the solution to each of the following systems in determinant form:

   (a) $2x - 3y = 4$ (b) $x_1 + x_3 + x_4 = 1$
   $x + y - 2z = 1$ $2x_1 + x_2 + x_3 = -1$
   $x - y - z = 5$ $x_1 - x_2 + x_4 = 2$
    $x_2 - 2x_3 - x_4 = 1$

7. Solve for x:

   $$\begin{vmatrix} x & 0 & 0 & 1 \\ 0 & x & 0 & 0 \\ 0 & 0 & x & 0 \\ 1 & 0 & 0 & x \end{vmatrix} = 0$$

8. For what values of k is the following system determinative?
$$kx + y = 1$$
$$y + z = 1$$
$$z + x = 1$$

9. For what values of k does the following system have a solution other than the trivial solution $(0, 0, 0)$?
$$x + 2y - z = kx$$
$$2x + y - z = ky$$
$$x - 2y + z = kz$$

10. Show that if the three lines, $a_1x + b_1y = c_1$, $a_2x + b_2y = c_2$, and $a_3x + b_3y = c_3$ are concurrent, then
$$\begin{vmatrix} a_1 & b_1 & c_1 \\ a_2 & b_2 & c_2 \\ a_3 & b_3 & c_3 \end{vmatrix} = 0.$$

Review Problems, Chapter Seven

You should be able to answer the following questions without referring back to the text.

1. If t is any real number and r and s are given numbers, solve the system
$$x \cos t - y \sin t = r$$
$$x \sin t + y \cos t = s.$$

2. Let a, b, c, d, r, and s be given numbers. Suppose x and y are numbers such that
$$ax + by = r$$
$$cx + dy = s,$$
and suppose (u,v) is a solution to the system
$$au + cv = 0$$
$$bu + dv = 0.$$
Show that $ru + sv = 0$.

3. Determine the values of a, b, and c so that the graph of the equation $y = ax^2 + bx + c$ passes through the points $(0,3)$, $(-1,6)$, and $(2,9)$.

4. Let $u = 3 - 2i$, $v = 5 + 6i$, and $w = 10 - 2i$. Find real numbers s and t such that $su + tv = w$.

5. The number pair $(0,0)$ is a solution to the system
$$(6 - k)x - 2y = 0$$
$$-2x + (3 - k)y = 0.$$
For what values of k does the system have a solution other than $(0,0)$?

6. Find a solution to the system
$$3x - y + 2z = 0$$
$$2x + 3y - z = 0.$$

7. Show that the following system is inconsistent unless $2r - s - 3t = 0$.

$$x + 3y = r$$
$$2x - 3z = s$$
$$2y + z = t.$$

8. Show that

$$\begin{vmatrix} x & y & 1 \\ x_1 & y_1 & 1 \\ x_2 & y_2 & 1 \end{vmatrix} = 0$$

is the equation of the line that is determined by the points (x_1, y_1) and (x_2, y_2).

9. An automobile factory makes both six- and eight-cylinder cars that are priced at \$2200 and \$2500 respectively. During one week the plant used 2560 pistons and produced cars worth \$839,000. How many cars of each type were made?

10. Suppose four horses—A, B, C, and D—are entered in a race and the odds on them, respectively, are 6 to 1, 5 to 1, 4 to 1, and 3 to 1. If you bet \$1 on A, then you receive \$6 if A wins, or you realize a net gain of \$5. You lose your dollar if A loses. How should you bet your money to guarantee that you win \$12 no matter how the race comes out?

Miscellaneous Problems, Chapter Seven

The exercises that follow are designed to test your ability to apply your knowledge of systems of equations and the theory of matrices to more difficult problems.

1. Solve the following system:

$$xy = 4$$
$$y = 2x^2 - 4x + 2$$

2. Solve the following system:

$$\log (x^2/y^3) = 7$$
$$\log x^3y^2 = 4$$

3. Solve the following system:

$$2^x = 32^y$$
$$3 = x^2 - 12y^2 + 2x$$

4. Show that the three lines that are defined by the equations $x - 2y - 3 = 0$, $2x + y + 1 = 0$, and $3x + 4y + 5 = 0$ are concurrent.

5. Suppose you have a combination of ten coins consisting of nickels, dimes, and quarters whose total value is \$1.25. How many of each coin do you have?

6. Suppose you have a rectangular sheet of paper. Can you trim one edge of the paper to obtain a rectangle whose area and perimeter are half the area and perimeter of the original sheet? Can you do it by trimming two edges?

7. Solve the following system:

$$x_1 + x_2 = 10$$
$$x_2 + x_3 = 9$$
$$x_3 + x_4 = 8$$
$$x_4 + x_5 = 7$$
$$x_5 + x_6 = 6$$
$$x_6 + x_7 = 5$$
$$x_7 + x_8 = 4$$
$$x_8 + x_9 = 3$$
$$x_1 + x_9 = 2$$

8. Show that $\begin{vmatrix} 1 & 1 & 1 \\ x_1 & x_2 & x_3 \\ x_1^2 & x_2^2 & x_3^2 \end{vmatrix} = (x_3 - x_1)(x_2 - x_1)(x_3 - x_2).$

9. Solve for x.

$$\begin{vmatrix} x & 1 & -2 \\ -2 & x+1 & 1 \\ -1 & 3 & x-6 \end{vmatrix} = 0$$

10. Suppose that a, b, c, and d are numbers such that (i) $a^2 + b^2 = 1$, (ii) $c^2 + d^2 = 1$, and (iii) $ac + bd = 0$. Show that (iv) $a^2 + c^2 = 1$, (v) $b^2 + d^2 = 1$, and (vi) $ab + cd = 0$.

CHAPTER EIGHT

PERMUTATIONS, COMBINATIONS, THE BINOMIAL THEOREM, AND PROBABILITY

One of the significant trends in the modern-day use of mathematics is the increasing use of probability and statistics to describe the world in which we live. To obtain a working knowledge of these topics would require much more space than we have available in this book. There are, however, many basic concepts that are interesting in themselves and do not require extensive treatment. In this chapter we shall consider some of these elementary notions that are basic to an understanding of probability and statistics.

67 FACTORIAL NOTATION AND THE FUNDAMENTAL PRINCIPLE

Products of successive integers, such as $1 \cdot 2 \cdot 3 \cdot 4$, will appear so many times in the following pages that it is convenient to have a special notation for them.

DEFINITION 67-1. *Let n be a positive integer. The symbol **n**! is read "n factorial," and represents the product of all the positive integers from 1 to n; that is, n! = 1 · 2 · . . . · n. The symbol O! is defined as O! = 1. (Note the similarity between this meaning and the special definition for zero exponents.)*

For example, $5! = 1 \cdot 2 \cdot 3 \cdot 4 \cdot 5 = 120$ and $3! = 1 \cdot 2 \cdot 3 = 6$. The following theorem stems directly from the definition of $n!$.

THEOREM 67-1. *If n and r are positive integers, and r < n, then*

$$n! = r!(r + 1)(r + 2) \ldots n.$$

The next example illustrates how Theorem 67-1 is used to simplify expressions that involve factorials.

EXAMPLE 67-1. Simplify the expression $\dfrac{5! - 4!}{6!}$.

Solution. According to Theorem 67-1, $5! = 4! \cdot 5$ and $6! = 4! \cdot 5 \cdot 6$. Hence,

$$\frac{5! - 4!}{6!} = \frac{4!(5 - 1)}{4! \cdot 5 \cdot 6} = \frac{4}{30} = \frac{2}{15}.$$

EXAMPLE 67-2. Find the number n for which $\dfrac{(n + 2)!}{n!} = 56$.

Solution. According to Theorem 67-1,

$$\frac{(n + 2)!}{n!} = \frac{n!(n + 1)(n + 2)}{n!} = (n + 1)(n + 2).$$

Thus, $$(n + 1)(n + 2) = 56,$$
$$n^2 + 3n - 54 = 0,$$
$$(n - 6)(n + 9) = 0,$$
$$n = 6 \text{ or } n = -9.$$

Since we defined factorials for non-negative numbers only, the symbol $(-9)!$ is meaningless.   The solution to our problem is therefore $n = 6$.

If n is a large integer, then $n!$ will be an extremely large number. For example, $20! = 2,432,902,008,176,640,000$.   The use of logarithms makes computations with such large numbers much easier. Table IV (p. 400) contains the common logarithms of $n!$ for values of n between 1 and 100.

EXAMPLE 67-3.   Calculate $N = \dfrac{33!\,37!}{51!}$.

Solution.   From Table IV,

$$\log N = \log 33! + \log 37! - \log 51!$$
$$= 36.9387 + 43.1387 - 66.1906$$
$$= 13.8768.$$

The approximate value of N is $7.53 \cdot 10^{13}$.

Let us analyze the following problem.   A freshman engineering student has a choice of six engineering departments in which to enroll (electrical, mechanical, and so on), and after graduation a choice of three services (Army, Navy, and Air Force) in which to serve. How many different academic-service careers can he choose (Electrical-Army, Aeronautical-Air Force, and so forth)?   We can use a diagram of the situation to count the various possibilities.   In Fig. 67-1 we have shown the "paths" that our student may follow.   Such a diagram is called a **tree.**   The student starting at point S may choose any one of the six engineering branches of the tree, and then a service branch.   We find the number of possible choices he might make simply

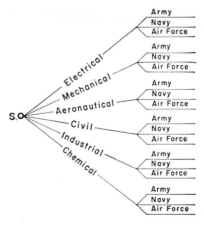

Figure 67-1

by counting the number of service branches shown. There are 18. Note that each of the six engineering branches is the base of three service branches. Therefore, the total number of possibilities facing our student can be expressed as the product $6 \cdot 3 = 18$.

This example illustrates a principle that is of fundamental importance in problems that deal with enumeration.

FUNDAMENTAL PRINCIPLE. *Suppose we have two operations—Operation (i) and Operation (ii)—such that there are m possible outcomes of Operation (i) and, after Operation (i) has been performed, n possible outcomes of Operation (ii). Then the combined operation that consists of performing Operation (i) and then Operation (ii) has mn possible outcomes.*

Our freshman engineering student had six courses of study and three branches of the service from which to choose. The operations referred to in the Fundamental Principle are (i) selecting an engineering major and (ii) selecting a branch of service. There are six possible outcomes of Operation (i) and three possible outcomes of Operation (ii), so there are $6 \cdot 3$ possible outcomes of the combined operation.

The Fundamental Principle can be extended to any number of operations.

EXAMPLE 67-4.   How many four-letter code words can be formed from the letters of the alphabet?

Solution.   In this problem there are four operations involved: selecting a first letter, selecting a second letter, selecting a third letter, and selecting a fourth letter. Since the alphabet contains 26 letters, each operation has 26 possible outcomes. Using the extension of the Fundamental Principle to four operations, we see that the number of possible four-letter words is $26 \cdot 26 \cdot 26 \cdot 26 = 26^4$.

EXAMPLE 67-5.   How many two-letter code words can be made from the alphabet if no letter is used more than once?

Solution.   There are 26 choices for the first letter. After the first letter has been chosen, there are only 25 choices for the second letter.

Therefore, the number of two-letter words that can be constructed without using a letter more than once is $26 \cdot 25 = 650$.

EXAMPLE 67-6. In how many ways may a chairman, vice-chairman, and secretary be selected from among the members of a six-man committee?

Solution. There are six choices for chairman. After the chairman has been selected, there are five possibilities for vice-chairman, and then four choices for secretary. There are therefore $6 \cdot 5 \cdot 4 = 120$ possible ways to fill the positions.

Problems 67

1. Simplify the following:

   (a) $\dfrac{8!}{11!}$

   (b) $\dfrac{5! - 8!}{4! - 7!}$

   (c) $\dfrac{(n-1)!\,(n+1)!}{(n!)^2}$

   (d) $\dfrac{(2n)!}{2n!}$

2. Using Table IV, calculate:

   (a) $\dfrac{21!}{7!}$

   (b) $(13!)(21!)$

   (c) $\dfrac{16! \cdot 24!}{81!}$

   (d) $6!17! - 7!16!$

3. How many 4-digit numbers can be formed? (The first digit cannot be 0).

4. Draw a tree to illustrate how many 3-digit numbers greater than 665 can be formed from the digits 2, 4, 6, and 8.

5. If two dice are tossed, in how many different ways can they fall? (The question is not how many sums can be formed!)

6. The travel bureau informs you that the following possible reservations are available for your trip from New York to Corpus Christi: to Columbus, Ohio, by rail or air; to Savannah by rail or boat; from Columbus to Little Rock by air or rail; from Little Rock to Corpus Christi by rail; from Savannah to New Orleans by rail; from New Orleans to Corpus Christi by air, rail, or boat. Draw a tree that will show all the possible ways you can make the trip.

7. A man has 12 shirts and 18 ties. How many different shirt-tie combinations can he wear? Suppose 4 shirts and 8 ties are green, and that 8 shirts and 10 ties are blue. How many shirt-tie combinations can he wear if his wife objects to a blue and green combination?

8. How many seating arrangements are possible for a class of 25 students in a classroom with 60 chairs?   Suppose the front row contains 10 chairs and that there are 5 girls in the class.   How many seating arrangements are possible if the front row is reserved for the 5 girls and the other rows are reserved for the boys?

9. Suppose that mathematics is offered at 8, 9, 10, 1, and 2 o'clock; English at 9 and 2 o'clock; and chemistry at 8, 10, and 1 o'clock.   How many different schedules are possible for a student who is taking these 3 courses?

10. How many possible 4-letter code words can be written in which (a) the first letter does not appear again in the word? (b) the same letter is not permitted to appear side by side?

68   PERMUTATIONS

A **permutation** of a set of objects is an arrangement of the objects in some order.   The arrangements *ABDC* and *BADC* are two different permutations of the letters *A*, *B*, *C*, and *D*.   Now we ask, "How many different permutations of these four letters are possible?" We can find the answer easily by using the Fundamental Principle stated in the preceding section.   Note that there are four choices for the first letter of an arrangement of the letters *A*, *B*, *C*, and *D*. Once we make this choice, we have three possible choices for the second letter, two choices for the third letter, and only one choice for the final letter.   Thus there are $4 \cdot 3 \cdot 2 \cdot 1 = 4! = 24$ different permutations of the four letters.   By reasoning in exactly the same way with any number of objects we can establish the following theorem.

THEOREM 68-1.   *The number of permutations of n objects (n is a positive integer) is n!.*

In addition to considering the possible arrangements of an entire set of objects, we often consider the selection and arrangement of a certain number of them.   Examples 67-5 and 67-6 represent this type of problem.   In Example 67-5 we found the number of possible arrangements of 2 letters selected from a set of 26.   We call each such arrangement a "permutation of 26 things taken 2 at a time."

Example 67-6 dealt with permutations of six things taken three at a time.

DEFINITION 68-1.   *The number of different ordered sets of r objects that can be selected from a set of n objects is called the **number of permutations of n objects taken r at a time**.   This number is denoted by the symbol P_r^n.*   (*Note that* $r \leq n$.)

EXAMPLE 68-1.   A football coach has a squad of 60 players.   How many different teams can he field, when two teams made up of the same men are considered as different teams if the men are assigned to different positions?

Solution.   We represent the answer by the symbol P_{11}^{60}; that is, the number of permutations of 60 objects taken 11 at a time.   To calculate this number, it is convenient to number the positions 1, 2, . . . , 11.   There are 60 candidates from which to choose a man to fill the first position, 59 choices for the second, 58 for the third, and so on, until there remains but one position to be filled.   At this point ten men have already been used, so there are 50 choices for the last position.   Hence, $P_{11}^{60} = 60 \cdot 59 \cdot \ldots \cdot 50$.

Note that in Example 68-1, $n = 60$ and $r = 11$.   The number of choices for the last position was equal to the number of men who were left after the first $r - 1$ positions were filled; that is, there were $n - (r - 1) = n - r + 1$ possible choices for the last position.   The number of permutations was simply the product of all the integers from $n - r + 1$ to n.   This result is valid when n and r are any positive integers ($n \geq r$).

THEOREM 68-2.

$$P_r^n = n(n - 1)(n - 2) \ldots (n - r + 1).$$

To consider a special case of Theorem 68-2, note that $P_n^n = n!$. This result agrees with Theorem 68-1.

So far we have been talking about the number of possible arrangements of *different* objects, but now we turn to a somewhat more complicated problem.   Suppose we have six signal flags—three red, two yellow, and one blue—and wish to make signals by arranging the flags vertically on a staff. How many signals can we make? Since there are six flags, we know that there are 6! ways of arranging them on the staff, but some of these arrangements are indistinguishable from others. We seek the number of distinguishable arrangements; let us call this number R. Now consider the following two operations:

(i) selecting a distinguishable arrangement of the flags,

and

(ii) ordering the flags in any given arrangement in such a way that the result doesn't change the signal (interchanging the two yellow flags, for example).

The first operation, we have said, has R possible outcomes, and we can easily calculate the number of possible outcomes of the second operation. There are 3! possible arrangements of the three red flags, 2! arrangements of the two yellow flags, and 1! = 1 arrangement of the blue flag. Hence, there are 3!2!1! arrangements of the six flags in any given signal. According to the Fundamental Principle, the combination of Operations (i) and (ii) has $R \cdot 3!2!1!$ outcomes. Every one of the 6! arrangements of the six flags on the staff can be effected by successively performing Operations (i) and (ii), so it follows that $R3!2!1! = 6!$ or $R = \dfrac{6!}{3!2!1!} = 60$.

In general, *if we have a set of n objects, r_1 of which are of one kind, r_2 of a second kind, . . . , and r_p of a pth kind ($r_1 + r_2 + \ldots + r_p = n$), then the number of distinguishable permutations of the n objects is given by the formula*

68-1
$$R = \frac{n!}{r_1!r_2! \ldots r_p!}.$$

We derive this formula by applying the same reasoning we used in the example of the signal flags. Note that if each of the n objects in the given set is distinct from all the others, then $r_1 = r_2 = \ldots = r_p = 1$, and Equation 68-1 reduces to $R = n!$. That is, Equation 68-1 also gives the formula for the number of permutations of n distinct objects.

EXAMPLE 68-2. How many distinguishable permutations of the letters in the word DIVIDED are possible?

Solution. The seven letters of the word DIVIDED form a class of objects of which three are of one kind (the D's), two are of a second kind (the I's), one (the E) is of a third kind, and one (the V) is of a fourth kind. According to Equation 68-1, there are $R = \dfrac{7!}{3!\,2!\,1!\,1!} =$ 420 distinguishable permutations of these letters.

We used Equation 68-1 to count the number of possible arrangements of a set of objects, some of which are of one kind, some of a second kind, and so on. Let us now look at the reverse problem—**partitioning** a given ordered set of objects. We might, for example, have six white flags arranged vertically on a staff and ask, "How many possible selections can we make if we select three flags to be dyed red, two to be dyed yellow, and one to be dyed blue." One possible selection would be to take the first, third, and fifth flags to be dyed red, the second and sixth to be dyed yellow, and the fourth to be dyed blue; but, of course, there are many other possible selections. If we make a selection, dye the flags, and replace them in their original positions on the staff, we will have one of the signals we were talking about earlier. In fact, different selections produce different signals, and different signals correspond to different selections. The problem of partitioning or grouping the flags so that three are to be dyed red, two are to be dyed yellow, and one is to be dyed blue is therefore essentially the same problem as determining the number of signals that can be made using three red flags, two yellow flags, and one blue flag. Since we found that there were 60 possible signals, we see that there are 60 ways to select the flags to be dyed.

In general, *if we have a set of n distinct objects, and if we wish to partition the set into p classes, the first class consisting of r_1 objects, the second of r_2 objects, . . . , and the pth of r_p objects (where $r_1 + r_2 + \ldots + r_p = n$), then the number of possible partitions is the number R given by Equation 68-1.*

EXAMPLE 68-3. An instructor decides to assign grades to 30 students as follows: 2 A's, 3 B's, 6 C's, 9 D's, and 10 E's. In how many ways can the class be graded?

Solution. If we let R denote the number of possible ways of assigning grades, then according to Formula 68-1

$$R = \frac{30!}{2!3!6!9!10!}.$$

(You might use logarithms to find how large this number is.)

EXAMPLE 68-4.   A group of three men are to be selected from ten salesmen in the home office to be transferred to a new office.   In how many ways can the selection be made?

Solution.   This problem can be approached from the standpoint of partitioning the ten men into two classes, the first class comprising three men to be transferred, and the second class consisting of seven men to be kept at the home office.   According to Equation 68-1, the number of such partitions is

$$R = \frac{10!}{3!7!} = 120.$$

Problems 68

1. Prove:

(a) $P_r^n = \dfrac{n!}{(n-r)!}$ (b) $\dfrac{P_r^n}{r!} = \dfrac{P_{n-r}^n}{(n-r)!}$

2. Use Table IV to evaluate:
   (a) P_5^{26} (c) P_{39}^{52}
   (b) P_{17}^{38} (d) P_{17}^{71}

3. How many baseball teams can be formed from a squad of 15 players if
   (a) two teams made up of the same men are different if the men are assigned different positions?
   (b) same assumption as (a) except that 3 of the men can be used only as pitchers?
   (c) every man can play every position but two teams are considered the same whenever the same men play regardless of position? (This is a partitioning problem.)

4. How many code words can be made from the letters of the word STUPID if
   (a) the code words consist of 4 letters?
   (b) the code words consist of 5 letters and must begin with a vowel?

5. How many different football teams can be formed from a squad that consists of 20 linemen, 3 quarterbacks, 8 halfbacks and 4 fullbacks?

6. How many 6-digit numbers can be formed that consist of 3 ones and 3 twos?

7. Four men, 3 women, and 2 children stand in a row to pose for pictures. A photo is taken of each possible lineup. How many photos are taken? When the pictures are developed they are so blurred that you can identify an individual only as a man, woman, or child. How many "different" pictures are there?

8. A committee of 9 people is to be split into 3 subcommittees that contain 4, 3, and 2 members. In how many ways can the subcommittee assignments be made?

9. Three men and 3 women are to be seated around a round table. Two seating arrangements are considered the same if one arrangement can be "rotated" into the other. How many ways may the men and women be seated if

    (a) there are no restrictions on where they sit?

    (b) men and women must be seated alternately?

The type of permutations involved in part (a) of this problem are termed **circular permutations.** What is the number of circular permutations of n objects?

10. In the game of bridge, 13 cards are dealt to each of 4 players. How many different deals are possible? How many deals are possible in which each player gets 1 ace?

69   COMBINATIONS

A permutation of n objects taken r at a time results from selecting and arranging r objects from among n. Thus, the ordered set of cards that consists of the 2, 3, 4, 5, and 6 of spades is one of the permutations of the 52 cards of a standard deck taken five at a time. Another such permutation is the ordered set that consists of the 3, 2, 4, 5, and 6 of spades. According to permutation theory, these sets are considered different, but to a poker player they represent the same hand. He is only interested in *which* cards are in his hand, not in their relative order within the hand. The answer to the question, "How many different five-card poker hands are possible?" is therefore not P_5^{52}, but a considerably smaller number. Let us denote the number of possible five-card poker hands (order within the hands being neglected) by C, and proceed to calculate this number. Consider the following two operations:

    (i) selecting five cards from a deck of 52,

and

    (ii) rearranging a set of five cards.

We have said that there are C possible outcomes of the first operation, and, after it has been performed, there are 5! possible outcomes of the second operation.   According to the Fundamental Principle of Section 67, there are $C \cdot 5!$ possible outcomes of the combined operation.   But these two operations performed successively yield all possible permutations of 52 cards taken five at a time.   Therefore,

$$C \cdot 5! = P_5^{52} \quad \text{or} \quad C = \frac{P_5^{52}}{5!}.$$

The example of the poker hands illustrates a general selection problem.

DEFINITION 69-1.   *The number of different sets of r objects that can be selected from a set of n objects, when the order within the set of r objects is disregarded, is called the number of* **combinations** *of n things taken r at a time.   We will use the symbol* C_r^n *to denote this number.*

To find the number C_r^n, we can proceed along the lines we followed in the example of the poker hands.   Every permutation of n things taken r at a time can be effected by the successive operations of selecting r objects from the n objects, and then by rearranging this set of r objects.   The symbol C_r^n represents the number of possible outcomes of selecting r objects, and there are $r!$ arrangements of any selection.   Hence, there are $C_r^n \cdot r!$ permutations of n things taken r at a time.   But there are P_r^n permutations of n objects taken r at a time, and therefore $C_r^n \cdot r! = P_r^n$.   If $r = 0$, we define $C_0^n = 1$. We have proved the following theorem.

THEOREM 69-1.   *If n is a positive integer, and r is an integer such that* $0 \le r \le n$, *then*

69-1 $$C_r^n = \frac{P_r^n}{r!} = \frac{n(n-1)\ldots(n-r+1)}{r!} = \frac{n!}{r!(n-r)!}.$$

A second way to prove Theorem 69-1 is to note that a combination of r objects selected from n objects is obtained by partitioning the set of n objects into two classes; the first class consists of those objects we select, and the second class consists of those objects that we do not select.   There are r objects in the first class and $n-r$ objects in the second.   Thus, we can regard C_r^n as the number of partitions of a set of n objects into two classes that contain r and $n - r$ objects. According to Equation 68-1,

$$R = \frac{n!}{r!(n-r)!} = C_r^n.$$

EXAMPLE 69-1. A man has one penny, one nickel, one dime, one quarter, and one half-dollar in his pocket.   He reaches into his pocket and pulls out three coins.   How many different sums can he produce by this process?

Solution.   There are $C_3^5 = \dfrac{5!}{3!2!} = 10$ sets of three coins that can be selected from five coins.   The order within any group of three is irrelevant because we wish only to find the sum.   Hence, there are ten different sums.

EXAMPLE 69-2.   Suppose the U.S. Senate contains 49 Democrats and 47 Republicans.   How many committees consisting of five Democrats and four Republicans can be formed?

Solution.   Consider the following operations:

(i) selecting the Democratic committee members

and

(ii) selecting the Republican committee members.

There are C_5^{49} possible outcomes of the first operation and C_4^{47} outcomes of the second operation.   Hence, according to the Fundamental Principle of Section 67, there are $C_5^{49} \cdot C_4^{47}$ possible different committees.

It is sometimes necessary to consider situations in which the objects from which combinations are to be selected are not all distinct.   For instance, consider the problem in Example 69-1 if the man has one penny, one nickel, one dime, one quarter, and two half-dollars in his pocket.   Every sum that occurs in Example 69-1 could arise in this case, and in addition there are those sums that occur when two of the three coins drawn are half-dollars.   In fact, there are exactly four additional sums, since the two half-dollars may be paired with any one of the remaining four coins.   Thus, the total number of sums in this case is $C_3^5 + 4 = 14$.   We won't attempt to write a formula covering all such examples; each case can be treated individually.   If the numbers involved are not too large, it may help to draw a tree to illustrate the problem.

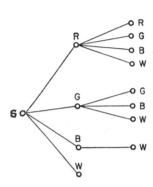

Figure 69-1

EXAMPLE 69-3.   An urn contains two red, two green, one blue, and one white ball.   How many different color combinations of two balls may be selected?

Solution.   The number of combinations that consist of two different colors is clearly the number of combinations of four colors taken two at a time; that is, C_2^4.   In addition, there are those combinations that consist of two red or two green balls.   Thus, the total number of color combinations is $C_2^4 + 2 = 8$. The tree in Fig. 69-1 illustrates this example.   Note that we were careful not to repeat branches that would give us the same combination but a different permutation.

Problems 69

1. Calculate:
   (a) C_5^7
   (b) C_2^{14}
   (c) C_1^n
   (d) C_{n-1}^n
   (e) C_n^n
   (f) C_{n-2}^{n-1}

2. Prove:
   (a) $C_{n-r}^n = C_r^n$
   (b) $C_{r-1}^n + C_r^n = C_r^{n+1}$

3. Solve for n:
   (a) $C_3^{n+1} = 2C_2^n$
   (b) $C_1^n = 5$
   (c) $C_{n-1}^{n+1} = 15$
   (d) $C_{n-1}^{n+1} = kC_{n-2}^n$

4. How many basketball games are played in the Big Ten if each team plays every other team twice?

5. How many different bridge hands of 13 cards can be dealt from a deck of 52 cards?   Use Table IV to compute your answer.

6. An employer is going to give a $50 raise to 10 of his 25 employees and a $25 raise to the others.   In how many ways can he grant the raise?

7. Consider 7 points, no three of which are collinear.
   (a) How many lines are determined?
   (b) How many triangles whose vertices are the given points are determined?

8. Ten couples are planning a picnic.   They agree that 3 men will build the fire and that 7 women will be in charge of the food.   If only 1 member of each couple is to be given a job, how many different groups of workers are possible?

9. How many councils of 4 seniors, 3 juniors, 2 sophomores, and 1 freshman can be formed from a student senate group that consists of 5 members from each class?

10. How many baseball teams can be formed from a squad of players that consists of 6 outfielders, 7 infielders, 3 catchers, and 10 pitchers?

70   THE BINOMIAL THEOREM

We call the expression $(a + b)$ a **binomial** to indicate that it is the sum of two terms.   Let us calculate a few powers of this binomial by direct multiplication:

$$(a + b)^1 = a + b$$

$$(a + b)^2 = (a + b)(a + b)$$

$$= a^2 + ba + ab + b^2$$

70-1
$$= a^2 + 2ab + b^2$$

$$(a + b)^3 = (a + b)(a + b)(a + b)$$

$$= a^3 + a^2b + aba + ba^2 + b^2a + bab + ab^2 + b^3$$

$$= a^3 + 3a^2b + 3ab^2 + b^3.$$

To multiply out a large power of a binomial would be quite laborious, so let us examine the above products and try to find a pattern that will enable us to write the expansion of a binomial power without using direct multiplication.

From the definition of the power of a number,

70-2
$$(a + b)^n = (a + b)(a + b) \ldots (a + b),$$

where there are n factors on the right-hand side of Equation 70-2. Our problem is to express this product as a sum of terms such as those found in Equations 70-1.   We therefore must first determine precisely what kind of terms will appear in the expansion.

Each term in the expansion of $(a + b)^n$ arises from the multiplication of a's and b's, where we choose either the letter a or the letter b from each of the parentheses on the right-hand side of Equation 70-2. We might, for example, say that we got the term aba in the expansion of $(a + b)^3$ shown in Equations 70-1 by choosing the letter a from the first and third parentheses, and b from the second. If we choose the letter b from r parentheses, then we must choose the letter a from $n - r$ parentheses, since there are n parentheses from which to choose a's and b's. When we multiply these a's and b's together, we get the product $a^{n-r}b^r$. The expansion of $(a + b)^n$ is therefore a sum of terms of the form $a^{n-r}b^r$, where r is one of the numbers 0, 1, 2, . . . , n. If $n = 6$, for example, the expansion contains terms of the form a^6, a^5b, a^4b^2, a^3b^3, a^2b^4, ab^5, b^6. Our problem now is to determine the number of terms of each type that occur in the expansion of $(a + b)^n$.

For a given number r, the product $a^{n-r}b^r$ may arise in several different ways. For example, the product $a^{n-2}b^2$ can occur when we choose b's from the first two parentheses (and a's from the rest), again when we choose b's from the first and third parentheses, and so on. The number of terms of the form $a^{n-2}b^2$ that can occur is equal to the number of ways of choosing the letter b from 2 of the n parentheses, and this number is C_2^n. By reasoning in exactly the same way, we see that the number of terms of the form $a^{n-r}b^r$ that occur in the expansion of $(a + b)^n$ is C_r^n. This result is stated in the following theorem.

THEOREM 70-1 (**The Binomial Theorem**). *If n is a positive integer and a and b are any two numbers, then*

$$(a + b)^n = C_0^n a^n b^0 + C_1^n a^{n-1}b^1 + \ldots + C_r^n a^{n-r}b^r + \ldots$$
70-3
$$+ C_{n-1}^n ab^{n-1} + C_n^n a^0 b^n$$

$$= a^n + na^{n-1}b + \ldots + C_r^n a^{n-r}b^r + \ldots + nab^{n-1} + b^n.$$

Since the quantities C_r^n appear as coefficients in the expansion of a power of a binomial, they are frequently called the **binomial coefficients.**

EXAMPLE 70-1.   Calculate $(a + b)^5$.

Solution.   According to Equation 70-3,

$$(a + b)^5 = a^5 + 5a^4b + C_2^5\, a^3b^2 + C_3^5\, a^2b^3 + 5ab^4 + b^5.$$

When the binomial coefficients that appear in this expansion are evaluated, we find that

$$(a + b)^5 = a^5 + 5a^4b + 10a^3b^2 + 10a^2b^3 + 5ab^4 + b^5.$$

EXAMPLE 70-2.   Show that $C_0^n + C_1^n + \ldots + C_n^n = 2^n$ for any positive integer n.

Solution. The Binomial Theorem is true when a and b are any two numbers; in particular, it is true when the two numbers are both 1. Thus,

$$(1 + 1)^n = C_0^n \, 1^n + C_1^n \, 1^{n-1}1^1 + \ldots + C_n^n \, 1^n,$$
$$2^n = C_0^n + C_1^n + \ldots + C_n^n.$$

EXAMPLE 70-3.   Find the binomial expansion of $(x^2 - 1/y)^4$.

Solution. We can use the Binomial Theorem with the substitution $a = x^2$ and $b = -1/y$ to obtain

$$\left(x^2 - \frac{1}{y}\right)^4 = (x^2)^4 + 4(x^2)^3 \left(-\frac{1}{y}\right) + C_2^4(x^2)^2 \left(-\frac{1}{y}\right)^2$$
$$+ 4(x^2) \left(-\frac{1}{y}\right)^3 + \left(-\frac{1}{y}\right)^4$$
$$= x^8 - \frac{4x^6}{y} + \frac{6x^4}{y^2} - \frac{4x^2}{y^3} + \frac{1}{y^4}.$$

EXAMPLE 70-4.   Compute an approximate value of $(1.01)^7$.

Solution. Using the Binomial Theorem, we find that
$$(1.01)^7 = (1 + .01)^7$$
$$= 1^7 + 7(1)^6(.01) + 21(1)^5(.01)^2 + \ldots + (.01)^7$$
$$= 1 + 7(.01) + 21(.01)^2 + 35(.01)^3 + \ldots + (.01)^7$$
$$= 1 + .07 + .0021 + .000035 + \ldots + .00000000000001.$$
It appears that, to three decimal places, $(1.01)^7 = 1.072$.

Problems 70

1. Find the 5th term in the expansions of each of the following:

(a) $(x + y)^7$

(b) $(2x + y)^{17}$

(c) $\left(2x^2 - \frac{i}{2}y\right)^{10}$

(d) $\left(2x^2 + \frac{i}{2y}\right)^{10}$

2. What is the binomial expansion of $(a - b)^n$?

3. Prove that: $C_0^n - C_1^n + C_2^n - C_3^n + \ldots + (-1)^n C_n^n = 0$.

4. Show that if n is even, then $C_0^n + C_2^n + \ldots + C_n^n = 2^{n-1}$. (*Hint:* Use the result of the preceding problem and Example 70-2.)

5. Find the term that involves x^2 in each of the following:
(a) $(a - x^{1/2})^6$ (b) $(1/x - x)^4$.

6. Find and simplify the 4th term in the expansion of each of the following:

(a) $\left(2x - \dfrac{1}{2x}\right)^{10}$ (c) $(x^{-1} - x^{1/2})^8$

(b) $(\tfrac{1}{2}x^{1/3} + \tfrac{1}{3}y^{1/2})^{12}$ (d) $(3 \log x - 2^v)^6$

7. Using the Binomial Theorem, compute approximately:
(a) $(1.02)^{10}$ (c) $(102)^5$
(b) $(.98)^4$ (d) 99^5

8. Write the complete expansion of the following:
(a) $(1 + i)^5$ (c) $(1 + \tan x)^6$
(b) $(1 + i)^4$ (d) $(\sec x - 1)^3$

9. Show that $\sin^{10} x + \cos^{10} x = 1 - 5 \cos^2 x + 10 \cos^4 x - 10 \cos^6 x + 5 \cos^8 x$.

10. According to DeMoivre's Theorem (Section 49),
$$(\cos \theta + i \sin \theta)^2 = \cos 2\theta + i \sin 2\theta.$$
Now if the left side is multiplied out, we obtain the equation
$$\cos^2 \theta - \sin^2 \theta + 2i \sin \theta \cos \theta = \cos 2\theta + i \sin 2\theta.$$
Hence, $\cos 2\theta = \cos^2 \theta - \sin^2 \theta$ and $\sin 2\theta = 2 \sin \theta \cos \theta$. Use DeMoivre's Theorem and the Binomial Theorem to develop a formula for $\sin 4\theta$.

71   THE SIGMA NOTATION

Each term of the sum in Equation 70-3 can be obtained from the expression $C_r^n a^{n-r} b^r$ by replacing the letter r with one of the numbers $0, 1, 2, \ldots, n$. The Binomial Theorem, therefore, gives the following "directions" for expanding the expression $(a + b)^n$: "Replace the letter r in the expression $C_r^n a^{n-r} b^r$ with each of the numbers $0, 1, 2, \ldots,$ n in turn, and add up all the terms that result." Directions like these occur so often in mathematics that we have a special symbol for them. If $A(r)$ is some mathematical expression and n is a positive integer, then the symbol $\sum\limits_{r=0}^{n} A(r)$ means, "Successively replace the letter r in the expression $A(r)$ with the numbers $0, 1, 2, \ldots, n$ and add up the resulting terms." The symbol Σ is the Greek letter sigma, and it is used to suggest "sum" since we are to add a number of terms. This notation is merely a symbolism by which we avoid having to write out the sum $A(0) + A(1) + A(2) + \ldots + A(n)$. We needn't start counting at $r = 0$, but could start at any number less than n. Thus,

$$\sum_{r=1}^{n} A(r) = A(1) + A(2) + \ldots + A(n)$$

and

$$\sum_{r=6}^{8} A(r) = A(6) + A(7) + A(8),$$

for example. The letter r is called the **index of summation.** We may use any letter as the index of summation; for example,

$$\sum_{k=7}^{10} A(k) = A(7) + A(8) + A(9) + A(10) = \sum_{r=7}^{10} A(r).$$

EXAMPLE 71-1.   Evaluate $\sum_{r=0}^{5} r^2$.

Solution. $\sum_{r=0}^{5} r^2 = 0^2 + 1^2 + 2^2 + 3^2 + 4^2 + 5^2 = 55.$

We will use the sigma notation not only here and elsewhere in this book, but you will also encounter it often in later mathematics courses. *In terms of this symbolism the Binomial Theorem reads*

71-1 $$(a + b)^n = \sum_{r=0}^{n} C_r^n a^{n-r} b^r.$$

Let us examine the coefficients of the terms in the expansion of $(a + b)^n$. The term involving $a^{n-r} b^r$ is

$$C_r^n a^{n-r} b^r = \frac{n(n-1) \ldots (n-r+1)}{r!} a^{n-r} b^r.$$

Thus, we may express the coefficient of the quantity $a^{n-r} b^r$ as a fraction. To get the numerator of this fraction we calculate a product of integers—the first integer is n; each succeeding integer is obtained by subtracting 1 from the factor that precedes it; the last integer in the product is 1 more than the exponent of a.   The denominator is the factorial of the exponent of b.   Once we note this fact, we can readily calculate, for example, that the coefficient of the term a^7b^3 in the expansion of $(a + b)^{10}$ is $\dfrac{10 \cdot 9 \cdot 8}{3!} = 120$.

Next we observe that there is one term (the number 1) in the expansion of $(a + b)^0$, two terms in the expansion of $(a + b)^1$, three terms in the expansion of $(a + b)^2$, and in general, $n + 1$ terms in the expansion of $(a + b)^n$.   An ingenious scheme for calculating the binomial coefficients, known as Pascal's Triangle, is illustrated below.

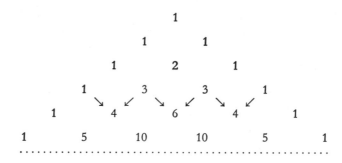

The first row lists the coefficients in the expansion of $(a + b)^0$, the second row lists the coefficients in the expansion of $(a + b)^1$, the third row lists the coefficients for $(a + b)^2$, and so on.   Each number in the array, except the ones on the edges, is obtained by adding the two numbers nearest it in the row above.   Thus, as the arrows indicate, in the fifth row we have $4 = 1 + 3$, $6 = 3 + 3$, and $4 = 3 + 1$.   This method yields the binomial coefficients because

71-2 $C_r^{n+1} = C_{r-1}^n + C_r^n$ (see Problem 2(b), Section 69).

Thus, the number 6 in the fifth row of Pascal's Triangle is C_2^4, and Equation 71-2 states that $C_2^4 = C_1^3 + C_2^3 = 3 + 3$.   You should also note the symmetry of Pascal's Triangle; it is an expression of the equality $C_{n-r}^n = C_r^n$ (see Problem 2a, Section 69).

Another way to evaluate the binomial coefficients is based on a relationship between C_{r+1}^n and C_r^n, which we now proceed to find. According to Equation 69-1,

$$C^n_{r+1} = \frac{n(n-1)\ldots(n-r)}{(r+1)!}$$

$$= \left[\frac{n(n-1)\ldots(n-r+1)}{r!}\right]\frac{(n-r)}{(r+1)}.$$

The fraction inside the brackets is C^n_r, so we have

71-3 $$C^n_{r+1} = \frac{(n-r)}{(r+1)}C^n_r.$$

Equation 71-3 is an example of a **recursion formula.** If we write the binomial coefficients for a given number n in a finite sequence $C^n_0, C^n_1, \ldots, C^n_r, C^n_{r+1}, \ldots, C^n_n$, the recursion formula enables us to find, one by one, all the binomial coefficients that follow one that we know. But we know that $C^n_0 = 1$ for any n, so we can use Equation 71-3 to find, one by one, the values of all the binomial coefficients for any positive integer n.

EXAMPLE 71-2.   Find the first four terms of the expansion $(x+y)^{21}$.

Solution.   We use the recursion formula with $n = 21$, together with the fact that $C^{21}_0 = 1$, to write

$$C^{21}_0 = 1$$

$$C^{21}_1 = \left(\frac{21-0}{1}\right)1 = 21 \quad (r = 0 \text{ in Equation 71-3})$$

$$C^{21}_2 = \left(\frac{21-1}{2}\right)21 = 210$$

$$C^{21}_3 = \left(\frac{21-2}{3}\right)210 = 1330.$$

Thus, $(x+y)^{21} = x^{21} + 21x^{20}y + 210x^{19}y^2 + 1330x^{18}y^3 + \ldots.$

Problems 71

1. Find the 5th term in the expansion of each of the following:
   (a) $(a+b)^{12}$
   (c) $(1-ix)^8$
   (b) $(2y-3x^2)^7$
   (d) $(\sin x - \cos x)^9$

2. Find the first four terms in the expansion of each of the following:
   (a) $(x+y)^{30}$
   (c) $(a-2b)^{19}$
   (b) $(a+x)^{120}$
   (d) $(2x-4y^2)^{13}$

3. Expand $(x + y + z)^4$ by writing it as $[x + (y + z)]^4$.

4. Calculate $(3 + 5i)^6$.

5. Let n be a positive integer and x and h be any numbers. Expand and simplify:

$$\frac{(x + h)^n - x^n}{h}.$$

6. Let $A(n) = \left(1 + \dfrac{1}{n}\right)^n$. Show that

$$A(n) = \sum_{r=0}^{n} C_r^n \left(\frac{1}{n}\right)^r.$$

Calculate $A(1)$, $A(2)$, and $A(5)$.

7. Write out the indicated sum, but do not perform the addition.

(a) $\displaystyle\sum_{r=1}^{4} \frac{\sin r}{r}$

(b) $\displaystyle\sum_{r=0}^{5} \frac{x^r}{r!}$

(c) $\displaystyle\sum_{r=0}^{7} (-1)^r 2^{3-r}$

(d) $\displaystyle\sum_{r=1}^{k} \frac{(-1)^r}{r+k}$

8. Show that $(a - b)^n = \displaystyle\sum_{r=0}^{n} (-1)^r C_r^n\, a^{n-r} b^r$

9. $\dfrac{\displaystyle\sum_{r=0}^{10} C_r^{10}\, 2^{10-r} 3^r}{\displaystyle\sum_{r=0}^{8} C_r^8\, 3^{8-r} 2^r} = ?$

10. Solve for x:

(a) $\displaystyle\sum_{r=0}^{7} C_r^7\, x^{7-r} 3^r = 0$

(b) $\displaystyle\sum_{r=0}^{10} C_r^{10}\, x^r = 0$

72 PROBABILITY

If a person draws a card from a standard bridge deck of 52 cards, what are his chances of turning up an ace? What are his chances of drawing the ace of spades? Questions of this kind involve the theory of probability, which we will discuss in the next few sections.

When we analyze the questions posed in the first paragraph, we note that there are 52 possible cards from which to choose, and that there seems to be no reason to assume that any one card is more likely to be drawn than any other. We shall say that the drawing of a card is a **trial** that can result in one of 52 **equally likely outcomes**. If we are interested in the probability of drawing an ace from a deck of cards, we call the drawing of an ace a **success,** and the drawing of any other card a **failure.** Since there are 52 equally likely possible outcomes, of which only 4 are successes, it seems reasonable to say that the chances of drawing an ace are 4 in 52. This relationship is usually expressed in ratio form by saying, "The probability of drawing an ace is $\frac{4}{52} = \frac{1}{13}$." To compute the probability of drawing the ace of spades from a deck of cards, we note that there is only one way of achieving success, so the probability of success is $\frac{1}{52}$. These notions are formalized in the following definition.

DEFINITION 72-1. *If a trial can result in one of n equally likely outcomes, among which s are considered as successes and the rest failures, then the* **probability** *of success is* $p = s/n$.

EXAMPLE 72-1. What is the probability of making a 3 in one throw of a die?

Solution. Throwing a die can result in six possible numbers, all of which, we suppose, are equally likely. Since there is only one possible success, the probability of making a 3 is $\frac{1}{6}$.

EXAMPLE 72-2. What is the probability of making a 7 in one throw of a pair of dice?

Solution. We first count the number of possible outcomes. Each number that can turn up on one die can be paired with the six possible numbers that can turn up on the other, giving a total of 36 possible outcomes. (Note: There are not 36 possible *sums.*) Now we count the ways in which a 7 can be made. The combinations that add up to 7 are (1, 6), (2, 5), (3, 4), (4, 3), (5, 2), and (6, 1), so there are six possible ways of making a 7. The probability of making a 7 is therefore $p = \frac{6}{36} = \frac{1}{6}$.

If all the n possible outcomes of a trial are considered successes $(s = n)$, then the probability of success is $p = n/n = 1$; while if all the outcomes are failures, the probability of success is $p = 0/n = 0$. Thus, *a probability of 1 indicates certain success, while a probability of 0 indicates certain failure.* If s of n possible outcomes are successes and the rest are failures, then the number of failures is $n - s$. The probability q of failure is $q = (n - s)/n = 1 - s/n = 1 - p$. Hence, *the probability of failure is 1 minus the probability of success*, and *the probability of success is 1 minus the probability of failure.*

EXAMPLE 72-3.   What is the probability of making a 1, 2, 3, 4, or 5 in a throw of one die?

Solution.   Since there is only one possible outcome that is a failure, the probability q of failure is $q = \frac{1}{6}$.   Thus, the probability of success is $p = 1 - q = \frac{5}{6}$.

To calculate probabilities from Definition 72-1, we need to know the number of possible outcomes and the number of possible successes.   We shall find our previous study of combinations useful in this connection.

EXAMPLE 72-4.   What is the probability of being dealt a five-card poker hand containing all spades?

Solution.   There are C_5^{52} possible five-card poker hands.   We can form C_5^{13} five-card hands from the 13 spades.   Hence, the probability of being dealt a hand containing five spades is

$$p = \frac{C_5^{13}}{C_5^{52}} = \frac{13!\,5!\,47!}{8!\,5!\,52!} = .004952.$$

The **expectation** of winning any prize is defined as the value of the prize times the probability of winning it.   If n possible outcomes of a game have occurrence probabilities of $p_1, p_2, \ldots, p_n$ (where $\sum_{r=1}^{n} p_r = 1$), and if the amounts to be paid on the corresponding outcomes are $A_1, A_2, \ldots, A_n$, then the **total expectation,** or the **expectation of the game,** is

$$E = \sum_{r=1}^{n} p_r A_r = p_1 A_1 + p_2 A_2 + \ldots + p_n A_n.$$

EXAMPLE 72-5.   There are three one-dollar bills and two five-dollar bills in a box.   You are allowed to draw one bill and keep it.   What is the expectation of this game?   (This amount might be considered the price you should pay for the privilege of playing.)

Solution. The probability of drawing a one-dollar bill is $\frac{3}{5}$, and the probability of drawing a five-dollar bill is $\frac{2}{5}$. Thus the total expectation is

$$E = (\tfrac{3}{5})(1.00) + (\tfrac{2}{5})(5.00) = 2.60.$$

The examples in this section and the following sections are mostly concerned with cards, dice, or the random selection of an object from a box. These examples were chosen not primarily for their practical importance, but rather because it is easy to agree in these situations that certain outcomes are equally likely, and the possible outcomes of a trial can be precisely counted. But we can't calculate the probability of your passing this course by counting the different grades it is possible for you to receive, because it is clear that the different grades are not equally likely. In many scientific applications of probability this type of complication (among others) occurs, and it is necessary to use more refined techniques to arrive at some solution. When we use the phrase "number of outcomes" in this book, assume that it means "number of equally likely outcomes."

Problems 72

1. What is the probability that the sum 11 will appear in a single throw of 2 dice?

2. A box contains 7 red, 5 white, and 4 black balls. What is the probability of your drawing at random one red ball? One black ball?

3. A committee of 4 people is to be selected at random from a group of 7 women and 13 men. What is the probability that the committee will consist of 2 men and 2 women?

4. What is the probability of your being dealt a bridge hand (13 cards) that consists of all honor cards (A, K, Q, J or 10's)?

5. A card is drawn from a deck. What is the probability that it will be a black face card (K, Q, or J)?

6. A box contains 7 red, 5 white, and 4 black balls. What is the probability of your drawing at random 2 white balls?

7. What is the probability of your throwing a sum less than 5 in a single roll of a pair of dice? What is the expectation of the game if a person wins $2 for throwing a sum less than 5 and $1 for any other sum?

8. A bag contains ten slips that are numbered from 1 to 10. If you draw a number divisible by 3, you win $3. If the number you pick is

divisible by 5, then you win $5. Otherwise you win nothing. What is the expectation of the game?

9. One card is drawn from a deck. What is the probability that it is either a king or queen? What is the probability that it is neither a king nor a queen?

10. A coin is tossed 3 times. What is the probability of its coming up heads 3 times? What is the probability of tossing at least one tail?

11. What is the probability that a sum less than 7 will appear in a single throw of 2 dice? What is the probability that a sum of 13 will appear?

12. In poker, what is the probability of being dealt
 (a) a royal flush (ace, king, queen, jack, ten of the same suit)?
 (b) a straight flush (five cards in numerical sequence of the same suit, but not a royal flush)?
 (c) a flush (five cards in the same suit but not a straight or royal flush)?

73 COMBINED PROBABILITIES

We know (Example 72-2) that the probability of making a 7 in a single throw of a pair of dice is $\frac{1}{6}$. Similarly, we can calculate that the probability of making an 11 is $\frac{1}{18}$. In this section we will learn how we can use this information to answer such questions as, "What is the probability of making a 7 followed by an 11 in two throws of a pair of dice?" and "What is the probability of making a 7 or an 11 in a single throw?"

To find the probability of making a 7 followed by an 11 we must divide the number of ways of achieving this result by the number of ways a pair of dice may turn up in two throws. Now there are six ways of making 7 on the first throw and two ways of making 11 on the second. From the Fundamental Principle of Section 67 we see that there are therefore $6 \cdot 2$ ways of making a 7 followed by an 11; that is, there are $6 \cdot 2$ ways of achieving success. Since there are 36 equally likely outcomes to a throw of a pair of dice, we have, again by the Fundamental Principle, $36 \cdot 36$ equally likely possible outcomes of two successive throws. Hence, the probability of making a 7 followed by an 11 is $\dfrac{6 \cdot 2}{36 \cdot 36} = \dfrac{1}{6} \cdot \dfrac{1}{18} = \dfrac{1}{108}$. We now observe that this probability could have been calculated directly by simply multiplying the probabilities of making a 7 and of making an 11. This example illustrates a general theorem.

THEOREM 73-1. *If the probability of success in one trial is p_1, and if, after this trial has been successful, the probability of success in a second trial is p_2, then the probability of successful outcomes in both trials is p_1p_2.*

Proof. If n_1 is the number of equally likely possible outcomes of the first trial, and s_1 is the number of possible successes, then $p_1 = s_1/n_1$. If n_2 is the number of equally likely possible outcomes of the second trial after the first has occurred, and s_2 is the number of possible successes after the first trial has succeeded, then $p_2 = s_2/n_2$. Now according to the Fundamental Principle of Section 67, the number of possible outcomes of the two successive trials is n_1n_2, and the number of successes is s_1s_2. Hence, the probability of two successful outcomes is $p = s_1s_2/n_1n_2 = p_1p_2$.

Note that our definition of what constitutes "success" may be different in the two trials. For example, we might say that a 7 on the first throw is a success, while an 11 is necessary to make the second throw successful. Theorem 73-1 may easily be extended to cases involving more than two trials.

EXAMPLE 73-1. What is the probability of drawing in succession the A, K, and Q of spades from a standard deck of cards, if we assume that the cards are not replaced in the deck after they have been drawn?

Solution. The probability of drawing the ace of spades is $\frac{1}{52}$. After the ace has been drawn, there are 51 cards left, so the probability of drawing the king of spades is $\frac{1}{51}$. Similarly, after the first two trials have been successful, the probability of drawing the queen of spades is $\frac{1}{50}$. Theorem 73-1 then tells us that the probability of drawing the three cards in the order stated is $(\frac{1}{52})(\frac{1}{51})(\frac{1}{50})$.

EXAMPLE 73-2. A box contains 5 red, 7 white, and 8 black balls. What is the probability of drawing a red ball and then a white ball if (i) the first ball drawn is not replaced in the box, or (ii) the first ball drawn is replaced?

Solution. The probability of drawing a red ball is $\frac{5}{20} = \frac{1}{4}$ in either case. After a red ball is drawn, the probability of drawing a white ball is $\frac{7}{19}$ in the first case and $\frac{7}{20}$ in the second case. Thus, the probability of drawing a red and then a white ball is $\frac{7}{76}$ in the first case and $\frac{7}{80}$ in the second case.

Now let's examine the probability of making *either* a 7 *or* an 11 in a single throw of a pair of dice. Here, a successful outcome can be one of 2 types, either the spots on the dice add up to 7 or to 11. To count the total number of ways of succeeding, we need only count the number of ways of making a 7 and the number of ways of making an 11 and add them. We find that there are 6 + 2 ways in which a successful throw can occur. Since there are 36 possible ways a pair of dice may fall, the probability of making a 7 or an 11 is $(6 + 2)/36 = \frac{6}{36} + \frac{2}{36} = \frac{1}{6} + \frac{1}{18} = \frac{2}{9}$. Thus, the probability of making a 7 or an 11 is the sum of the probabilities of making either one.

Suppose we now consider a problem that sounds much the same as the preceding one. "If we draw a single card from a standard bridge deck, what is the probability that it will be *either* an ace *or* a spade?" Here again, a successful outcome will be one of two types, and we must count the number of possible successes. There are four ways of drawing an ace and 13 ways of drawing a spade, but there are not 4 + 13 ways of drawing an ace or a spade. If we simply add 4 and 13, it means that we are counting the drawing of the ace of spades twice. There are only 16 ways of achieving a successful result and hence the probability of drawing an ace or a spade from a standard deck of 52 cards is $\frac{16}{52} = \frac{4}{13}$.

We use the following definition to distinguish between the situations illustrated by the preceding two examples.

DEFINITION 73-1. *If the successful outcomes of a given trial are grouped into a number of types in such a way that each success is of just one type, then we have grouped the successes into* **mutually exclusive types.**

In computing the probability of making either a 7 or an 11 in a single throw of a pair of dice, the successful outcomes can be grouped into two types: making a 7 and making an 11. These types of outcomes are mutually exclusive for if we throw an 11, we can't very well throw a 7, too. In computing the probability of drawing a spade or an ace, we can group the successful outcomes into two types:

drawing a spade and drawing an ace.   But these types of outcomes are not mutually exclusive because we could pick the spade ace at one draw.   Of course, it is possible to group the successful outcomes in more than one way.   In particular, the successful outcomes of drawing a spade or an ace can be grouped into the following mutually exclusive types: drawing a spade and drawing a non-spade ace.

We will now prove a theorem that concerns the probability of success when the successful outcomes are grouped into mutually exclusive types.

THEOREM 73-2.   *If the successful outcomes of a given trial are grouped into two mutually exclusive types, and if the probability of a success of one type is p_1 and the probability of a success of the other type is p_2, then the probability of a successful outcome of the trial is $p_1 + p_2$.*

Proof.   If there are n possible outcomes of the trial, s_1 of which are successes of one type and s_2 of which are successes of the other type, then the total number of successes is $s_1 + s_2$.   The probability that the trial will be successful then is $p = (s_1 + s_2)/n = s_1/n + s_2/n = p_1 + p_2$.   (Where did we utilize the fact that the types were mutually exclusive?)

It is easy to extend Theorem 73-2 to cases in which the successful outcomes are grouped into more than two mutually exclusive types.

EXAMPLE 73-3.   What is the probability of making a 7 followed by an 11 or two consecutive 7's in two throws of a pair of dice?

Solution.   We have already seen that the probability of making a 7 followed by an 11 is $(\frac{1}{6})(\frac{1}{18})$, and according to Theorem 73-1, the probability of 2 consecutive 7's is $(\frac{1}{6})(\frac{1}{6})$.   Hence, we can use Theorem 73-2 to find that the probability of one or the other of these successes is $(\frac{1}{6})(\frac{1}{18}) + (\frac{1}{6})(\frac{1}{6}) = \frac{1}{27}$.

The next example illustrates how we can use various methods to solve a probability problem.

EXAMPLE 73-4.   What is the probability of throwing a 7 at least once in two throws of a pair of dice?

Solution 1.   The successful outcomes of the trial consisting of two throws of a pair of dice can be grouped into the following *two* mutually exclusive types. We could make 7 on the first throw, or fail to make 7 on the first throw and make it on the second throw. The probability of making a 7 on any given throw is $\frac{1}{6}$. The probability of failing to make a 7 on any given throw is $\frac{5}{6}$, so the probability of throwing a non-seven followed by a 7 is $(\frac{5}{6})(\frac{1}{6}) = \frac{5}{36}$. The probability of making a 7 at least once is therefore $\frac{1}{6} + \frac{5}{36} = \frac{11}{36}$.

Solution 2. We might also consider the following *three* mutually exclusive types of successes: making a 7 on the first throw and a non-seven on the second, a non-seven on the first throw followed by a 7 on the second, or a 7 on both throws. The probabilities of these successes are $(\frac{1}{6})(\frac{5}{6})$, $(\frac{5}{6})(\frac{1}{6})$, and $(\frac{1}{6})(\frac{1}{6})$ respectively, so the probability of making a 7 at least once is $\frac{5}{36} + \frac{5}{36} + \frac{1}{36} = \frac{11}{36}$.

Solution 3. The probability of *not* making a 7 in two successive throws is $(\frac{5}{6})(\frac{5}{6})$. Hence, the probability of throwing at least one 7 is $1 - \frac{25}{36} = \frac{11}{36}$.

Problems 73

1. A coin is tossed twice. What is the probability that
   (a) a head will come up on the first toss and a tail on the second?
   (b) a tail will come up on the first toss and a head on the second?
   (c) one head and one tail will come up on the two tosses?

2. A pair of dice is thrown twice. What is the probability that
   (a) two 8's will fall?
   (b) two 10's will fall?
   (c) two 8's or two 10's will fall?
   (d) either an 8 or a 10 will fall on both throws?

3. A box contains 5 red, 6 white, and 9 black balls. Two balls are selected at random—that is, successively without being replaced in the box. What is the probability that
   (a) both balls will be red?
   (b) both balls will be of the same color?
   (c) at least one black ball will be drawn?
   (d) the balls will be of different color?

4. Two boxes each contain 6 red poker chips and 4 white poker chips. One chip is selected at random from the first box and placed in the second. What is the probability that
   (a) a chip selected at random from the second box will be white?
   (b) two chips selected at random from the second box will both be red?

5. How many pairs of dice must be thrown simultaneously in order that the probability of making a 2 on at least one of the pairs will be greater than $\frac{1}{2}$? How many times must you throw one pair of dice in order that the probability of making a 2 on the next throw will be greater than $\frac{1}{2}$?

6. What is the probability of throwing either a 7 or an 11 on 5 successive throws of a pair of dice?

7. Two boxes each contain a certain number of bills. You can select a box at random and select a bill at random. What is the mathematical expectation of the game if
   (a) one box contains three $10 bills and one $5 bill, and the second box contains three $5 bills and one $1 bill?
   (b) one box contains three $10 bills and one $1 bill, and the second box contains four $5 bills?
   (c) one box contains three $10 bills and three $5 bills, and the second box contains one $5 bill and one $1 bill?

8. You draw two cards from a deck of cards. You win $1 if they are of the same color, $5 if they are of the same suit, and $10 if they are of the same denomination. (Two black 5's pay a total of $11.) What is the mathematical expectation of the game?

9. A box contains 4 red and 6 white balls. One ball is drawn from the box and replaced by a white ball. Then two more balls are drawn. What is the probability that the second drawing will produce two balls of the same color?

10. Four recruits whose shoe sizes are 7, 8, 9, and 10 report to the supply clerk to be issued shoes. The supply clerk selects one pair of shoes of each of the four required sizes and hands them at random to the men. What is the probability that
    (a) no man will receive the correct size?
    (b) exactly 2 men will receive the correct size?
    (c) exactly 3 men will receive the correct size?
    (d) each man will receive the correct size?

74   THE BINOMIAL DISTRIBUTION

In this section we shall be concerned with a number of independent trials—for example, tossing a coin ten times. Two trials are called **independent** if the outcome of one does not affect the outcome of the other. For example, in two successive throws of a die, it is clear that the outcome of one roll does not affect the outcome of the following roll. If a dozen dice are thrown, the particular number that appears on one die has no effect on the number appearing on any other die. Thus, successive rolls of a die, or simultaneous throws of several dice, are independent trials. In this section we shall be concerned with the probability of obtaining exactly r successes in n independent trials.

EXAMPLE 74-1. What is the probability of making exactly three 7's in five throws of a pair of dice?

Solution. An example of a successful sequence of throws is three consecutive 7's followed by two non-seven's. We will label this sequence $(7, 7, 7, -, -)$. Other successful sequences are $(7, -, 7, -, 7)$, $(-, 7, -, 7, 7)$, and so on. Now let's count the number of possible successful sequences. We can make a successful sequence by replacing three blanks in the array $(-, -, -, -, -)$ with 7's—that is, by choosing three places out of five to be labeled "7." Since there are C_3^5 ways of choosing three things from among five, it follows that there are $C_3^5 = 10$ possible successful sequences. If p denotes the probability of making a 7 in one throw of a pair of dice, and if $q = 1 - p$ denotes the probability of failing to throw a 7, then the probability that any particular successful sequence will occur is p^3q^2.

For example, the probability of obtaining the sequence $(7, -, 7, 7, -)$ is $pqppq = p^3q^2$. There are ten different successful sequences and the probability of obtaining each is p^3q^2. Since the different types of successful sequences are mutually exclusive, the probability of obtaining a successful sequence is the sum of the probabilities of each type of success. The probability of making exactly three 7's in five throws is therefore

$$p_3 = \underbrace{p^3q^2 + p^3q^2 + \ldots + p^3q^2}_{10 \text{ terms}} = 10\,p^3q^2 = C_3^5\,p^3q^2.$$

We know that p, the probability of making a 7 in one throw of a pair of dice, is $\frac{1}{6}$. Hence, $q = \frac{5}{6}$, and $p_3 = 10(\frac{1}{6})^3(\frac{5}{6})^2 = .0322$.

The method used to solve the preceding example can be used to establish the following theorem.

THEOREM 74-1 (**The Binomial Law**). *If the probability of success in a single trial is p and if $q = 1 - p$, then the probability p_r that exactly r* *successes will occur in n independent trials is given by the formula*

74-1 $$p_r = C_r^n \, p^r q^{n-r},$$

where C_r^n is a binomial coefficient.

EXAMPLE 74-2. What is the probability of making at least two 7's in three throws of a pair of dice?

Solution.   Let p_r denote the probability of making r 7's in three throws. Since the probability p of success in a single trial is $\frac{1}{6}$, we have (Theorem 74-1)

$$p_2 = C_2^3 \, (\tfrac{1}{6})^2(\tfrac{5}{6}) = \tfrac{15}{216}$$

and

$$p_3 = C_3^3 \, (\tfrac{1}{6})^3(\tfrac{5}{6})^0 = \tfrac{1}{216}.$$

We want to find the probability of making *at least* two 7's in three throws—that is, the probability of making exactly two 7's or exactly three 7's.   Thus, the required probability is

$$p_2 + p_3 = \tfrac{16}{216} = \tfrac{2}{27} = .0741.$$

Suppose we throw a die and consider it a successful throw if a 1 or a 2 turns up.   The probability of success is clearly $p = \frac{1}{3}$.   Now suppose we throw a dozen dice and consider the number of 1's or 2's that occur.   If p_r denotes the probability that exactly r dice will turn up a 1 or a 2, the Binomial Law states that $p_r = C_r^{12} \, (\frac{1}{3})^r(\frac{2}{3})^{12-r}$. A table giving p_r for $0 \leq r \leq 12$ follows.

r	p_r	r	p_r	r	p_r
0	.0077	5	.1907	9	.0033
1	.0462	6	.1112	10	.0005
2	.1272	7	.0477	11	.0000
3	.2119	8	.0149	12	.0000
4	.2384			Total	.9997

The last two entries are 0 to four decimal places.

As r increases from 0 to 4, the numbers p_r in the table also increase. As r increases from 4 to 12, the numbers p_r decrease.   The **most likely number of successes** is 4.   To find the most likely number of successes for any binomial distribution, we must find the largest probability p_r. According to Theorem 74-1,

$$\frac{p_{r+1}}{p_r} = \frac{C_{r+1}^n p^{r+1} q^{n-r-1}}{C_r^n p^r q^{n-r}} = \frac{C_{r+1}^n p}{C_r^n q}.$$

Using Equation 71-3 to simplify the right-hand side of this last equation, we get

$$\frac{p_{r+1}}{p_r} = \frac{(n-r)p}{(r+1)q}.$$

Therefore,

$$\frac{p_{r+1}}{p_r} > 1 \quad \text{if} \quad \frac{(n-r)p}{(r+1)q} > 1.$$

In other words,

$$p_{r+1} > p_r \quad \text{if} \quad np - rp > rq + q.$$

We can simplify the inequality on the right by using the fact that $p + q = 1$ to find that

74-2   if $(n+1)p > r+1$, then $p_{r+1} > p_r$.

Similarly,

74-3   if $(n+1)p < r+1$, then $p_{r+1} < p_r$.

Using these inequalities, we can easily prove the following theorem.

THEOREM 74-2. *Let p be the probability of success in a single trial, and let n be the number of trials. If $(n + 1)p$ is not an integer, then the most likely number of successes is $[(n + 1)p]$.*

Proof. Let $m = [(n+1)p]$. Then

$$m < (n+1)p < m+1.$$

If r is any integer such that $0 \leq r < m$, then

$$r+1 \leq m < (n+1)p$$

and according to Inequality 74-2, $p_r < p_{r+1}$. Thus, by choosing $r = 0, 1, 2, \ldots, m - 1$, we see that the following inequalities are valid:

74-4 $p_0 < p_1 < \ldots < p_{m-1} < p_m$.

If r is an integer such that $m \leq r \leq n$, then

$$r + 1 \geq m + 1 > (n + 1)p,$$

and according to Inequalities 74-3, $p_{r+1} < p_r$. If we let $r = m$, $m + 1, \ldots, n - 1$, we find that the following inequalities are valid:

74-5 $p_m > p_{m+1} > \ldots > p_n.$

From Inequalities 74-4 and 74-5, we conclude that m is the most likely number of successes.

If we use Theorem 74-2 with the data in the table on p. 327, we see that $(n + 1)p = \frac{13}{3}$, and $[(n + 1)p] = [\frac{13}{3}] = 4$. Thus, the most likely number of successes as calculated by the formula in Theorem 74-2 is the same as the number that was found from the table on p. 327.

If the number $(n + 1)p$ is an integer, Theorem 74-2 does not apply. By reasoning as we did in the proof of Theorem 74-2, we can show that *if $(n + 1)p$ is an integer m, then the numbers $m - 1$ and m are the two most likely numbers of successes, and $p_{m-1} = p_m$.* We leave the proof of this statement for the problems.

You should not get the impression that if m is the most likely number of successes, then the probability p_m is large. It can be shown by more advanced methods that even though p_m is the largest probability of a binomial distribution, p_m is very small if the number of trials n is very large.

> EXAMPLE 74-3.   Suppose a box contains 4 red balls and 1 white ball. A trial consists of drawing a ball and then replacing it in the box and the trial is a success if the ball that is drawn is white. In 100 trials, what is the most likely number of successes and what is the probability of obtaining the most likely number of successes?
>
> *Solution.*   The number of trials is $n = 100$; the probability of success is $p = \frac{1}{5}$. Thus $(n + 1)p = \frac{101}{5}$ and according to Theorem 74-2, the most likely number of successes is $[\frac{101}{5}] = 20$. According to Equation 74-1,
>
> $$p_{20} = C^{100}_{20} \left(\tfrac{1}{5}\right)^{20}\left(\tfrac{4}{5}\right)^{80}.$$
>
> If we use logarithms and Tables I and IV (pp. 393-394, 400) we find that $p_{20} = .0994$. Thus, even though the most likely number of successes is 20, the chances are less than 1 in 10 of having exactly 20 successes.

Problems 74

1. A trial consists of drawing a card from a deck and discarding it, and is a success if an ace is drawn. Can you use Equation 74-1 to calculate the probability of obtaining exactly 1 success in 4 trials?

2. A coin is tossed 10 times.
   (a) What is the probability that exactly 5 tosses will come up heads?
   (b) What is the probability that at least 5 heads will turn up?
   (c) How many heads are most likely to turn up?

3. If you throw 12 dice, how many would most likely turn up 1? What is the probability that exactly this many would be 1?

4. Using the data in the table on p. 327, we find that the most likely number of successes is 4. What is the probability of 3, 4, or 5 successes?

5. A box contains 10 white and 3 red balls. A trial consists of drawing two balls and then replacing them in the box. What is the most likely number of successes in 10 trials if a trial is called a success when
   (a) both balls are white?
   (b) the balls are of different color?
   (c) both balls are of the same color?

6. Three cards are drawn from a deck and then replaced. What is the most likely number of times that 3 cards of the same suit will be drawn if 100 drawings are made? What is the probability of obtaining this most likely number?

7. A pair of dice is thrown. You win if a 7 or an 11 appears. You lose if a 2 or a 12 appears, and if any other number appears, the throw is a draw. If the dice are thrown 20 times, what is the most likely number of times that
   (a) you will win?
   (b) you will either win or lose?

8. A man offers to bet you even money that when throwing a pair of dice he will throw a 7 before the sixth roll. Should you take the bet?

9. A die is thrown 6 times. Define the function f by the statement: $f(x)$ is the probability that the number 1 will occur x times. What is the domain of f? Draw a graph of f. Calculate $\sum\limits_{r=0}^{2} f(r)$.

10. A coin is tossed 15 times. Define the function p by the statement: $p(x)$ is the probability that x of the tosses will come up heads. For what values of x is $p(x)$ a maximum? What is this maximum value? Compute $\sum\limits_{r=6}^{9} p(r)$.

$$\cos t = x \qquad \sec t = \frac{1}{x} \qquad \tan t = \frac{y}{x}$$

$$\sin t = y \qquad \csc t = \frac{1}{y} \qquad \cot t = \frac{x}{y}$$

$$\cos^2 t + \sin^2 t = 1$$

$$\tan t = \frac{\sin t}{\cos t} \qquad \cot t = \frac{1}{\tan t} \qquad \csc t = \frac{1}{\sin t}$$

$$\cot t = \frac{\cos t}{\sin t} \qquad \qquad \sec t = \frac{1}{\cos t} \qquad \text{elementary Identities}$$

$$\tan^2 t + 1 = \sec^2 t \qquad \qquad \cos^2(t) + \sin^2(t) = 1$$

1. $\cos(u \mp v) = \cos u \cos v \pm \sin u \sin v$

2. $\cos\left(\frac{\pi}{2} - u\right) = \sin u$

3. $\cos(u) = \sin\left(\frac{\pi}{2} - u\right)$

4. $\sin(-u) = -\sin(u)$

5. $\cos(-u) = \cos(u)$

6. $\sin(u \pm v) = \sin u \cos v \pm \cos u \sin v$

7. $\sin(2t) = 2\sin(t)\cos(t)$

8. $\cos(2u) = \cos^2 u - \sin^2 u$

$$= 1 - 2\sin^2 u$$

$$= 2\cos^2 u - 1$$

9. $\tan(u+v) \quad \dfrac{\tan u + \tan v}{1 - \tan u \tan v}$

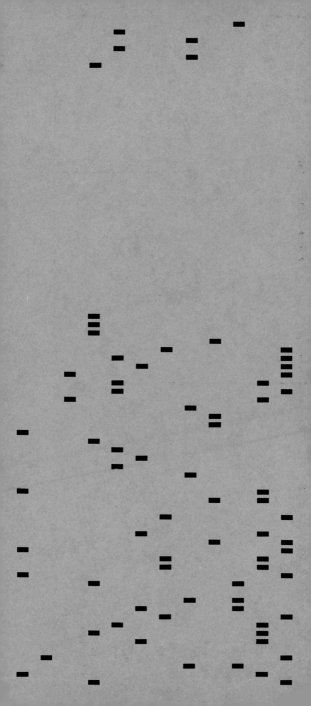

MONCUS WILLIAM C JR

MONCUS WILLIAM C JR   625250
STUDENT NAME   ALPHA NUMBER
PENG 254/56,9112 DEC 16 66 FRSH
PROGRAM OF STUDY SOCIAL SECURITY NUMBER THIS CARD EXPIRES CLASS

KENNESAW JUNIOR COLLEGE, MARIETTA, GEORGIA

IDENTIFICATION CARD

THIS IS A RECEIPT FOR PAYMENT OF FEES

CASHIER'S STAMP

PAID
No. 3
SEP 26 1966
KENNESAW
JR. COLLEGE

VALID ONLY WHEN OFFICIALLY STAMPED

↑ SIGN YOUR NAME HERE
SIGNATURE

CUT ON HEAVY LINES TO FIT WALLET

YOU HAVE JUST RECEIVED A FEE CARD AND AN I.D. CARD.
TAKE THESE CARDS AND YOUR COURSE SCHEDULE TO THE
CASHIER'S STATION. YOUR PAYMENT OF FEES SHOULD BE
IN THE EXACT AMOUNT DUE THE COLLEGE. WE URGE
YOU TO USE CHECK OR MONEY ORDER. PAYMENT OF FEES
BY CASH WILL BE AT YOUR OWN RISK. CHECKS SHOULD
BE MADE PAYABLE TO KENNESAW JUNIOR COLLEGE.

YOU MAY PICK UP YOUR I.D. CARD IN THE REGISTRAR'S
OFFICE APPROXIMATELY THREE (3) DAYS AFTER REGIS-
TRATION.

FINAL TERM GRADES WILL BE POSTED AT THE CLOSE
OF EACH QUARTER IN THE DIVISION IN WHICH THE
COURSE IS TAUGHT. YOUR NAME WILL NOT BE SHOWN
ON THE POSTED LIST OF GRADES. HOWEVER, YOU CAN
IDENTIFY YOUR GRADE BY MEANS OF YOUR ALPHA NUM-
BER, WHICH IS PRINTED AT THE TOP OF YOUR I.D. CARD.

LATE PENALTY FEES WILL APPLY AFTER 5:00 P.M.,
ON THE DAY FOLLOWING REGISTRATION.

HACKETT GROUP

11. Let p be the probability of success in a single trial and let n be the number of independent trials. If $(n + 1)p$ is an integer m, show that the numbers m and $m - 1$ are the most likely numbers of successes and that $p_m = p_{m-1}$.

75 EMPIRICAL PROBABILITY

As we said earlier, we have confined our examples of probability to situations in which most people would probably agree that certain outcomes are "equally likely." It seems clear that the probability of throwing a 1 in a single throw of a die is $\frac{1}{6}$, that the probability of drawing the ace of spades from a deck of cards is $\frac{1}{52}$, and so on. These are examples of what statisticians call *a priori* **probability.** But there are situations in which it is not possible to determine the probability of success by finding the ratio of the number of possible successful outcomes to the number of equally likely outcomes. In such situations the determination of the probability of an outcome is found experimentally. A probability that is found experimentally is called an **empirical probability.**

In order to determine an empirical probability of a certain outcome, we make a frequency count. Let us suppose that we are given a die so obviously imperfect that we doubt that the probability of throwing a 3, for example, is $\frac{1}{6}$. In order to determine the probability that a 3 will occur, we make a number of throws, say N of them. If S denotes the number of times that a 3 appears, then we take the empirical probability of a 3 appearing to be S/N. For example, if a 3 appeared 30 times in 100 throws, then the empirical probability would be $\frac{3}{10}$. Of course, the confidence we place in this probability depends a great deal on the number N. If N were 20, it is doubtful that the result would be at all reliable, but if N were 100,000, then we would expect the ratio S/N to represent rather accurately the probability of a 3 occurring. Essentially, the process of finding the empirical probability of a particular outcome by making frequency counts is an attempt to predict future behavior by past performance. The more information we possess about the history of a trial, the surer we feel about our predictions concerning the future outcome of this trial.

EXAMPLE 75-1.   In May, Bill Clout was batting .333 for the Columbus Jets baseball team.   What is the probability that he will get at least one hit in four official appearances at the plate?

Solution.   We take the probability of Clout's getting a hit in one official appearance as $\frac{1}{3}$.   The probability of his failing to hit is therefore $\frac{2}{3}$, and hence the probability of his failing to hit in four consecutive appearances is $(\frac{2}{3})^4 = \frac{16}{81}$.   The probability of his getting at least one hit is thus $1 - \frac{16}{81} = \frac{65}{81} = .802$.

There are two things we should note in Example 75-1.   First, even though Clout is averaging one hit in three times at the plate, we do not conclude that he will surely get at least one hit in four appearances.   We only say that he probably will, and we are about .8 sure.   Second, we would feel more confident about this figure if our observations had been made near the end of the season when Clout has been at bat many times, rather than during the opening weeks of the season when he had batted only a few times.

To illustrate further the necessity for being careful in making predictions about empirical probability, let us consider the following situation.   Suppose we have a die that we suspect, but do not know, is weighted so as to make a 1 or a 2 appear more often than these numbers would on a true die.   To test this hypothesis, we throw the die 12 times and note the number of times that a 1 or a 2 appears.   Suppose there are seven times on which a 1 or a 2 appears.   Now what conclusion can we draw?   Since the probability of making a 1 or a 2 is $\frac{1}{3}$, we might say that there should be only four appearances of a 1 or a 2 and hence 7 appearances "prove" that the die is weighted.   However, let us consult the table on p. 327, which shows the probability of making a 1 or a 2 exactly r times in 12 throws when the die is "perfect."   From the table, we see that the probability that there are seven times in which either a 1 or a 2 appears is .0477.   (Note that the probability of four appearances is only .2384.)   Now we must make a decision.   Is the occurrence of seven successes sufficiently rare to justify our making any conclusion or not?   This type of problem is an important one which is extensively treated in statistics, and we will not pursue the matter further at this point.   In this particular problem, however, you might agree that the evidence is suggestive, but hardly conclusive.   Determining what is conclusive evidence in such instances is really a matter of agreement concerning the limits of variation allowed

Problems 75

1. A coin is tossed 10 times and comes up heads each time. What is the empirical probability that the coin will come up heads on the 11th toss? What is the *a priori* probability that the coin will come up heads on the 11th toss? What is the a priori probability that a coin will come up heads 10 consecutive times?

2. Suppose that birth records indicate that the number of boys and the number of girls born each year are equal. What is the probability that a family of 7 children selected at random will consist of
    (a) all boys?
    (b) exactly 4 boys?
    (c) more boys than girls?

3. A certain drug that was used to treat 1000 patients with a certain illness was found to be of benefit in 200 cases. A doctor uses the drug to treat 10 of his patients. What is the probability that
    (a) none of the patients will benefit from the use of the drug?
    (b) all the patients will benefit from the use of the drug?
    (c) more than $\frac{1}{2}$ of the patients will benefit from the use of the drug?

4. In a primary election in a certain city 4000 people register as Democrats and 3000 people register as Republicans. The day before the general election you choose 10 names from the phone book and make calls to remind them to vote. Assuming there are no Independents, what is the probability that you contact an equal number of Democrats and Republicans?

5. Suppose that the weather bureau records show that the 300 days of the month of April for the past 10 years could be grouped into 120 sunny days and 180 cloudy days or grouped into 150 warm days and 150 cold days. What is the probability that there will be no more than 1 week of cloudy weather in the month of April? What is the probability that exactly 15 days in the month of April will be warm and sunny?

6. If past records indicate that 25% of the students who enroll for a certain mathematics course do not make a passing grade, what is the probability that no students will fail in a class of 30? How many students are most likely to fail?

Review Problems, Chapter Eight

You should be able to answer the following questions without referring back to the text.

1. How many odd numbers of two digits can be formed from the digits 1, 2, 3, 4, 5?

2. Simplify: (a) $\dfrac{(n+1)!+n!}{n!}$ (b) $\dfrac{(n+1)!-n!}{n}$

3. A **diagonal** of a polygon is a line that joins 2 non-adjacent vertices. How many diagonals does a pentagon have? How many diagonals does an n-sided polygon have?

4. How many different 7-digit numbers can be formed from the digits 1, 2, and 3? How many of these numbers are greater than 3,000,000?

5. How many distinguishable permutations of the letters in the words BEER BOTTLE can be formed? How many of them start with B? How many of them contain the word BEER (for example, TOBEERLTEB)?

6. Find the 5th term of the expansion $(a^2 - \frac{1}{2}x)^9$.

7. An instructor with a class of 40 students calls on 5 students chosen at random every day for recitation. What is the probability that an unprepared student will escape detection for 5 consecutive days?

8. Compute: $\displaystyle\sum_{r=0}^{5} C_r^5\, 2^r$.

9. Suppose you are playing a game in which you draw a card from a deck and are paid nothing if it is an ace or a face card. Otherwise you are paid the same number of dollars as the denomination of the card. What is the expectation of the game?

10. A baby has 11 letter blocks that consist of 4 S's, 4 I's, 2 P's, and 1 M. The baby places the blocks all in a row and all right side up. What is the probability that he will spell the word MISSISSIPPI? If he selects 3 blocks and places them right side up in a row, what is the probability that he will spell the word IMP?

11. An examination of medical records reveals that the mortality rate of a certain disease is .2. A doctor is treating 6 patients with this disease. How many patients are most likely to survive? What is the probability that less than half of his patients will survive?

12. Jack has 3 coins and Jill has 4 coins. They both toss all their coins and whoever gets the greatest number of heads wins. If each gets the same number of heads, Jack will win. What is the probability that Jill will win?

Miscellaneous Problems, Chapter Eight

These exercises are designed to test your ability to apply your knowledge of permutations, combinations, the Binomial Theorem, and probability to somewhat more difficult problems.

1. If k and n are positive integers, solve the following equation for k and n:
$$kC_2^n = C_2^{2n}.$$

2. Show that $C_r^n \left(\dfrac{1}{n}\right)^r \leq \dfrac{1}{r!}$ and hence that

$$\left(1 + \frac{1}{n}\right)^n \leq \sum_{r=0}^{n} \frac{1}{r!}.$$

3. Prove that

$$\sum_{r=0}^{n} (C_r^n)^2 = C_n^{2n}.$$

4. A deck is made up of cards that are numbered from 1 to 10 inclusive. You draw two cards from the deck at random. If the sum of the numbers on the cards you draw is even, you win \$1, and if the sum is odd, you lose \$1. Is the game fair?

5. Three boxes each contain 5 white, 3 red, and 2 blue poker chips. One chip is selected at random from the first box and placed in the second. Two chips are then selected at random from the second box and placed in the third box. Finally 3 chips are selected at random from the third box. What is the probability that all three chips will be of different color?

6. Suppose that you draw balls successively without replacing them from a box that contains 3 red and 7 white balls until you pick a red ball. How many drawings will you most likely make?

7. A pig pen is divided into 4 sections, say A, B, C, and D. In the evening the farmer places 3 black and 2 red pigs in each section. During the night 1 pig in pen A gets into pen B. Then 1 pig in pen B escapes to pen C, and in succession a pig goes from pen C to pen D and one goes from pen D to pen A. What is the probability that after this exchange the color distribution of pigs in each section will be the same as it was originally?

8. Ten rooms are numbered from 1 to 10 and connected by doorways as follows. Room 1 is connected to rooms 2 and 3; room 2 is also connected to rooms 4 and 5; room 3 is also connected to rooms 5 and 6; room 4 is connected to rooms 7 and 8; room 5 is connected to rooms 8 and 9; and room 6 is connected to rooms 9 and 10. Suppose there are 24 people in room 1 who move from room to room at random, but never go from a room with a larger number to a room with a smaller number. Where would you expect to find the people when they stopped wandering?

9. Let p_r be the probability of making r heads in 5 tosses of a coin. Define the function f by the equations

$f(x) = p_r$ if $r - \frac{1}{2} < x \leq r + \frac{1}{2}$ $(r = 0, 1, 2, 3, 4, 5)$.
Draw the graph of f. Define the function F by the statement: $F(x)$ is the probability that the number of heads made in 5 tosses is equal to or less than x. Draw the graph of F.

10. Although we have not discussed the following type of probability problem, you might think about it. If you glance at your watch, what is the probability that the second hand will be exactly at the 30-second mark? What is the probability that it will be between the 29-second mark and the 31-second mark?

11. Box A contains 3 red balls and 1 white ball. Box B contains 3 white balls and 1 red ball. A ball is selected at random from box A and placed in box B; then a ball is selected at random from box B and returned to box A. This procedure is continued until either (a) 1 box contains 4 red balls and the other box contains 4 white balls, or (b) each box contains 2 red and 2 white balls. If the game ends in situation (a), you receive \$1, and if it ends in situation (b), you receive nothing. How much should you pay to play the game?

CHAPTER NINE

SEQUENCES

You will recall from Chapter Two that a function consists of two sets of numbers: the *domain* and the *range,* and *a rule of correspondence* that assigns to each number of the domain a number of the range.   In this chapter we deal with a special class of functions called *sequences.*   A **sequence** is simply a function whose domain consists only of integers.   We could, for example, construct a sequence showing the annual traffic fatalities in the United States from 1900 to the present.   To each of the integers 1900, 1901, 1902, and so on, which represent one of the years under consideration, we assign the number of traffic fatalities that occurred in that year.   If we denote the function so defined by f, then $f(1937) = 39{,}643$; $f(1943) = 23{,}823$; and so on.

A sequence is determined if we assign a number to correspond to each integer in a certain (given) set of integers. In this chapter we shall only discuss sequences whose domain consists of the entire set of positive integers; that is, the numbers 1, 2, 3, ...

76 BASIC CONCEPTS

Sequences are a special kind of function, but the notation that we use for them is different from the notation we usually use for functions. Instead of using a symbol such as $f(n)$ to denote the number that corresponds to a given integer n, we shall use a symbol such as y_n. Thus, in a given sequence, we might use y_3 to denote the number that corresponds to 3, y_{157} to denote the number that corresponds to 157, and so forth. The numbers $y_1, y_2, \ldots$ are called the **terms** of the sequence, and we denote the entire sequence by the symbol $\{y_n\}$. The positive integers are ordered; that is, there is a first integer, a second, a third, and so on, and this ordering induces an order among the terms of a sequence $\{y_n\}$. Thus, y_1 is the first term of the sequence $\{y_n\}$, and y_{17} is the seventeenth term.

EXAMPLE 76-1. Let $\{y_n\}$ be the sequence in which $y_n = 3n - \dfrac{70}{n}$. We can write this sequence as $\left\{ 3n - \dfrac{70}{n} \right\}$. Find y_2, y_5, and y_7.

Solution. By direct substitution we obtain $y_2 = 3 \cdot 2 - \frac{70}{2} = 6 - 35 = -29$, $y_5 = 15 - 14 = 1$, and $y_7 = 21 - 10 = 11$.

One way to define a sequence $\{y_n\}$ is to write an explicit formula for y_n in terms of n. We defined the sequence in Example 76-1 by this method. Another way to define a sequence is to give the first term of the sequence and a formula that tells how to calculate any term (other than the first) if the preceding term is known. A formula of this type is called a **recursion formula,** an example of which we have already seen in connection with the binomial coefficients (Equation 71-3).

EXAMPLE 76-2. Let $\{y_n\}$ be the sequence in which $y_1 = 1$ and $y_n = 3y_{n-1} - 1$ for $n > 1$. Find the first five terms.

Solution. The equation $y_n = 3y_{n-1} - 1$ tells us that we can find the term y_n by multiplying the preceding term by 3 and subtracting 1 from the result. Since we know the first term, we can find succeeding terms one at a time. Thus,

$$y_2 = 3y_1 - 1 = 3 \cdot 1 - 1 = 2,$$

$$y_3 = 3y_2 - 1 = 3 \cdot 2 - 1 = 5,$$

$$y_4 = 3y_3 - 1 = 3 \cdot 5 - 1 = 14,$$

$$y_5 = 3y_4 - 1 = 3 \cdot 14 - 1 = 41.$$

We won't try to explain how we can arrive at a formula for y_n, but you can easily check to see that the formula

76-1
$$y_n = \frac{3^{n-1} + 1}{2}$$

does give the correct values for the four listed terms. You should also be able to show that this formula yields $y_1 = 1$ and satisfies the equation $y_n = 3y_{n-1} - 1$. "Mathematical induction" (which we shall discuss in the next section) is required to show that Formula 76-1 is the only formula for y_n such that both $y_1 = 1$ and $y_n = 3y_{n-1} - 1$.

A sequence $\{y_n\}$ is determined by a rule that assigns to each positive integer n a number y_n. You should not conclude that any sequence is defined by either an explicit formula as in Example 76-1 or by a recursion formula as in Example 76-2. A sequence may be completely determined by some statement that can't be written as an equation.

EXAMPLE 76-3. Let $\{y_n\}$ be the sequence of digits in the decimal representation of $\sin \pi/3$. Find the first few terms of this sequence.

Solution. We know that $\sin \pi/3 = \sqrt{3}/2 = .866025 \ldots$ Thus $y_1 = 8$, $y_2 = 6$, and so on. We have no formula to calculate y_n for each n, but the number y_{34}, for example, is completely determined and we could find it if we cared to.

We often associate with a sequence $\{y_n\}$ another sequence $\{S_n\}$ that is called the sequence of **partial sums** of $\{y_n\}$. The terms of the sequence $\{S_n\}$ are defined by the formula

$$S_n = \sum_{r=1}^{n} y_r = y_1 + y_2 + \ldots + y_n.$$

(See Section 71 for the meaning of the summation symbol Σ).   Thus,

$$S_1 = y_1,$$
$$S_2 = y_1 + y_2 = S_1 + y_2,$$
$$S_3 = y_1 + y_2 + y_3 = S_2 + y_3,$$

and so on.   Clearly

$$S_n = S_{n-1} + y_n.$$

We shall calculate the numbers S_n for two special types of sequences in Sections 78 and 79, and you will meet the concept of partial sums again in your work in calculus.

EXAMPLE 76-4.   Let $\{y_n\}$ be the sequence given by the formula $y_n = \dfrac{1}{n(n+1)}$.   Find the first five terms of the corresponding sequence of partial sums.

Solution.

$$S_1 = y_1 = \frac{1}{1 \cdot 2} = \tfrac{1}{2},$$

$$S_2 = S_1 + y_2 = \tfrac{1}{2} + \frac{1}{2 \cdot 3} = \tfrac{2}{3},$$

$$S_3 = S_2 + y_3 = \tfrac{2}{3} + \frac{1}{3 \cdot 4} = \tfrac{3}{4},$$

$$S_4 = S_3 + y_4 = \tfrac{3}{4} + \frac{1}{4 \cdot 5} = \tfrac{4}{5},$$

$$S_5 = S_4 + y_5 = \tfrac{4}{5} + \frac{1}{5 \cdot 6} = \tfrac{5}{6}.$$

On the basis of these results, we are strongly tempted to conclude that $S_6 = \tfrac{6}{7}$, and indeed that $S_n = \dfrac{n}{n+1}$.   It is easy to show that such a conclusion would be correct, for

$$y_n = \frac{1}{n(n+1)} = \frac{1}{n} - \frac{1}{n+1}$$

and, therefore,

$$S_n = (1 - \tfrac{1}{2}) + (\tfrac{1}{2} - \tfrac{1}{3}) + (\tfrac{1}{3} - \tfrac{1}{4}) + \ldots + \left(\frac{1}{n} - \frac{1}{n+1}\right).$$

When we remove the parentheses, the sum "collapses" to

$$S_n = 1 - \frac{1}{n+1} = \frac{n}{n+1}.$$

Problems 76

1. Is every sequence a function? Is every function a sequence?

2. Find the first 5 terms of the following sequences.

   (a) $\left\{\dfrac{3n-1}{2}\right\}$

   (b) $\{y_n\}$ if $y_n = 3(\frac{1}{2})^n$

   (c) $\left\{\dfrac{1 \cdot 3 \cdot 5 \cdot \ldots \cdot (2n-1)}{(2n)!}\right\}$

   (d) $\{y_n\}$ if $y_n = 1 - (-1)^n$

   (e) $\left\{\sin \dfrac{n\pi}{2}\right\}$

   (f) $\{y_n\}$ if $y_n = \dfrac{1}{n} \log 10^n$

3. Find the first 5 terms of the sequence $\{y_n\}$ if:

   (a) $y_1 = 3, y_n = 2y_{n-1} + 1$

   (b) $y_1 = 2, y_{n+1} = (-y_n)^{-1}$

   (c) $y_1 = 1, y_n = \frac{1}{2}ny_{n-1}$

   (d) $y_1 = 2, y_n = y_{n-1}^2$

   (e) $y_1 = 3, y_2 = 2$, and
       $y_n = \frac{1}{2}(y_{n-1} + y_{n-2})$

   (f) $y_1 = 1, y_n = n \sin\left[\dfrac{\pi}{2}(2y_{n-1} + 1)\right]$

4. Try to guess a simple formula that gives a sequence whose first 5 terms are:

   (a) $3, \frac{3}{2}, \frac{3}{4}, \frac{3}{8}, \frac{3}{16}$

   (b) $2, 5, 8, 11, 14$

   (c) $1, 3, 7, 15, 31$

   (d) $2, \dfrac{-4}{1 \cdot 2}, \dfrac{8}{1 \cdot 2 \cdot 3}, \dfrac{-16}{1 \cdot 2 \cdot 3 \cdot 4}, \dfrac{32}{1 \cdot 2 \cdot 3 \cdot 4 \cdot 5}$

5. Find S_1, S_2, S_3, and S_4, where $\{S_n\}$ is the sequence of partial sums of the sequence $\{y_n\}$, if:

   (a) $y_n = (-1)^n$

   (b) $y_n = 1 - (-1)^n$

   (c) $y_1 = 1, y_n = \dfrac{-y_{n-1}}{n(n-1)}$

   (d) $y_1 = -7, y_n = 2^n + y_{n-1}$

6. Find the first 5 terms of the sequence $\{x_n\}$ if:

   (a) $x_n = \sum_{r=1}^{n} (\frac{1}{2})^r$

   (b) $x_n = \sum_{r=1}^{n} \cos \pi r$

   (c) $x_n = \sum_{r=1}^{n} 3r$

   (d) $x_1 = 1$, and $x_n = \sum_{r=1}^{n-1} x_{n-r}$

7. After 2 min, a certain yeast plant produces 1 new plant (by budding) every min, and this new plant in turn begins producing plants at the end of 2 min at the rate of 1 per min. Starting with 1 plant, there will be 1 plant at the end of the first and second min, 2 plants at the end of 3 min, and 3 plants at the end of 4 min. How many plants are there

at the end of 7 min?   (The sequence defined in this way is the famous
Fibonacci Sequence).

8. Let y_n be the digit in the nth decimal place of the decimal expansion of $\frac{1}{7}$.
Write the first 8 terms of the sequence $\{y_n\}$ and find y_{43}.

77 MATHEMATICAL INDUCTION

To specify the sequence $\{y_n\}$ of Example 76-2 we did two things;
(i) we gave the first term and (ii) we stated a recursion formula; that
is, a rule for calculating the successor of any term.   Since y_1 was
known, we used the recursion formula to calculate its successor y_2.
After we found y_2, we calculated its successor y_3, and so on.   Clearly,
we could find any term, for example y_{123}, by proceeding step by step.
Many sequences that arise in applications of mathematics are of this
type, and we often wish to find a formula that gives the nth term y_n
in terms of n.   We usually arrive at the formula by guesswork, but
we establish the validity of the formula by the process of mathematical
induction.   The process of **mathematical induction** is based on the
following axiom.

THE INDUCTION AXIOM.   *The only sequence of numbers $\{a_n\}$ that possesses
the properties*

(i) $a_1 = 0$, *and*
(ii) *whenever $a_k = 0$, then $a_{k+1} = 0$,*

is the sequence in which every term is zero; that is, $a_n = 0$ for every n.

Reworded, the Induction Axiom states that "If the first term of a
sequence is 0, and if every term that is 0 is followed by a term that
is 0, then every term of the sequence is 0."   If a sequence possesses
properties (i) and (ii), it is easy to see, for example, that $a_3 = 0$.
For according to Property (i), $a_1 = 0$ and according to Property (ii),
every 0 term is followed by a 0 term, and hence $a_2 = 0$.   But now
we can use Property (ii) again to see that the 0 second term is followed by a 0 term, so $a_3 = 0$.   The axiom asserts that if n is any
given positive integer, we can carry out this process n times and arrive
at the conclusion that $a_n = 0$.

Beginners usually find the Induction Axiom a little subtle to apply.
It is easy to check whether or not Property (i) holds, but how
do we verify Property (ii)?   We must show that whenever $a_k = 0$,

then $a_{k+1} = 0$. To this end we *assume* that $a_k = 0$ and show that the equality $a_{k+1} = 0$ stems logically from this assumption. We do not have to *prove* that $a_k = 0$ for any k except $k = 1$. Perhaps a simple example will clear up this point.

EXAMPLE 77-1. Let $\{a_n\}$ be a sequence such that $a_1 = t$, where t is a given number, and $a_n = (a_{n-1})^2$ for $n > 1$ (that is, each term after the first is the square of the preceding term). Show that this sequence possesses Property (ii) of the Induction Axiom.

Solution. We must show that if $a_k = 0$, then $a_{k+1} = 0$. Now according to the recursion formula for the sequence, we have

$$a_{k+1} = [a_{(k+1)-1}]^2 = a_k{}^2.$$

Thus, if $a_k = 0$, then $a_{k+1} = 0^2 = 0$, and the sequence therefore possesses Property (ii) of the Induction Axiom. We have not shown that any term of the sequence is 0; we have merely shown that if the sequence contains any 0 terms, then each of them is followed by a 0 term. The value of the first term $a_1 = t$ determines whether or not this sequence consists only of 0's. If $t = 0$, then $a_1 = 0$, and the sequence possesses Property (i) of the Induction Axiom. Therefore the sequence contains only 0's. If $t \neq 0$, then the sequence does not possess Property (i) (although it still possesses Property (ii)), and the sequence contains no 0 terms.

The next theorem is an important consequence of the Induction Axiom.

THEOREM 77-1. *If $\{a_n\}$ and $\{b_n\}$ are two sequences that possess the properties*

(i) $a_1 = b_1$ *and*
(ii) *whenever $a_k = b_k$, then $a_{k+1} = b_{k+1}$,*

then $a_n = b_n$ for every positive integer n.

Proof. Let $\{c_n\}$ be the sequence made up of the differences between the corresponding terms of the sequences $\{a_n\}$ and $\{b_n\}$; that is, $c_n = a_n - b_n$. We shall show that the terms of the sequence $\{c_n\}$ satisfy both properties of the Induction Axiom. According to the first condition of this theorem,

$$c_1 = a_1 - b_1 = 0.$$

Further, if $c_k = 0$, then $a_k = b_k$. Thus, according to the second condition of this theorem, $a_{k+1} = b_{k+1}$, and hence

$$c_{k+1} = a_{k+1} - b_{k+1} = 0.$$

Therefore, whenever $c_k = 0$, then $c_{k+1} = 0$. We see that the sequence $\{c_n\}$ satisfies both conditions of the Induction Axiom, and hence $c_n = 0$ for every n. It follows that $a_n = b_n$ for every n.

When a sequence is defined in terms of a recursion formula, we may be able to guess the formula for the nth term after writing out a number of the early terms. Theorem 77-1 provides a way to determine whether or not our guess is correct.

EXAMPLE 77-2. Let $\{a_n\}$ be the sequence for which $a_1 = 3$ and $a_n = na_{n-1}$ for $n > 1$. Find a formula for a_n.

Solution. The first few terms of the sequence $\{a_n\}$ are $3, 3 \cdot 2, 3 \cdot 2 \cdot 3,$ $3 \cdot 2 \cdot 3 \cdot 4, 3 \cdot 2 \cdot 3 \cdot 4 \cdot 5$. These terms suggest that the formula we seek is $a_n = 3n!$. To prove that this formula is correct, we let $\{b_n\}$ be the sequence that is determined by the equation $b_n = 3n!$ and apply Theorem 77-1. Clearly, $a_1 = b_1$, so Condition (i) of Theorem 77-1 is satisfied. It follows from the recursion formula for the sequence that

$$a_{k+1} = (k + 1)a_{(k+1)-1} = (k + 1)a_k$$

for any positive integer k. If, for some k, $a_k = b_k = 3k!$, then it follows that

$$a_{k+1} = (k + 1) \cdot 3k! = 3(k + 1)! = b_{k+1}.$$

Hence, the sequences $\{a_n\}$ and $\{b_n\}$ also satisfy Condition (ii) of Theorem 77-1, and they are therefore the same sequences; that is, $a_n = b_n = 3n!$ for any integer n.

EXAMPLE 77-3. Show that for every positive integer n,

$$\sum_{r=1}^{n} r = 1 + 2 + \ldots + n = \frac{n(n + 1)}{2}.$$

Solution. Consider the sequences $\{a_n\}$ and $\{b_n\}$, where

$$a_n = \sum_{r=1}^{n} r \quad \text{and} \quad b_n = \frac{n(n + 1)}{2}.$$

We have $a_1 = 1$, and $b_1 = \frac{1}{2} \cdot 1 \cdot 2 = 1$, so $a_1 = b_1$. Suppose that for some k, $a_k = b_k$. By definition,

$$a_{k+1} = \sum_{r=1}^{k+1} r = \sum_{r=1}^{k} r + (k+1) = a_k + (k+1).$$

Since we have assumed that $a_k = b_k$, we may write

$$a_{k+1} = b_k + (k+1) = \frac{k(k+1)}{2} + (k+1)$$

$$= \frac{(k+1)(k+2)}{2} = b_{k+1}.$$

The two conditions of Theorem 77-1 are therefore satisfied, so we can conclude that $a_n = b_n$ for every n.

Problems 77

1. Let $\{a_n\}$ be a sequence such that $a_1 = 2$.
   (a) If $a_n = 3a_{n-1}$, show that $a_n = 2 \cdot 3^{n-1}$.
   (b) If $a_n = a_{n-1} + 5$, show that $a_n = 5n - 3$.
   (c) If $a_n = a_{n-1}^2$, show that $a_n = 2^{2^{n-1}}$.
   (d) If $a_n = \frac{a_{n-1}}{n}$, show that $a_n = \frac{2}{n!}$.

2. Which of the sequences in the preceding problem possess Property (ii) of the Induction Axiom?

3. Let $\{y_n\}$ be a sequence with a given first term y_1. Suppose that $y_n = y_{n-1} + d$, where d is a given number, for $n > 1$. Show that $y_n = y_1 + (n-1)d$.

4. Let $\{y_n\}$ be a sequence with a given first term y_1. Suppose that $y_n = ry_{n-1}$, where r is a given number, for $n > 1$. Show that $y_n = y_1 r^{n-1}$.

5. Let $\{y_n\}$ be a sequence such that $y_1 = 5$. Find a formula for y_n if the recursion formula for the sequence is:
   (a) $y_n = \frac{1}{4}y_{n-1}$
   (b) $y_n = 2ny_{n-1}$
   (c) $y_n = -\frac{n}{(n+1)}y_{n-1}$
   (d) $y_n = y_{n-1} + n - 1$

6. If $\{y_n\}$ is the sequence in which $y_1 = 2$ and $y_n = (y_{n-1})^{-1}$ for $n > 1$, show that
$$y_n = \frac{3 + (-1)^{n+1}}{3 + (-1)^n}.$$

7. Use mathematical induction to show that the formula $y_n = \frac{3^{n-1} + 1}{2}$ is the only formula that yields the sequence of Example 76-2.

8. Show that:

(a) $2 + 4 + 6 + \ldots + 2n = n(n + 1)$

(b) $\dfrac{1}{1 \cdot 2} + \dfrac{1}{2 \cdot 3} + \ldots + \dfrac{1}{n(n + 1)} = \dfrac{n}{n + 1}$

(c) $1^2 + 2^2 + 3^2 + \ldots + n^2 = \dfrac{n(n + 1)(2n + 1)}{6}$

9. Show that:

(a) $\sum\limits_{r=1}^{n} (\tfrac{1}{2})^r = 1 - (\tfrac{1}{2})^n$

(b) $\sum\limits_{r=1}^{n} (-1)^r = \dfrac{(-1)^n - 1}{2}$

10. Discuss what happens when you attempt to use mathematical induction

to prove that the sum $\sum\limits_{r=1}^{n} r$ is equal to

(a) $\dfrac{n(n + 1)}{2} + \log 2.$

(b) $\dfrac{n(n + 1)}{2} + 9(n - 1)(n + 1).$

78 ARITHMETIC PROGRESSIONS

An **arithmetic progression** (abbreviated as **A.P.**) is a sequence $\{y_n\}$ that is determined by the equation

78-1 $y_n = y_1 + (n - 1)d,$

where y_1 and d are given numbers.

> EXAMPLE 78-1. Find the first five terms of the A.P. $\{y_n\}$ if $y_1 = 5$ and $d = -2.$
>
> *Solution.* According to Formula 78-1, $y_n = 5 - 2(n - 1) = 7 - 2n.$ Hence, $y_1 = 5, y_2 = 3, y_3 = 1, y_4 = -1,$ and $y_5 = -3.$

If y_n and y_{n+1} are any two consecutive terms of the A.P. that is determined by Equation 78-1, then

$$y_{n+1} - y_n = y_1 + nd - y_1 - (n - 1)d = d.$$

The number d is therefore the difference between any two consecutive terms of the progression. Conversely, if $\{y_n\}$ is a sequence such that $y_{n+1} - y_n = d$ for every positive integer n, then we can use mathematical induction (see Exercise 3 of Problems 77) to show that $\{y_n\}$ is an A.P.

EXAMPLE 78-2.   The numbers 5, 8, 11, 14, and 17 are the first five terms of an A.P. $\{y_n\}$.   Find the formula for y_n and find the 12th term.

Solution.   We can compute d from any two consecutive terms; for instance, $d = 11 - 8 = 3$, or $d = 14 - 11 = 3$.   Since $y_1 = 5$, $y_n = 5 + (n - 1)3 = 3n + 2$, and therefore $y_{12} = 38$.

EXAMPLE 78-3.   Suppose $\{y_n\}$ is an A.P. with $y_4 = 24$ and $y_8 = 36$. Find the formula for y_n.

Solution.   The required formula is $y_n = y_1 + (n - 1)d$, and we are to determine y_1 and d.   Now $y_4 = y_1 + 3d$, and $y_8 = y_1 + 7d$, and since we know the values of y_4 and y_8, we have the system of two linear equations.

$$y_1 + 3d = 24$$

$$y_1 + 7d = 36.$$

These equations can be easily solved and yield $d = 3$ and $y_1 = 15$. It follows that $y_n = 15 + (n - 1)3 = 12 + 3n$.

There is a simple way to find the sum of a given number of terms of an A.P.   To illustrate the method of finding the formula for the sum of n terms of an A.P., let us find the sum of the first seven terms of the A.P. $\{3n - 1\}$.   We first write the sum in the order that the terms appear in the A.P.   Then we reverse the order and add the two equations:

$$S_7 = 2 + 5 + 8 + 11 + 14 + 17 + 20$$
$$S_7 = 20 + 17 + 14 + 11 + 8 + 5 + 2$$
$$\overline{2S_7 = 22 + 22 + 22 + 22 + 22 + 22 + 22}$$

$$2S_7 = 7 \cdot 22$$

$$S_7 = \tfrac{1}{2} \cdot 7 \cdot 22 = 77.$$

Using this calculation as a model, we now derive the formula for the sum of the first n terms of an A.P. $\{y_n\}$.   We obtain each term of an A.P. by adding the number d to its predecessor or by subtracting d from its successor.   Thus, for example, $y_2 = y_1 + d$, $y_3 = y_2 + d = y_1 + 2d$, and so on; and $y_{n-1} = y_n - d$, $y_{n-2} = y_{n-1} - d = y_n - 2d$, and so on.   With these facts in our possession we can write the sum $S_n = \sum_{r=1}^{n} y_r$ in two ways and add the two equations:

$$S_n = y_1 + (y_1 + d) + (y_1 + 2d) + \ldots + (y_n - 2d) + (y_n - d) + y_n$$
$$S_n = y_n + (y_n - d) + (y_n - 2d) + \ldots + (y_1 + 2d) + (y_1 + d) + y_1$$
$$2S_n = (y_1 + y_n) + (y_1 + y_n) + (y_1 + y_n) + \ldots + (y_1 + y_n)$$
$$2S_n = n(y_1 + y_n).$$

Thus, the formula for the sum of the first n terms of an A.P. is

78-2
$$\sum_{r=1}^{n} y_r = S_n = \frac{n}{2}(y_1 + y_n).$$

Formula 78-2 states that *the sum of the first n terms of an A.P. is obtained by multiplying the number of terms to be added by the average of the first and last terms considered.*

EXAMPLE 78-4.   Find the sum of the first 100 odd positive integers.

Solution.   The sequence of odd positive integers is the A.P. $\{2n - 1\}$. The first term is 1, the difference d is 2, and $y_{100} = 199$. According to Formula 78-2,

$$S_{100} = \tfrac{100}{2}(1 + 199) = (100)^2 = 10,000.$$

EXAMPLE 78-5.   A carpenter was hired to construct 192 window frames.   The first day he made five frames, and each day thereafter he made two more frames than he had the day before.   How long did it take him to finish the job?

Solution.   The numbers of frames completed each day form an A.P. whose first few terms are 5, 7, 9, . . . , with $y_1 = 5$ and $d = 2$.   Let n be the number of days required to complete the job.   Then $S_n = 192$ and $y_n = 5 + 2(n - 1) = 2n + 3$.   Hence,

$$S_n = \frac{n}{2}(5 + 2n + 3) = n(n + 4),$$

$$192 = n(n + 4),$$

$$n^2 + 4n - 192 = 0,$$

$$(n - 12)(n + 16) = 0.$$

It follows that $n = 12$ or $n = -16$.   Since n must be positive, we see that the solution is $n = 12$.

EXAMPLE 78-6.   If $\{y_n\}$ is an A.P. with $d = -2$ and $S_8 = 72$, find the terms y_1 and y_8.

Solution. The two fundamental Formulas 78-1 and 78-2 lead to the following system of equations for y_1 and y_8:

$$y_8 = y_1 - 14$$

$$72 = 4(y_1 + y_8).$$

We can solve this system to find that $y_1 = 16$ and $y_8 = 2$.

There is a close relationship between an A.P. and a linear function. You will recall that a linear function f is defined by an equation $f(x) = mx + b$. The domain of f is understood to be the set of all real numbers, unless otherwise specified. If we form the sequence $\{y_n\}$, where $y_n = f(n)$, we see that

$$y_{n+1} - y_n = f(n + 1) - f(n)$$

$$= [m(n + 1) + b] - [mn + b]$$

$$= m.$$

Further, $y_1 = f(1) = m + b$. Thus, every linear function f that is defined by the equation $f(x) = mx + b$ determines an A.P. $\{y_n\}$, where $y_n = f(n)$. The first term of this A.P. is $m + b$, and $d = m$. Conversely, you can easily verify that every A.P. $\{y_n\}$, where $y_n = y_1 + (n - 1)d$, determines a linear function f that is defined by the equation $f(x) = dx + (y_1 - d)$. Then $f(n) = y_n$. In other words, *we can consider an A.P. as a linear function whose domain consists of the positive integers.* The relationship between an A.P. and a linear function is illustrated graphically in Fig. 78-1.

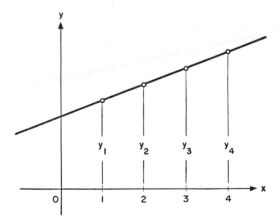

Figure 78-1

Problems 78

1. Suppose that $\{y_n\}$ is an A.P.
   (a) If $y_1 = 3$, $d = -2$, find y_7 and S_7.
   (b) If $y_1 = 3$, $y_7 = 13$, find S_7 and d.
   (c) If $y_1 = 3$, $S_7 = 42$, find y_7 and d.
   (d) If $y_3 = 4$, $y_8 = 24$, find y_1, d, and S_8.
   (e) If $d = 2$, $S_{12} = 72$, find y_1 and y_{12}.
   (f) If $y_1 = -3$, $d = 5$, $S_N = 18$, find y_N.

2. Show that the sum of the first n odd integers is n^2.

3. Find a formula for the sum of the first n even integers.

4. How many positive multiples of 7 are less than 300?   What is their sum?

5. A man started work in 1945 at an annual salary of $5000 and received a $200 raise each year.   In what year did his income reach $7000?

6. Two hundred logs are stacked in the following manner: 20 logs in the bottom row, 19 in the next row, and so on.   How many rows are there, and how many logs are in the top row?

7. Find the first 4 terms of the A.P. $\{y_n\}$ if $y_n = f(n)$, where f is the linear function defined by the equation:
   (a) $f(x) = 3x + 2$ (c) $f(x) = \frac{1}{2}x + \frac{1}{4}$
   (b) $f(x) = -4x + 1$ (d) $f(x) = 1 - 2x$

8. Find the equation that defines a linear function f such that $y_n = f(n)$ if $\{y_n\}$ is an A.P. that is defined by the following equations.   Sketch a graph of f showing the points that correspond to the terms of the A.P.
   (a) $y_1 = 2$, $d = -1$ (c) $y_1 = -5$, $y_n = y_{n-1} + 3$
   (b) $y_n = 3 + 4n$ (d) $d = 3$, $S_7 = 21$

9. Find the following sums:
   (a) $\displaystyle\sum_{r=1}^{12} 3r$ (c) $\displaystyle\sum_{r=1}^{82} (3 - r)$
   (b) $\displaystyle\sum_{r=1}^{23} (2r - 1)$ (d) $\displaystyle\sum_{r=4}^{30} (r + 2)$

10. The acceleration of a body falling in a vacuum is 32 fps per second. Each second that the body falls, it falls 32 ft farther than it did the second before.   If a body falls from rest, it falls 16 ft in the first second. How far does it fall in 10 sec?   How far does it fall in t sec?   (We are assuming that t is a positive integer here, but the formula is valid for all positive numbers t.)

11. A guy wire extends from the top of a 10-ft pole to a point on the ground 40 ft from the pole.   Starting 1 ft from the pole, vertical streamers

spaced 1 ft apart extend from the wire to the ground. How many ft of material are required for the streamers?

79   GEOMETRIC PROGRESSIONS

Another type of sequence that arises frequently in mathematical applications is the **geometric progression (G.P.).**   A sequence $\{y_n\}$ is a G.P. if each term is obtained from the formula

79-1 $$y_n = y_1 r^{n-1},$$

where y_1 is a given first term and r is a given number.   From this equation we see that $y_{n+1} = y_1 r^n$ and hence,

$$\frac{y_{n+1}}{y_n} = \frac{y_1 r^n}{y_1 r^{n-1}} = r.$$

Thus we see that the *quotient* of two consecutive terms of a G.P. is constant, whereas in an A.P., the *difference* between two consecutive terms is constant.   Conversely, we can show by mathematical induction (see Exercise 4 of Problems 77) that any sequence that is defined in terms of the recursion formula $y_{n+1} = r y_n$ is a G.P.

EXAMPLE 79-1.   The numbers 1, 2, 4, 8, and 16 are the first five terms of a G.P. $\{y_n\}$.   Find the formula for y_n and calculate y_7.

Solution.   Clearly, $y_1 = 1$ and $r = \frac{2}{1} = 2$.   Hence, $y_n = 1 \cdot 2^{n-1} = 2^{n-1}$, and $y_7 = 2^6 = 64$.

EXAMPLE 79-2.   The fifth term of a G.P. is 4 and the ratio of two consecutive terms is $\frac{2}{3}$.   Find the formula for y_n.

Solution.   We know that $r = \frac{2}{3}$; hence, $y_5 = y_1(\frac{2}{3})^4$.   But we also know that $y_5 = 4$, so we have $4 = y_1(\frac{2}{3})^4$.   Therefore, $y_1 = 4(\frac{2}{3})^{-4}$, and

$$y_n = 4(\tfrac{2}{3})^{-4}(\tfrac{2}{3})^{n-1} = 4(\tfrac{2}{3})^{n-5}.$$

It is easy to find a formula for the nth partial sum, S_n, of a G.P. We first write

79-2 $$S_n = y_1 + y_1 r + y_1 r^2 + \ldots + y_1 r^{n-1}.$$

Then we multiply both sides of Equation 79-2 by the number r to obtain the equation

79-3 $$rS_n = y_1r + y_1r^2 + \ldots + y_1r^{n-1} + y_1r^n.$$

Now we subtract each side of Equation 79-3 from the corresponding side of Equation 79-2 to obtain the equation

79-4 $$(1 - r)S_n = y_1 - y_1r^n.$$

If $r \neq 1$, we may solve Equation 79-4 for S_n;

79-5 $$S_n = y_1 \left(\frac{1 - r^n}{1 - r} \right).$$

EXAMPLE 79-3.   If $y_1 = 3$, $r = 2$, and $y_N = 768$ in a G.P., find N and S_N.

Solution.   The two fundamental formulas associated with geometric progressions are Equations 79-1 and 79-5.   After we substitute the given values of y_1, r, and y_N in these equations, we have the system of equations

$$768 = 3 \cdot 2^{N-1}$$

$$S_N = 3\frac{1 - 2^N}{1 - 2} = 3(2^N - 1).$$

From the first of these equations we obtain

$$2^{N-1} = 256 = 2^8,$$

so $N - 1 = 8$ and $N = 9$.   Since $2^{N-1} = 256$, we have $2^N = 256 \cdot 2 = 512$, and the second equation yields

$$S_9 = 3(512 - 1) = 1533.$$

EXAMPLE 79-4.   When a certain golf ball is dropped on a piece of pavement, it bounces to a height of three-fifths the distance from which it fell.   If the ball is dropped from a height of 100 inches, how far has it traveled when it hits the ground for the tenth time?   How high will it rise on the next bounce?

Solution.   The first time the ball hits the ground, it has fallen from a height of 100 inches.   It then bounces to a height of $100(\frac{3}{5})$ inches, from which height it hits the ground for the second time.   It then bounces to a height of $100(\frac{3}{5})(\frac{3}{5}) = 100(\frac{3}{5})^2$ inches, and so on.   The tenth time the ball hits the ground it will have fallen from a height of

$100(\tfrac{3}{5})^9$ inches and will then bounce to a height of $100(\tfrac{3}{5})^{10}$ inches. This figure answers the second question. To answer the first question, we observe that except for the original drop, the ball must bounce from the ground to a "peak" height and fall back to the ground on each bounce. Hence, the total distance D the ball travels before it hits the ground for the tenth time is

$$D = 100 + 2 \cdot 100(\tfrac{3}{5}) + 2 \cdot 100(\tfrac{3}{5})^2 + \ldots + 2 \cdot 100(\tfrac{3}{5})^9.$$

Starting with the second term, the sum on the right is the ninth partial sum of the G.P. with $y_1 = 200(\tfrac{3}{5})$ and $r = \tfrac{3}{5}$. From Formula 79-5 we see that

$$D = 100 + 200(\tfrac{3}{5}) \frac{1 - (\tfrac{3}{5})^9}{1 - \tfrac{3}{5}} = 100 + 300[1 - (\tfrac{3}{5})^9]$$

$$= 400 - 300(\tfrac{3}{5})^9.$$

Using logarithms, we find that $(\tfrac{3}{5})^9$ is about .01 and $D = 397$.

In the same way, we can show that when the ball hits the ground for the hundredth time, it will have traveled $400 - 300(\tfrac{3}{5})^{99}$ inches; and, indeed, when the ball hits the ground for the nth time (where n is any positive integer), it will have traveled $400 - 300(\tfrac{3}{5})^{n-1}$ inches. Thus, no matter how often the ball bounces, the distance it will travel will be less than 400 inches.

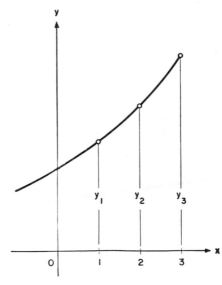

Figure 79-1

A G.P. is related to an exponential function in the same way that an A.P. is related to a linear function. If f is an exponential function that is defined by the equation $f(x) = ab^x$ $(b > 0)$, and if we let $y_n = f(n)$, then we see that

$$y_n = f(n) = ab^n = (ab)b^{n-1} = f(1)b^{n-1} = y_1 b^{n-1}.$$

Thus, an exponential function f defines a G.P. in which $r = b$ and $y_1 = ab$. Conversely, a G.P. $\{y_n\}$ (with $r > 0$) determines an exponential function f, defined by the equation $f(x) = y_1 r^{x-1}$, that possesses the property $y_n = f(n)$. The relationship between a G.P. and an exponential function is illustrated graphically in Fig. 79-1.

Problems 79

1. Formula 79-5 is meaningless if $r = 1$. What is the formula for S_n if $r = 1$?

2. Suppose that $\{y_n\}$ is a G.P.
   (a) If $y_1 = 5$, $r = 3$, find y_5 and S_5.
   (b) If $y_1 = 3$, $r = i$, find y_{17} and S_{17}.

3. Let $\{y_n\}$ be a G.P.
   (a) If $y_1 = 5$ and $y_5 = 80$, find all possible values of r and S_5.
   (b) If $y_1 = 1$ and $S_{12} = 42$, how many possible values of r are there?

4. The enrollment at a certain university increases at the rate of 3% per year. If there were 10,000 students enrolled in 1947, how many students were enrolled in 1957? What will be the first year in which the enrollment is more than double the enrollment of 1947?

5. One third of the air in a container is removed with each stroke of a vacuum pump. What fraction of the original amount of air remains in the container after 5 strokes? How many strokes are necessary to remove 99% of the air?

6. If we know that 3 numbers, a, b, and c, are consecutive terms of both an A.P. and a G.P., find all possible values of a, b, and c.

7. Find the value of each of the following:
   (a) $\sum\limits_{k=1}^{10} 3(2)^k$ (c) $\sum\limits_{k=1}^{5} (2^k + 3k)$
   (b) $\sum\limits_{k=1}^{10} 2^{-k}$ (d) $\sum\limits_{k=5}^{25} (\tfrac{1}{2})^k + (\tfrac{1}{3})^k$

8. Suppose that r is a number different from 1, and let n be a positive integer. Using synthetic division, show that
$$(r^n - 1) \div (r - 1) = \sum_{k=0}^{n-1} r^k.$$
Compare your result with Formula 79-5.

9. Write the first 4 terms of the G.P. $\{y_n\}$ that is defined by $y_n = f(n)$ if the exponential function f is defined by the equation:
   (a) $f(x) = 2^x$ (c) $f(x) = 4(\tfrac{1}{2})^x$
   (b) $f(x) = 3(10)^x$ (d) $f(x) = (\sin 3)^x$

10. Find the equation that defines an exponential function f such that $y_n = f(n)$ if $\{y_n\}$ is a G.P. that is defined by the following equations. Sketch a graph of f showing the points that correspond to the terms of the G.P.

(a) $y_1 = 3$, $r = \frac{2}{3}$ (b) $y_n = (.1)^{n-1}$

80   ARITHMETIC AND GEOMETRIC MEANS. THE SUM OF A G.P.

The **mean** (more precisely, the **arithmetic mean**) of two numbers a and b is their average, $(a + b)/2$. Thus, the mean of the numbers 3 and 7 is 5. If we observe that the three numbers 3, 5, 7 are the consecutive terms of an A.P., we are led to a generalization of the concept of the arithmetic mean of two numbers.

DEFINITION 80-1. *If we choose n numbers, each between two given numbers a and b, in such a way that the set of numbers that consists of the chosen numbers and the given numbers a and b forms the first n + 2 terms of an A.P., then we call the chosen numbers the* **nth arithmetic means** *of the numbers a and b.*

EXAMPLE 80-1.   Find the third arithmetic means of the numbers -3 and 9.

Solution.   According to Definition 80-1, we must find three numbers, y_2, y_3, and y_4, such that the numbers $y_1 = -3, y_2, y_3, y_4$, and $y_5 = 9$ form the first five terms of an A.P. First, we find a number d such that y_5 and y_1 are related by Equation 78-1; that is, $y_5 = y_1 + 4d$. Since $y_5 = 9$ and $y_1 = -3$, we immediately find that $d = 3$. Hence, $y_2 = 0$, $y_3 = 3$, and $y_4 = 6$.

The **geometric mean** of two positive numbers a and b is the number $\sqrt{ab}$. Thus, the geometric mean of 2 and 8 is 4. If we observe that the three numbers 2, 4, 8 are consecutive terms of a G.P., we are led to a generalization of the concept of the geometric mean of two numbers.

DEFINITION 80-2.   *If we choose n positive numbers, each between two given positive numbers a and b, in such a way that the set of numbers that consists* *of the chosen numbers and the given numbers a and b forms the first n + 2 terms of a G.P., then we call the chosen numbers the **nth geometric means** of the numbers a and b.*

EXAMPLE 80-2.   Find the fourth geometric means of the numbers $\frac{1}{2}$ and 16.

Solution.   According to Definition 80-2, we must find four positive numbers, y_2, y_3, y_4, and y_5, such that the numbers $y_1 = \frac{1}{2}$, y_2, y_3, y_4, y_5, and $y_6 = 16$ are the first six terms of a G.P.   First, we find the positive number r such that $16 = \frac{1}{2}r^5$ (Equation 79-1).   We see that $r = 2$, and the required means are therefore the numbers $y_2 = 1$, $y_3 = 2$, $y_4 = 4$, and $y_5 = 8$.

EXAMPLE 80-3.   If a and b are two positive numbers, show that their first arithmetic mean is not less than their first geometric mean.

Solution.   Since the arithmetic mean of a and b is $\frac{1}{2}(a + b)$ and the geometric mean is $\sqrt{ab}$, we must show that

$$\sqrt{ab} \leq \tfrac{1}{2}(a + b).$$

In order to demonstrate this inequality, we proceed as follows:

$$2\sqrt{ab} \leq (a + b),$$

$$4ab \leq (a + b)^2$$

$$4ab \leq a^2 + 2ab + b^2.$$

But this last inequality can be rearranged as

$$0 \leq a^2 - 2ab + b^2,$$

$$0 \leq (a - b)^2.$$

This final inequality is obviously correct, and we can reverse the steps in our reasoning to solve the problem.

In Example 79-4 we found that the distance traveled by a certain golf ball in n bounces was

$$D_n = 400 - 300(\tfrac{3}{5})^{n-1}.$$

We then concluded that no matter how long the ball bounces, the distance it travels is less than 400.   But if n is a very large integer, for example, 1,000,000, then the distance D_n is almost 400. In fact, since we can make the number $(\frac{3}{5})^{n-1}$ as small as we please by choosing a large enough value for n, we can make the difference between D_n and 400 as close to zero as we please. We say that the **limit** of D_n is 400.

Let $\{y_n\}$ be a G.P. that is defined by Equation 79-1. Then according to Equation 79-5, we can write the formula for the nth partial sum of the G.P. as

80-1
$$S_n = \frac{y_1}{1-r} - \left(\frac{y_1}{1-r}\right) r^n.$$

If $|r| < 1$, then we can make the second term of the right-hand side of Equation 80-1 as close to zero as we wish by making n large enough. (You can probably convince yourself of this fact by considering the value of an expression like $(\frac{1}{2})^n$, when n is a large number.) It follows that if $|r| < 1$, then $\frac{y_1}{1-r}$ closely approximates the sum S_n when n is a large number—in fact, the larger the number n, the closer the approximation. To express the fact that we can make the difference between S_n and $\frac{y_1}{1-r}$ as small as we please by making n large enough, we write:

80-2
$$\text{If } |r| < 1, \quad \lim_{n \to \infty} S_n = \sum_{k=1}^{\infty} y_k = \frac{y_1}{1-r}.$$

The symbol $\lim_{n \to \infty} S_n$ is read "the limit of S_n as n increases without bound." The symbol $\sum_{k=1}^{\infty} y_k$ is read "the sum of the sequence $\{y_n\}$."

EXAMPLE 80-4.   Find the limit of the partial sums of the G.P. $\{(\frac{1}{2})^n\}$.

Solution. Since $y_1 = \frac{1}{2}$ and $r = \frac{1}{2}$, we have, according to Equation 80-2

$$\lim_{n \to \infty} S_n = \frac{\frac{1}{2}}{1 - \frac{1}{2}} = 1.$$

In Fig. 80-1 the numbers S_1, S_2, S_3, S_4, are shown plotted on the number scale. We see that each time a point S_{k+1} is plotted, it bisects the segment between the points S_k and 1. Thus, even though the point S_n is *never* the point 1, it is clear that the point S_n is *very close to* the point **1** when n is a large number.

Figure 80-1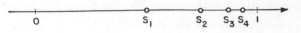

EXAMPLE 80-5.   Find $\sum\limits_{r=0}^{\infty} (\tfrac{1}{3})^r$.

Solution.   We are to find the sum of a geometric progression whose first term is 1 and for which $r = \tfrac{1}{3}$.   According to Equation 80-2,

$$\sum_{r=0}^{\infty} (\tfrac{1}{3})^r = \frac{1}{1 - \tfrac{1}{3}} = \tfrac{3}{2}.$$

Problems 80

1. Find the second arithmetic means of the following numbers:
(a) 4 and 10   (c) -3 and 7
(b) -1 and 1   (d) $\sqrt{2}$ and $6 + \sqrt{2}$

2. Find the second arithmetic means of the numbers k and k^2.

3. Find the third geometric means of the numbers 16 and 81.

4. Find the second arithmetic means and the second geometric means of the numbers $\tfrac{9}{2}$ and $\tfrac{4}{3}$.   Plot the points $(1,\tfrac{9}{2})$ and $(4,\tfrac{4}{3})$ and the points corresponding to the second arithmetic and geometric means.

5. Find 3 numbers a, b, and c that are between 2 and 18 such that their sum is 25, the numbers 2, a, b are consecutive terms of an A.P., and the numbers b, c, and 18 are consecutive terms of a G.P.

6. The number .111 . . . can be considered as the sum of the G.P. $\{(\tfrac{1}{10})^n\}$. In other words .111 . . . $= \sum\limits_{k=1}^{\infty} (\tfrac{1}{10})^k$.   Evaluate this sum.

7. Follow the procedure indicated in the preceding problem to evaluate .3333 . . .   and .9999 . . . .

8. Inside a square that has sides 1 ft long a second square is constructed whose vertices are the mid-points of the sides of the first square.   Similarly, a third square is constructed whose vertices are the mid-points of the second square.   If this sequence of constructions is continued,
(a) find the area of the 10th square,
(b) find the area of the nth square,
(c) find the sum of the areas of the first 10 squares,
(d) find the limit of the sum of the areas of the squares.

9. Find the value of each of the following sums:

(a) $\sum\limits_{k=0}^{\infty} (-\frac{1}{2})^k$　　　　　　　　　　(c) $\sum\limits_{k=5}^{\infty} 81(\frac{2}{3})^k$

(b) $\sum\limits_{k=0}^{\infty} (.57)^k$　　　　　　　　　　(d) $\sum\limits_{k=100}^{\infty} (\frac{1}{2})^k$

10. A function f whose domain is the set of all real positive numbers is defined by the equation

$$f(x) = \sum\limits_{k=0}^{\infty} (1 + x)^{-k}.$$

Sketch the graph of the function f.

81　MATHEMATICAL INDUCTION APPLIED TO SEQUENCES OF STATEMENTS

Preceding sequences have consisted of numbers, one number being associated with each positive integer n. In this section we are going to discuss sequences of statements; that is, with each positive integer n we will associate some mathematical statement P_n. Some examples of such statements follow.

Illustration 81-1. P_n is the statement "$1 + 2 + \ldots + n = \frac{1}{2}n(n + 1)$,"

Illustration 81-2. P_n is the statement "$1! + 2! + \ldots + n!$ is an odd number,"

Illustration 81-3. P_n is the statement "$(n + 1)^n < n^{n+1}$,"

Illustration 81-4. P_n is the statement "$2^n - 1$ is a perfect square."

We shall explain one way to determine whether or not a sequence $\{P_n\}$ of statements contains only true statements. For any integer n the corresponding statement P_n of Illustration 81-1 is true, as we showed in Example 77-3. We shall show in Example 81-1 that all the statements of the sequence of Illustration 81-2 are also true. In Illustration 81-3, statements P_1 and P_2 are false, but we shall show (in Example 81-3) that all the other statements in that sequence are true. The only true statement of the sequence of Illustration 81-4 is P_1, but the methods we will discuss in this section are not the way to show that a statement such as P_3 is false.

With a given sequence of statements $\{P_n\}$ we shall associate in a simple way a sequence of numbers $\{a_n\}$. If P_n is a true statement, we let $a_n = 0$, and if P_n is a false statement, we let $a_n = 1$. We can now use our Induction Axiom to prove the following theorem.

THEOREM 81-1. *If $\{P_n\}$ is a sequence of statements that possesses the properties*

  (i) *P_1 is true and*
  (ii) *whenever P_k is true, then P_{k+1} is true,*

then P_n is a true statement for every positive integer n.

Proof. Properties (i) and (ii) of the sequence of statements $\{P_n\}$ imply that the corresponding sequence of numbers $\{a_n\}$ possesses the properties (i) $a_1 = 0$ and (ii) whenever $a_k = 0$, then $a_{k+1} = 0$. It follows from the Induction Axiom that $a_n = 0$ for every positive integer n. Hence, for each n, P_n is a true statement.

EXAMPLE 81-1. Use Theorem 81-1 to show that the sum $\sum_{r=1}^{n} r!$ is an odd number for every positive integer n.

Solution. We are to verify that the sequence of statements $\{P_n\}$ of Illustration 81-2 consists only of true statements. Since P_1 is the statement "1 is an odd number," it is true, and we see that the sequence $\{P_n\}$ possesses Property (i) of Theorem 81-1. Suppose that P_k is a true statement; that is, that the sum $1! + 2! + \ldots + k!$ is odd. Then, since $(k+1)! = 1 \cdot 2 \cdot \ldots \cdot (k+1)$ is an even number, it follows that $\sum_{r=1}^{k+1} r! = \sum_{r=1}^{k} r! + (k+1)!$ is an odd number; that is, that the statement P_{k+1} is true. Hence, the sequence $\{P_n\}$ possesses Property (ii) of Theorem 81-1, and it follows that all the statements in the sequence are true. In other words, $\sum_{r=1}^{n} r!$ is an odd number for every positive integer n.

EXAMPLE 81-2. Let x be any real number. Show that $|\sin nx| \leq n|\sin x|$ for every positive integer n.

Solution. Let $\{P_n\}$ be the sequence in which P_n is the statement "$|\sin nx| \leq n|\sin x|$." Then P_1 is the statement "$|\sin x| \leq |\sin x|$," which is surely true. We must also show that the truth of the statement P_k implies that statement P_{k+1} also is true. For any k, we have

$$|\sin (k + 1)x| = |\sin (kx + x)|$$
$$= |\sin kx \cos x + \cos kx \sin x|$$
$$\leq |\sin kx \cos x| + |\cos kx \sin x|$$
$$\leq |\sin kx| + |\sin x|.$$

Hence, if P_k is true (that is, if $|\sin kx| \leq k|\sin x|$), we see that

$$|\sin (k + 1)x| \leq |\sin kx| + |\sin x| \leq k|\sin x| + |\sin x|$$
$$= (k + 1)|\sin x|.$$

Thus, the statement P_{k+1},

$$|\sin (k + 1)x| \leq (k + 1)|\sin x|,$$

is true whenever P_k is true. The two conditions of Theorem 81-1 are satisfied, so we conclude that statement P_n is true for any positive integer n.

EXAMPLE 81-3. Show that, for $n \geq 3$, $(n + 1)^n < n^{n+1}$.

Solution. With a little algebra, we can show that the above inequality is equivalent to the statement

$$\left(\frac{n + 1}{n}\right)^n < n.$$

We will call this last inequality the statement P_n. It is clear that the sequence $\{P_n\}$ does not possess Property (i) of Theorem 81-1, but we will show that it does possess Property (ii). For any positive integer k it is clearly true that

$$\frac{k + 2}{k + 1} < \frac{k + 1}{k}.$$

Hence,

$$\left(\frac{k + 2}{k + 1}\right)^{k+1} < \left(\frac{k + 1}{k}\right)^{k+1} = \left(\frac{k + 1}{k}\right)^k \cdot \left(\frac{k + 1}{k}\right).$$

If P_k is true (that is, if $\left(\frac{k + 1}{k}\right)^k < k$) then

$$\left(\frac{k + 2}{k + 1}\right)^{k+1} < k\left(\frac{k + 1}{k}\right) = k + 1,$$

which simply states that P_{k+1} is true.   Hence, $\{P_n\}$ possesses Property (ii)—that is, every true statement of the sequence is followed by a true statement.   If we replace our original sequence $\{P_n\}$ with a sequence $\{Q_n\}$ that is obtained from $\{P_n\}$ by neglecting the first two terms ($Q_1 = P_3$, $Q_2 = P_4$, and so on), it is clear that $\{Q_n\}$ will also possess Property (ii).   The sequence $\{Q_n\}$ is the sequence of statements

$$\text{``}(n + 3)^{n+2} < (n + 2)^{n+3}.\text{''}$$

The sequence $\{Q_n\}$ also possesses Property (i), for Q_1 is the statement

$$\text{``}(1 + 3)^3 < (1 + 2)^4\text{''}$$

or

$$\text{``}64 < 81.\text{''}$$

According to Theorem 81-1, it follows that statement Q_n is true for each n, and therefore statement P_n is true for each $n \geq 3$.

Problems 81

1. Let P_n, be the statement "$n = n + 1$."   Does the sequence $\{P_n\}$ possess Property (ii) of Theorem 81-1?

2. Use mathematical induction to prove Equation 78-2.

3. Use mathematical induction to prove Equation 79-5.

4. Show that for any positive integer n if $0 < a < b$, then $a^n < b^n$.

5. Use mathematical induction to prove that $\log n < n$ for every positive integer n.

6. Let $\{y_n\}$ be the Fibonacci Sequence that is defined by the equations
$$y_1 = 1, y_2 = 2, y_{n+2} = y_n + y_{n+1}.$$
Prove that
$$\sum_{r=1}^{n} y_r = y_{n+2} - 2.$$

7. Use mathematical induction to show that if n is a positive integer, then $x - y$ is a factor of $x^n - y^n$.

8. Use mathematical induction to show that if n is an odd positive integer, then $x + y$ is a factor of $x^n + y^n$.

9. Use mathematical induction to prove that for any positive integer n:
(a) $n^2 - 3n + 4$ is an even number.
(b) $2n^3 - 3n^2 + n$ is divisible by 6.

10. Suppose that $a > -1$.   Show that for every positive integer n
$$(1 + a)^n \geq 1 + na.$$
Where does your proof break down if $a < -1$?

Review Problems, Chapter Nine

You should be able to answer the following questions without referring back to the text.

1. (a) Let $\{y_n\}$ and $\{z_n\}$ be A.P.'s. Show that $\{y_n + z_n\}$ is an A.P.
   (b) Let $\{y_n\}$ and $\{z_n\}$ be G.P.'s. Show that $\{y_n z_n\}$ is a G.P.

2. (a) Let $\{y_n\}$ be an A.P. If z_n is the arithmetic mean of y_n and y_{n+1}, is the sequence $\{z_n\}$ an A.P.? If z_n is the geometric mean of y_n and y_{n+1}, is $\{z_n\}$ an A.P.? If z_n is the geometric mean of y_n and y_{n+1}, is $\{z_n\}$ a G.P.?
   (b) Answer the questions in part (a) if $\{y_n\}$ is a G.P.

3. Is the sequence $\{\log n\}$ an A.P.? Calculate $\sum\limits_{k=1}^{50} \log k$.

4. If $\{y_n\}$ is a G.P. of positive terms, show that $\{\log y_n\}$ is an A.P.

5. Evaluate:

   (a) $i^{\sum\limits_{r=1}^{208} (2r-1)}$

   (b) $(-1)^{\sum\limits_{r=0}^{n} 2^r}$

6. Twenty rungs are equally spaced along a ladder. The bottom rung is $2\frac{1}{2}$ ft long and the top rung is $1\frac{1}{2}$ ft long. How many linear ft of wood were required to make all the rungs?

7. In a given equilateral triangle whose sides are 1 ft long, let us shade an equilateral triangle whose vertices are the mid-points of the sides of the given triangle. Next, in each of the 3 unshaded triangles formed by the first shading we shade an equilateral triangle whose vertices are the mid-points of an unshaded triangle. In the same way, we then shade 9 equilateral triangles inside each of the 9 unshaded triangles, and so on. If we continue this process indefinitely, what percentage of the original triangle will be shaded?

8. Prove that $2^n < n! < n^n$ for every integer $n \geq 4$.

9. Let a, b, and c be given numbers. Show that the sequence formed by taking differences of consecutive terms of the sequence $\{an^2 + bn + c\}$ is an A.P.

10. Let $y_n = \frac{1}{2}[1 + (-1)^{n+1}]$. Write out the first 5 terms of the sequence $\{y_n\}$. Let $a_n = \frac{1}{n} \sum\limits_{r=1}^{n} y_r$. Prove that if n is an even integer, then $a_n = \frac{1}{2}$.

Miscellaneous Problems, Chapter Nine

These problems are designed to test your ability to apply your knowledge of sequences and mathematical induction to somewhat more difficult problems.

1. A man invested \$100 on the first day of January for 10 consecutive years at 5% interest compounded annually. What was the value of his account just after he made his last deposit?

2. The product $P_n = y_1 \cdot y_2 \cdot \ldots \cdot y_n$ is called the **nth partial product** of the sequence $\{y_n\}$. Find a formula for the nth partial product of a G.P.

3. Is the inequality in Example 81-2 true if the sine function is replaced by the cosine function?

4. For what positive integers n is the inequality $\log n! > n$ true? Use mathematical induction to prove your answer.

5. Let $\{y_n\}$ be an A.P. Find a formula for the following sums:

   (a) $\sum\limits_{r=n}^{2n} y_r$ (b) $\sum\limits_{r=1}^{n} y_r^2$ (See 8(c) of Problems 77 for $\sum\limits_{r=1}^{n} r^2$.)

6. Let $\{y_n\}$ be the sequence that is defined by the equation $y_n = \sum\limits_{r=1}^{n} r$.

   Find a formula for $\sum\limits_{k=1}^{m} y_k$. (See 8(c) of Problems 77 for $\sum\limits_{r=1}^{n} r^2$.)

7. Billiard balls are placed in a rack in the form of an equilateral triangle. There are 5 balls along each side of the rack. A second layer of balls is placed on top of those in the rack so that there are 4 balls on a side; a third layer is placed on the second layer, and so on, so that a pyramid of balls is formed with one ball on top. How many balls does the pyramid contain? Find a formula for the number of balls in the pyramid if the bottom layer has n balls along each side of the rack.

8. Use mathematical induction to show that

$$\sum_{r=1}^{n} r^3 = \left[\frac{n(n+1)}{2}\right]^2.$$

9. A sequence $\{y_n\}$ is called an **harmonic progression** if the sequence $\left\{\dfrac{1}{y_n}\right\}$ is an A.P.

   (a) Write the first 4 terms of an H.P. if $y_1 = 1, y_2 = \frac{1}{2}$.
   (b) Write the first 4 terms of an H.P. if $y_1 = 2, y_2 = \frac{3}{2}$.
   (c) Make a logical definition of the harmonic mean of two numbers and find a formula for the harmonic mean of two numbers a and b.

CHAPTER TEN

INVERSE FUNCTIONS AND
TRIGONOMETRIC EQUATIONS

In this chapter we will review and extend our knowledge of functions. You will recall that the three elements that comprise a function are:

(i) a set of numbers called the **domain** of the function,
(ii) a set of numbers called the **range** of the function, and
(iii) a **rule** that assigns to each number x in the domain a number y in the range.

We *pick* a number in the domain and *get* a number in the range. We shall now look at what happens when we first pick a number in the range of a given function. Most of our attention will be devoted to trigonometric functions, but the ideas we develop here can be applied to other functions.

We will assume for convenience that *all the numbers we discuss in this chapter are real numbers.*

82 INVERSE FUNCTIONS

We will begin our discussion of inverse functions with an important example. Let f be the function that is determined by the equation $f(x) = \log x$. The domain of the logarithmic function f is the set

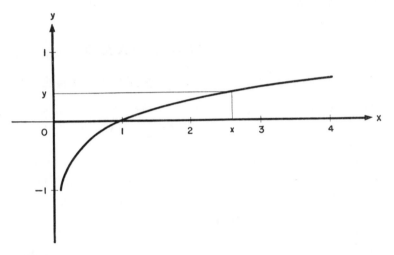

Figure 82-1

of all positive numbers, and its range is the set of all real numbers. Figure 82-1 shows the graph of f; the domain (the positive x-axis) and the range (the entire y-axis) are indicated by heavy lines. It is obvious how we can use the graph to find the number y in the range that corresponds to a given number x in the domain. It is equally obvious that we could pick the number y *first* and then find x. That is, with each real number y we can associate the positive number x that satisfies the equation $\log x = y$. From our study of logarithms we know that the number x is explicitly given by the equation $x = 10^y$. This equation defines a new function—its domain is the set of all real numbers, its range is the set of positive numbers, and its rule of correspondence is expressed by the equation $x = 10^y$. This function is *not the same* as the logarithmic function f, but it is certainly closely related to it. We say that this new function is the **inverse** of f and denote it by the symbol f^{-1}. The number that corresponds to a given real number y is 10^y, so we write $f^{-1}(y) = 10^y$.

In the case of the logarithmic function we can pick any number in the range and find exactly one corresponding number in the domain. In general, however, if we pick a number in the range of a function, then there may be several corresponding numbers in the domain. For example, if g is the function that is determined by the equation $y = x^2$, then to every positive number y there correspond two numbers: $x = \sqrt{y}$ and $x = -\sqrt{y}$. We don't have a rule of correspondence that assigns just one number x to each chosen number y. Our function g does not have an inverse.

We now lay down a rule that tells us when a function f has an inverse and how to define this inverse when it exists.

DEFINITION 82-1. *If for each number y in the range of a function f there is exactly one number x in the domain of f such that $f(x) = y$, then the function f has an **inverse function f^{-1}**. The domain of f^{-1} is the range of f, and the range of f^{-1} is the domain of f. The number that corresponds to a given number y in the range of f is the number x that satisfies the equation $y = f(x)$. Thus,*

$$x = f^{-1}(y) \quad \text{if, and only if,} \quad y = f(x).$$

EXAMPLE 82-1. Determine whether or not the function f that is defined by the equation $f(x) = x^3$ has an inverse function f^{-1}, and if it does, find the equation that determines f^{-1}.

Solution. Both the domain and the range of f consist of all the real numbers. If y is any real number, then there is exactly one real number x such that $f(x) = x^3 = y$; namely, $x = \sqrt[3]{y}$. Thus, the inverse function f^{-1} exists and is defined by the equation $f^{-1}(y) = \sqrt[3]{y}$.

We can easily see whether or not a function f has an inverse by looking at the graph of f. We merely draw a horizontal line through each point on the y-axis that is in the range of our function. If each such line cuts the graph exactly once (see Fig. 82-1, for example), the equation $f(x) = y$ has just one solution and the function f

has an inverse.   If a horizontal line through some point y cuts the
graph more than once, the equation $f(x) = y$ has more than one
solution, and the function f does not have an inverse.

EXAMPLE 82-2.   Determine whether or not the function f that is defined by the equation $f(x) = x^2 + 2x$ has an inverse function f^{-1},
and if it does, find the equation that defines f^{-1}.

Solution.   The domain of f is the set of all the real numbers.   The
graph of f (Fig. 82-2) shows us that the range of f is the set of all real
numbers $y \geq -1$.   If y is any number in the range of f (other than

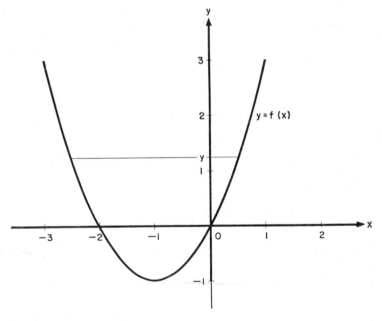

Figure 82-2

$y = -1$), it is evident from Fig. 82-2 that there are two numbers x
in the domain of f such that $f(x) = y$.   For example, the numbers 0
and -2 both correspond to $y = 0$.   Thus, the function f does not
have an inverse.

In Example 82-2 we see that a horizontal line cuts the graph of
the function f in two points and therefore f has no inverse.   We can
get a curve that is intersected only once by each horizontal line by
simply removing one of the "branches" of the curve in Fig. 82-2

(see Fig. 82-3).   The remaining branch is the graph of a *new function* *F* whose domain is the set of numbers $x \geq -1$, whose range is the set of numbers $y \geq -1$, and for which $F(x) = x^2 + 2x$.   The only difference between the original function f and the new function F is that the domain of F is smaller than the domain of f.   We have obtained the function F by **restricting the domain** of f.   Clearly,

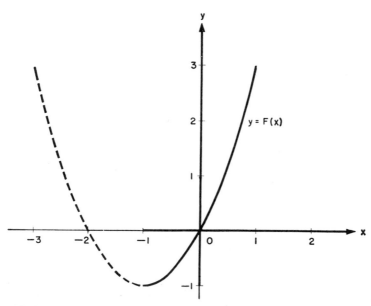

Figure 82-3

our new function F has an inverse.   You may use the Quadratic Formulas to see that the solutions to the equation $y = x^2 + 2x$ are $x = -1 + \sqrt{1 + y}$ and $x = -1 - \sqrt{1 + y}$.   Since the domain of F is the set of numbers $x \geq -1$, we see that $F^{-1}(y) = -1 + \sqrt{1 + y}$.

If F is any function that has an inverse, then F and its inverse F^{-1} have the "same" graph, except that the domain of F^{-1} consists of numbers on the vertical axis (Fig. 82-4).   Since the numbers in the domain of a function are usually pictured as lying along the horizontal axis, we turn the picture of the graph of F^{-1} over and then rotate it to make the y-axis point to the right (Fig. 82-5).   If we now re-label the axes so that the horizontal axis is the x-axis and the vertical axis is the y-axis, our graph is still the graph of the *function* F^{-1}, but now it is also the graph of the *equation* $y = F^{-1}(x)$ (Fig. 82-6).

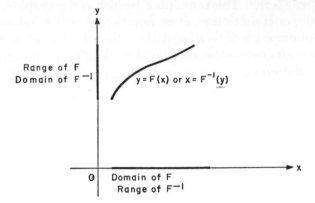

Figure 82-4

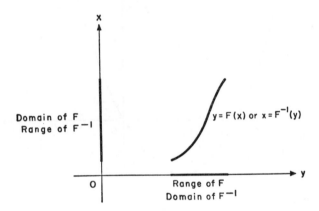

Figure 82-5

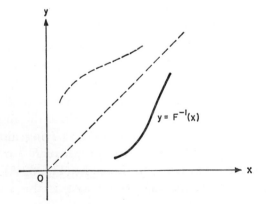

Figure 82-6

The dashed-line curve of Fig. 82-6 is the graph of the equation $y = F(x)$. If you study that figure, you will see that the graph of the equation $y = F^{-1}(x)$ may be obtained by reflecting the graph of the equation $y = F(x)$ about the line that bisects the first and third quadrants.

EXAMPLE 82-3. The domain of a function G is the set of numbers x such that $-1 \leq x \leq 0$, and $G(x) = \sqrt{1 - x^2}$. Find the graph of G^{-1}.

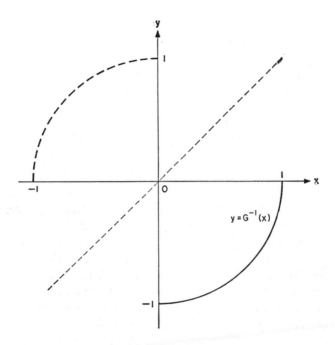

Figure 82-7

Solution. The graph of the equation $y = G(x)$ is the dashed-line curve in Fig. 82-7. We obtain the graph of G^{-1} (the solid curve) by reflecting the graph of G about the line $y = x$.

Problems 82

1. Let f be the exponential function that is defined by the equation $f(x) = 2^x$. Does f have an inverse f^{-1}? If so, how is it defined?

2. Determine whether or not the function f has an inverse f^{-1}, and if it does, find the equation that determines f^{-1}.

(a) $f(x) = 3x + 2$
(b) $f(x) = 1 - 6x$
(c) $f(x) = x^4$
(d) $f(x) = x^5$
(e) $f(x) = |x|$

(f) $f(x) = \dfrac{1}{x}$
(g) $f(x) = [x]$
(h) $f(x) = [x] - x$

3. Let f be the function that is defined by the equation $f(x) = \dfrac{2 - x}{3 + x}$. What is the domain of f? Find the equation that determines f^{-1}. What is the domain of f^{-1}? What is the range of f?

4. Restrict the domain of the function f that is defined by the equation $f(x) = x^2$ to obtain a function F that has an inverse F^{-1}. Can you find more than one such function F?

5. Suppose the function F has an inverse function F^{-1}. Let x be a number in the domain of F and let y be a number in the domain of F^{-1}.
   (a) Use Definition 82-1 to show that $F^{-1}[F(x)] = x$, and $F[F^{-1}(y)] = y$.
   (b) Verify the equations in part (a) if F is determined by the equation $F(x) = x/(1 + x)$.

6. Draw the graph of F and F^{-1} if F is determined by the following equations:
   (a) $F(x) = x + 1$
   (b) $F(x) = x^3$
   (c) $F(x) = 1 - x$
   (d) $F(x) = \sqrt[3]{x}$

7. Suppose F is a function with an inverse function F^{-1} that is the same as F; that is, F^{-1} and F have the same domain and range, and $F^{-1}(x) = F(x)$ for every x in their domain. Describe the graph of F. Give an example of a function F such that F^{-1} is the same as F.

8. For each of the functions f that are defined by the following equations, determine the range of f from the graph of f. Then, define a function F by restricting the domain of f such that F^{-1} exists. Draw the graph of your function F^{-1} and find the equation that determines F^{-1}.
   (a) $f(x) = x^2 + 2x - 3$
   (b) $f(x) = 1 + 2x - x^2$
   (c) $f(x) = x^2 - 2x$
   (d) $f(x) = \frac{1}{2}x - \frac{1}{4}x^2$
   (e) $f(x) = |x - 2|$
   (f) $f(x) = 2 - |x + 1|$

9. Suppose f and g are functions that have inverses such that the domain of g is the range of f. Let F be the function that is defined by the equation $F(x) = g[f(x)]$. Show that F has an inverse function F^{-1} and find the equation that expresses F^{-1} in terms of f^{-1} and g^{-1}.

83   INVERSE FUNCTIONS FOR THE SINE AND COSINE FUNCTIONS

The domain of the sine function is the set of all real numbers, and its range is the set of all numbers y such that $-1 \le y \le 1$. Since the sine function is periodic, it is clear that the equation $\sin x = y$ has infinitely many solutions for each number y in the range of the sine function. Therefore, the sine function does not have an inverse. But by restricting the domain of the sine function, we can construct a new function that does have an inverse. *We define the* **Sine function** (*the capital letter S distinguishes this new function from the sine function*) *as the function whose domain is the set of numbers x such that* $-\pi/2 \leq x \leq \pi/2$, *and whose rule of correspondence is expressed by the equation* $y = \sin x$. The solid curve in Fig. 83-1 is the graph of the Sine function; the dashed-line curve is the part of the graph of the sine function that we "removed."

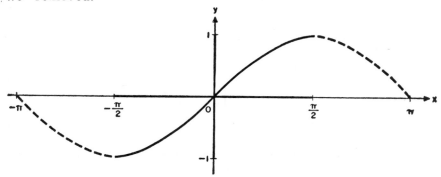

Figure 83-1

It is clear from Fig. 83-1 that the Sine function has an inverse, and we call this inverse function the **Arcsine function.** The domain of the Arcsine function is the set of numbers y such that $-1 \leq y \leq 1$, and its range is the set of numbers x that satisfy the inequalities $-\pi/2 \leq x \leq \pi/2$. If y is a number in the domain of the Arcsine function, we will denote the associated number in the range either by **Arcsin** y or **Sin⁻¹** y. Both these notations are in common use.

DEFINITION 83-1. *The Arcsine function is defined as follows:* $x =$ **Arcsin** $y =$ **Sin⁻¹** y *if, and only if,* (i) $\sin x = y$, *and* (ii) $-\pi/2 \leq x \leq \pi/2$.

EXAMPLE 83-1. Find Arcsin $\frac{1}{2}$.

Solution. We know from our previous study that $\sin \pi/6 = \frac{1}{2}$, and since $-\pi/2 \leq \pi/6 \leq \pi/2$, we see that Arcsin $\frac{1}{2} = \pi/6$.

EXAMPLE 83-2.   Find Arcsin (−.7895).

Solution.   We find from Table II that sin .91 = .7895, so sin (−.91) = −.7895.   Since −π/2 ≤ −.91 ≤ π/2, we see that Arcsin (−.7895) = −.91.

It follows from our discussion of the graphs of inverse functions in Section 82 that we can obtain the graph of the Arcsine function by reflecting the graph of the Sine function about the line $y = x$.   The graph of the equation $y =$ Arcsin x is shown in Fig. 83-2.

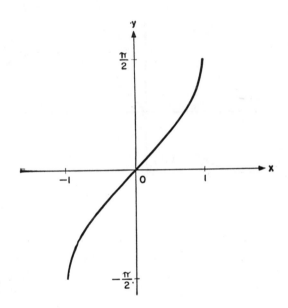

Figure 83-2

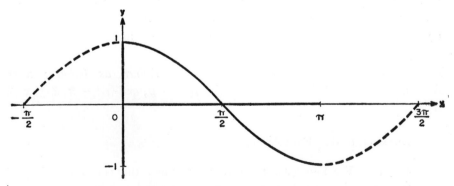

Figure 83-3

We can treat the cosine function in the same way we treated the sine function.   *We first define the* **Cosine function** (*again using a capital letter to distinguish this new function from the cosine function*) *as the function whose domain is the set of numbers x that satisfy the inequalities* $0 \leq x \leq \pi$, *and whose rule of correspondence is expressed by the equation* $y = \cos x$. The graph of the Cosine function is the solid curve in Fig. 83-3. Clearly, the Cosine function has an inverse; we call it the **Arccosine function.**   The domain of the Arccosine function is the set of numbers y such that $-1 \leq y \leq 1$, and its range is the set of numbers x that satisfy the inequalities $0 \leq x \leq \pi$.   The number corresponding to a given number y in the domain of the Arccosine function is denoted either by **Arccos y** or **Cos^{-1} y.**

DEFINITION 83-2.   *The Arccosine function is defined as follows:* $x =$ **Arccos y = Cos^{-1} y** *if, and only if,* (i) $\cos x = y$, *and* (ii) $0 \leq x \leq \pi$.
The graph of the equation $y =$ Arccos x is shown in Fig. 83-4.

EXAMPLE 83-3.   Calculate $\sin (\text{Cos}^{-1} \tfrac{3}{5})$.

Solution.   Let $t = \text{Cos}^{-1} \tfrac{3}{5}$. According to Definition 83-2, $\cos t = \tfrac{3}{5}$, and $0 \leq t \leq \pi$. In fact, since $\cos t > 0$, we know that $0 \leq t \leq \pi/2$. From the fundamental identity $\sin^2 t + \cos^2 t = 1$, we obtain the equation

$$\sin^2 t = 1 - (\tfrac{3}{5})^2 = \tfrac{16}{25}.$$

Since $0 \leq t \leq \pi/2$, we know that $\sin t \geq 0$, and therefore $\sin t = \tfrac{4}{5}$. Thus, we have $\sin (\text{Cos}^{-1} \tfrac{3}{5}) = \tfrac{4}{5}$.

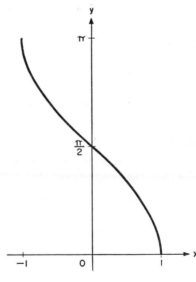

Figure 83-4

EXAMPLE 83-4.   Show that Arcsin x + Arccos $x = \pi/2$ for any number x such that $-1 \leq x \leq 1$.

Solution.   Let $u =$ Arcsin x.   Then $\sin u = x$, and $-\pi/2 \leq u \leq \pi/2$. Therefore, if we write $v = \pi/2 - u$, it follows that $0 \leq v \leq \pi$, and

$\cos v = \cos (\pi/2 - u) = \sin u = x.$ Since $0 \le v \le \pi$, and $\cos v = x$, we see from Definition 83-2 that $v = $ Arccos x. Thus,

$$\text{Arcsin } x + \text{Arccos } x = u + v = \frac{\pi}{2}.$$

Problems 83

1. Evaluate.

(a) Arcsin $\sqrt{3}/2$

(b) Arccos $-\frac{1}{2}$

(c) $\text{Sin}^{-1} .8573$

(d) $\text{Cos}^{-1} .4536$

(e) $\text{Sin}^{-1} 1 + \text{Cos}^{-1} 1$

(f) $\text{Sin}^{-1} \frac{1}{2} + \text{Cos}^{-1} (-\frac{1}{2})$

(g) Arccos $(\text{Sin}^{-1} 0)$

(h) Arcsin $(\text{Cos}^{-1} 1)$

2. Simplify.

(a) $\sin (\text{Sin}^{-1} x)$

(b) $\cos (\text{Cos}^{-1} x)$

(c) $\text{Sin}^{-1} (\sin x)$

(d) $\text{Cos}^{-1} (\cos x)$

3. Evaluate.

(a) $\cos (\text{Sin}^{-1} .8)$

(b) $\sin (\text{Arccos } \frac{12}{13})$

(c) $\sin (\text{Arccos } .28)$

(d) $\cos (\text{Sin}^{-1} .96)$

4. Evaluate.

(a) $\sin (2 \text{ Arccos } \frac{1}{2})$

(b) $\cos (2 \text{ Sin}^{-1} \frac{1}{2})$

(c) $\text{Cos}^{-1} (2 \sin \pi/6)$

(d) $\text{Sin}^{-1} (2 \cos 2\pi/3)$

5. Prove.

(a) $\text{Sin}^{-1} 2x \ne 2 \text{ Sin}^{-1} x$

(b) $\text{Cos}^{-1} u + \text{Cos}^{-1} v \ne \text{Cos}^{-1} (u + v)$

6. Prove.

(a) $\cos (\text{Arcsin } a + \text{Arccos } b) = b\sqrt{1 - a^2} - a\sqrt{1 - b^2}$

(b) $\sin (2 \text{ Arcsin } t) = 2t\sqrt{1 - t^2}$

(c) $\sin (\text{Cos}^{-1} y) = \cos (\text{Sin}^{-1} y)$

(d) $\cos (2 \text{ Cos}^{-1} y) = 2y^2 - 1$

7. Solve for t.

(a) $\text{Cos}^{-1} \frac{3}{5} - \text{Sin}^{-1} \frac{4}{5} = \text{Cos}^{-1} t$

(b) $\text{Sin}^{-1} (-\frac{5}{13}) + \text{Cos}^{-1} \frac{4}{5} = \text{Sin}^{-1} t$

8. Prove.

(a) $\text{Sin}^{-1} (-y) = -\text{Sin}^{-1} y$

(b) $\text{Cos}^{-1} (-y) = \pi - \text{Cos}^{-1} y$

9. Let $-1 \le u < v \le 1$. Determine which of the following numbers is larger.

(a) $\text{Sin}^{-1} u$ or $\text{Sin}^{-1} v$

(b) $\text{Cos}^{-1} u$ or $\text{Cos}^{-1} v$

(c) $\text{Sin}^{-1} (u - v)$ or $\text{Sin}^{-1} (v - u)$

(d) $\text{Cos}^{-1} (u - v)$ or $\text{Cos}^{-1} (v - u)$

10. In calculus the smaller area between a circle of radius r and a chord d units from the center of the circle is given by the formula $f(r) - f(d)$, where

$$f(x) = x\sqrt{r^2 - x^2} + r^2 \operatorname{Sin}^{-1} \frac{x}{r}.$$

Calculate the area between a circle with a radius of 1 and a chord that is one-half the distance from the center of the circle.

84 THE INVERSE FUNCTIONS FOR THE TANGENT AND COTANGENT FUNCTIONS

None of the trigonometric functions has an inverse, but we have just seen how to restrict the domain of the sine and cosine functions to produce new functions that do have inverses.   So let's apply the same procedure to the tangent and cotangent functions.   First, *we define the* **Tangent function** (*the capital letter distinguishes this new function from the tangent function*) *as the function whose rule of correspondence is expressed*

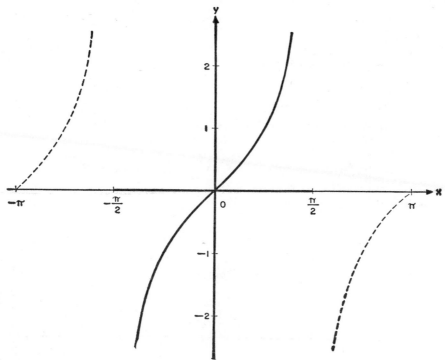

Figure 84-1

by the equation y = tan x, and whose domain is the set of numbers that satisfy the inequalities $-\pi/2 < x < \pi/2$.   The graph of the Tangent function is the solid curve in Fig. 84-1.

The Tangent function has an inverse, called the **Arctangent function.**   The domain of the Arctangent function is the set of all real numbers, and its range is the set of numbers between $-\pi/2$ and $\pi/2$.

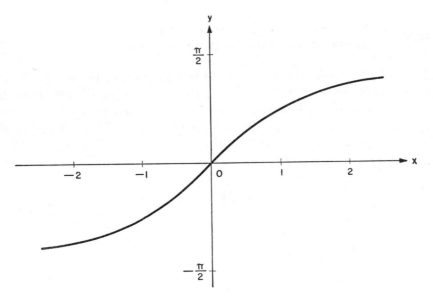

Figure 84-2

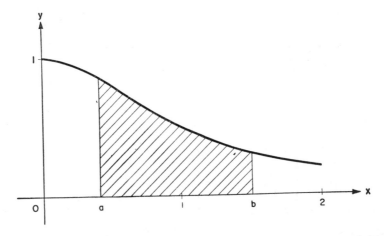

Figure 84-3

The number that is associated with a given real number y is denoted either by **Arctan** y or **Tan^{-1}** y.

DEFINITION 84-1.   *The Arctangent function is defined as follows:* $x = $ *Arctan* $y = $ *Tan^{-1}* y *if, and only if,* (i) *tan* $x = y$, *and* (ii) $-\pi/2 < x < \pi/2$.

We obtain the graph of the Arctangent function (Fig. 84-2) by reflecting the graph of the Tangent function about the line $y = x$.

> EXAMPLE 84-1.   Figure 84-3 shows the graph of the equation $y = 1/(1 + x^2)$ for values of $x \geq 0$. When you study calculus, you will find that the area bounded by the curve, the x-axis, and two vertical lines through the points a and b (the shaded area in the figure) is given by the formula $A = $ Arctan $b - $ Arctan a. What is this area if $a = 0$ and $b = 1$?

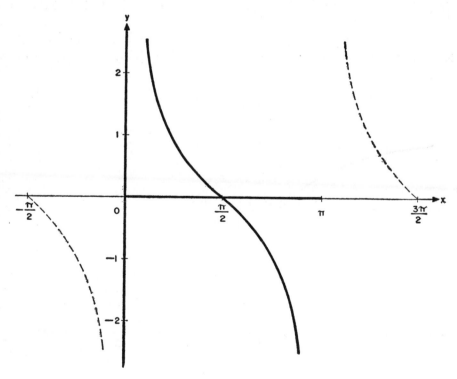

Figure 84-4

Solution. According to the formula we have just mentioned, $A =$ Arctan 1 — Arctan 0. You can easily find that Arctan $1 = \pi/4$ and Arctan $0 = 0$, and therefore $A = \pi/4$. (Inspect Fig. 84-3. **Does this** answer seem reasonable?)

We define the **Cotangent function** *as the function whose rule of correspondence is given by the equation* $y = \cot x$, *and whose domain is the set of numbers* $0 < x < \pi$. The graph of the Cotangent function is the solid curve shown in Fig. 84-4.

The Cotangent function has an inverse, called the **Arccotangent function.** The domain of the Arccotangent function is the set of all real numbers, and its range is the set of numbers between 0 and π. The number that is associated with a given real number y is denoted by **Arccot** y or **Cot**$^{-1}$ y.

DEFINITION 84-2. *The Arccotangent function is defined as follows:* $x =$ **Arccot** $y =$ **Cot**$^{-1}$ y *if, and only if,* (i) **cot** $x = y$ *and* (ii) $0 < x < \pi$.

We obtain the graph of the Arccotangent function (Fig. 84-5) by reflecting the graph of the Cotangent function about the line $y = x$.

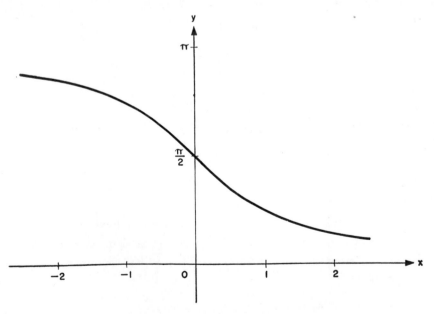

Figure 84-5

EXAMPLE 84-2.   Find Arctan 1 + Arccot 5.

Solution.   Using Table II, we find by interpolation that cot .197 = 5.
Since Arctan 1 = $\pi/4$ = .785, we have Arctan 1 + Arccot 5 = .197 +
.785 = .982.

EXAMPLE 84-3.   Show that if $x > 0$, then Arctan x = Arccot $\dfrac{1}{x}$.

Solution.   Let u = Arctan x.   Then tan $u = x$, and $-\pi/2 < u < \pi/2$.
In fact, since $x > 0$, we know that $0 < u < \pi/2$.   Since

$$\frac{1}{x} = \frac{1}{\tan u} = \cot u,$$

and $0 < u < \pi/2$, we have u = Arccot $1/x$; that is, Arctan x = Arccot $1/x$.

EXAMPLE 84-4.   Find sin (Arctan x), where x may be any real number.

Solution.   Let t = Arctan x.   Then tan $t = x$, and $-\pi/2 < t < \pi/2$.
Also (see Fig. 84-2), t and x have the same sign.   We wish to express
sin t in terms of x.   Since tan $t = x$, we have

$$\sin t = x \cos t,$$

$$\sin^2 t = x^2 \cos^2 t,$$

$$\sin^2 t = x^2(1 - \sin^2 t).$$

When we solve this last equation for $\sin^2 t$ we get

$$\sin^2 t = \frac{x^2}{1 + x^2}.$$

Therefore, either

$$\sin t = \frac{x}{\sqrt{1 + x^2}} \quad \text{or} \quad \sin t = \frac{-x}{\sqrt{1 + x^2}}.$$

Since t is between $-\pi/2$ and $\pi/2$, sin t and t have the same sign.
We have already seen that t and x have the same sign.   Now $x/\sqrt{1 + x^2}$
has the same sign as x, while $-x/\sqrt{1 + x^2}$ has the opposite sign, so
we conclude that

$$\sin t = \sin (\text{Arctan } x) = \frac{x}{\sqrt{1 + x^2}}.$$

We shall not discuss inverse functions for the cosecant and secant functions. They may be defined in the same way that the inverse functions for the other trigonometric functions are defined. For example, we introduce a "Secant" function and its inverse. If you master the concepts in this and the preceding section, you will have no trouble defining inverse functions for the secant and cosecant functions when you need to.

Problems 84

1. Evaluate.

(a) Arctan $\sqrt{3}$

(b) Arctan (-1)

(c) $\mathrm{Cot}^{-1}(-1)$

(d) $\mathrm{Cot}^{-1}\sqrt{3}$

(e) $\mathrm{Tan}^{-1}.2027$

(f) $\mathrm{Tan}^{-1}1.871$

(g) Arccot .0709

(h) Arccot (-7.096)

2. Express in terms of x.

(a) $\tan(\mathrm{Tan}^{-1}x)$

(b) $\cot(\mathrm{Cot}^{-1}x)$

(c) $\mathrm{Tan}^{-1}(\tan x)$

(d) $\mathrm{Cot}^{-1}(\cot x)$

(e) $\cos(\mathrm{Tan}^{-1}x)$

(f) $\sin(\mathrm{Cot}^{-1}x)$

(g) $\cos(\mathrm{Cot}^{-1}x)$

(h) $\tan(\mathrm{Cot}^{-1}1/x)$

3. Evaluate.

(a) $\sin(\mathrm{Tan}^{-1}.75)$

(b) $\cos(\mathrm{Arctan}-\tfrac{4}{3})$

(c) $\cos(\mathrm{Arccot}\,\tfrac{7}{24})$

(d) $\sin[\mathrm{Cot}^{-1}(-\tfrac{24}{7})]$

4. Express in terms of x.

(a) $\tan(2\,\mathrm{Tan}^{-1}x)$

(b) $\cot(2\,\mathrm{Cot}^{-1}x)$

(c) $\sin(2\,\mathrm{Arctan}\,x)$

(d) $\cos(2\,\mathrm{Arccot}\,x)$

5. For what values of x are the following equations valid?

(a) Arctan $2x = 2$ Arctan x

(b) $\mathrm{Tan}^{-1}\left(\dfrac{2x}{1-x^2}\right) = 2\,\mathrm{Tan}^{-1}x$

(c) Arccot $2x = 2$ Arccot x

(d) $\mathrm{Cot}^{-1}\left(\dfrac{x^2-1}{2x}\right) = 2\,\mathrm{Cot}^{-1}x$

6. Prove.

(a) $\tan(\tfrac{1}{2}\mathrm{Cos}^{-1}a) = \sqrt{\dfrac{1-a}{1+a}}$

(b) $\tan(\mathrm{Tan}^{-1}a + \mathrm{Tan}^{-1}1) = \dfrac{1+a}{1-a}$

(c) $\tan(\mathrm{Tan}^{-1}a - \mathrm{Tan}^{-1}b) = \dfrac{a-b}{1+ab}$

(d) $\tan(\mathrm{Cos}^{-1}a + \mathrm{Sin}^{-1}b) = \dfrac{\sqrt{(1-a^2)(1-b^2)}+ab}{a\sqrt{1-b^2}-b\sqrt{1-a^2}}$

7. For what values of x is the following equation valid?

$$\tan (2 \text{ Arcsin } x) = \frac{2\sqrt{1 - x^2}}{x(1 - x^2)}$$

8. Prove.

(a) $\text{Tan}^{-1} (-x) = -\text{Tan}^{-1} x$ (b) $\text{Cot}^{-1} (-x) = \pi - \text{Cot}^{-1} x$

9. Find the equation that relates $\text{Arctan } x$ and $\text{Arccot } 1/x$ if $x < 0$ (see Example 84-3).   What is the equation that relates $\text{Arctan } x$ and $\text{Arccot } x$?

10. Solve for t.

(a) $\text{Arctan } \frac{1}{3} + \text{Arctan } \frac{1}{2} = \text{Aresin } t$

(b) $\text{Arccot } \frac{1}{3} + \text{Arccot } \frac{1}{2} = \text{Arccos } t$

85 TRIGONOMETRIC EQUATIONS

Let y be any number that satisfies the inequalities $-1 \leq y \leq 1$. Then the equation $\sin x = y$ has infinitely many solutions.   For example, the equation $\sin x = \frac{1}{2}$ is satisfied by any number x that can be written either as $x = \pi/6 + 2k\pi$ or $x = 5\pi/6 + 2k\pi$, where k is an integer—positive, negative, or zero.   The complete solution to the equation $\sin x = \frac{1}{2}$ is the collection of all such numbers, and we shall denote this collection by using braces { }.   Thus, we write $\left\{ \frac{\pi}{6} + 2k\pi, \frac{5\pi}{6} + 2k\pi \right\}$ to represent the set of numbers

$$\frac{\pi}{6}, \frac{5\pi}{6}, \frac{13\pi}{6}, \frac{17\pi}{6}, -\frac{11\pi}{6}, -\frac{7\pi}{6}, \ldots$$

You should have no trouble using this notation to describe the sets of numbers that satisfy the more elaborate trigonometric equations that follow.

EXAMPLE 85-1.   Solve the equation $\sin^2 x = 1$.

Solution.   Clearly, $\sin^2 x = 1$ if, and only if, $\sin x = 1$ or $\sin x = -1$. The set of all solutions to the first of these equations is the set $\left\{ \frac{\pi}{2} + 2k\pi \right\}$, while the set $\left\{ \frac{3\pi}{2} + 2k\pi \right\}$ is the set of all the solutions to the second.   Therefore the solution to the equation $\sin^2 x = 1$ is the set

$$\left\{ \frac{\pi}{2} + 2k\pi, \frac{3\pi}{2} + 2k\pi \right\}.$$

EXAMPLE 85-2.   Solve the equation $\sin^2 x - 4 \sin x + 3 = 0$.

Solution.   In factored form, this equation reads

$$(\sin x - 3)(\sin x - 1) = 0,$$

and therefore $\sin x = 3$ or $\sin x = 1$.   There is no real number x for which $\sin x = 3$, and hence the set of solutions we are seeking consists of all the solutions to the equation $\sin x = 1$; that is, the set $\left\{\dfrac{\pi}{2} + 2k\pi\right\}$.

EXAMPLE 85-3.   Solve the equation $2 \sin^2 x + \cos^2 x - 4 \sin x + 2 = 0$.

Solution.   We replace $\cos^2 x$ with $1 - \sin^2 x$ and simplify:

$$2 \sin^2 x + 1 - \sin^2 x - 4 \sin x + 2 = 0,$$

$$\sin^2 x - 4 \sin x + 3 = 0.$$

This last equation was solved in Example 85-2.

EXAMPLE 85-4.   Solve the equation $\cos 2x + 3 \sin^2 x - 4 \sin x + 2 = 0$.

Solution.   We may use the identity $\cos 2x = 1 - 2 \sin^2 x$ to transform this equation into the equation that we solved in Example 85-2.

As in the case of algebraic equations, solutions may be "lost" or extraneous "solutions" may be introduced as you simplify a given trigonometric equation.   Thus, it is always wise to check your solutions by substituting in the given equations.

EXAMPLE 85-5.   Solve the equation $\sin x + \cos x = 1$.

Solution.   If we square both sides of this equation, we get

$$\sin^2 x + 2 \sin x \cos x + \cos^2 x = 1.$$

Since $\sin^2 x + \cos^2 x = 1$, and $2 \sin x \cos x = \sin 2x$, our problem reduces to solving the equation

$$\sin 2x = 0.$$

Now x is a solution to this last equation if $2x$ belongs to the set of numbers $\{k\pi\}$; that is, if x is in the set $\{k\pi/2\}$.   But not every number of this latter set satisfies the original equation.   The numbers $3\pi/2$ and π, for example, satisfy the equation $\sin 2x = 0$, but not the equation $\sin x + \cos x = 1$. You can easily check to see that those numbers in the set $\{k\pi/2\}$ that satisfy the equation $\sin x + \cos x = 1$ form the set $\{2k\pi, \pi/2 + 2k\pi\}$.

The trigonometric equation in Example 85-5 is of the form

85-1　　　　　　　　　$B \sin x + C \cos x = r.$

In Section 38 (Theorem 38-1), we showed that there were numbers A and b such that

$$B \sin x + C \cos x = A \sin (x + b).$$

Therefore, Equation 85-1 is equivalent to the equation

$$A \sin (x + b) = r,$$

where A and b are chosen in the way that is indicated in the proof of Theorem 38-1. To solve the equation of Example 85-5, we could have observed that

$$\sin x + \cos x = \sqrt{2} \sin \left(x + \frac{\pi}{4} \right).$$

The equation

$$\sin \left(x + \frac{\pi}{4} \right) = \frac{1}{\sqrt{2}}$$

is satisfied if $x + \pi/4$ is in the set $\{\pi/4 + 2k\pi, 3\pi/4 + 2k\pi\}$; that is, if x is in the set $\{2k\pi, \pi/2 + 2k\pi\}$.

Problems 85

1. Solve for x:
    (a) $\sqrt{3} \sin x + 2 = 0$　　　　　(c) $\sqrt{3} \tan x + 1 = 0$
    (b) $2 \cos x - 1 = 0$　　　　　　　(d) $\cot (x + 1) - \sqrt{3} = 0$

2. Solve for t:
    (a) $4 \sin^2 t - 1 = 0$　　　　　　(c) $2 \tan t - 2 \cot t + 3 = 0$
    (b) $6 \cos^2 t + 5 \cos t + 1 = 0$　(d) $2 \sec^2 t + 3 \sec t - 2 = 0$

3. Solve for x:
    (a) $\cos 2x + \sin x = 1$　　　　　(c) $4 \tan x + \sin 2x = 0$
    (b) $\sin 2x + \cos x = 0$　　　　　(d) $\tan 2x = \cos x$

4. Solve for t:
    (a) $\sin t = \sin (2t - \pi)$　　　　(c) $\cot t = \tan (2t - 3\pi)$
    (b) $\cos t = \sin (\pi - 3t)$　　　　(d) $\sec t = \csc (t + \pi/6)$

5. Solve for x:

    (a) $\sqrt{3}\cos x - \sin x = 1$ (b) $\sin x - 2\cos x = 1$

6. Solve the following systems of equations:

    (a) $\sin x + \cos y = 1$ (b) $y = a\sin x + b\cos x$

          $\sin 2x = \sin y$ $y = a\cos x + b\sin x,$

                                   where a and b are given numbers

                                   and $a \neq b$.

7. Solve for x:

    (a) $3\operatorname{Sin}^{-1} x = \pi/2$ (c) $\operatorname{Arcsin}(2x - x^2) = \operatorname{Arcsin}\frac{1}{2}$

    (b) $\operatorname{Arctan}(x - 1) = \pi/3$ (d) $\operatorname{Arccos}(x^2 - 2x) = \operatorname{Arccos} 1$

8. (a) Show that if $\sin a = \sin b$ and $\cos a = \cos b$, then $a = b + 2k\pi$.

    (b) Show that if $\sin a = \cos b$ and $\cos a = \sin b$, then $a + b = \pi/2 + 2k\pi$.

9. Solve for x: $\operatorname{Arctan} x = 2\operatorname{Sin}^{-1} x/2$.

10. Solve for r, θ, and ϕ, if $r > 0$, $0 \leq \theta \leq \pi$, $0 \leq \phi \leq 2\pi$.

$$r\sin\theta\cos\phi = 1$$
$$r\sin\theta\sin\phi = 1$$
$$r\cos\theta = 2.$$

86 GRAPHICAL SOLUTION OF TRIGONOMETRIC EQUATIONS

Certain trigonometric equations are quite difficult to solve by analytic methods. Many times we can find the solutions to such equations by means of graphs. To illustrate the use of graphical methods to solve trigonometric equations, we shall first solve an equation that we previously solved analytically.

    EXAMPLE 86-1. Solve the equation $\sin x + \cos x = 1$.

    Solution. We first write the equation as $\sin x = 1 - \cos x$. Then we graph the two equations $y = \sin x$ and $y = 1 - \cos x$ (Fig. 86-1). The x-coordinates of the points of intersection of these graphs are the solutions to the original equation. From Fig. 86-1 we obtain the same set of solutions as we did in Example 85-5—the set of numbers $\{2k\pi, \pi/2 + 2k\pi\}$.

    We cannot solve the equation in the next example by simple formulas such as we used in the last section. Nevertheless, it is a type of equation that arises frequently in certain kinds of applied problems.

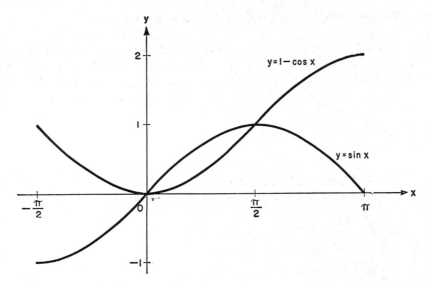

Figure 86-1

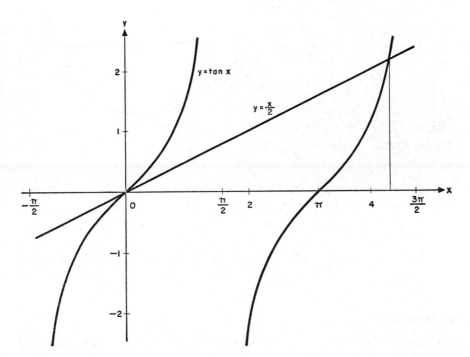

Figure 86-2

EXAMPLE 86-2.   Solve the equation $x - 2 \tan x = 0$.

Solution.   We write this equation as $x/2 = \tan x$. Its solutions are the x-coordinates of the points of intersection of the graphs of the equations $y = x/2$ and $y = \tan x$.   From Fig. 86-2 we see that two of the solutions to our equation are $x = 0$ and $x = 4.3$ (approximately).

EXAMPLE 86-3.   Solve the equation $x \sin x = 1$.

Solution.   We first observe, as we could have in the previous example, that if t is a solution, so is $-t$.   For $(-t) \sin (-t) = t \sin t$.   So if the right side of this equation is 1, so is the left side.   Therefore, we

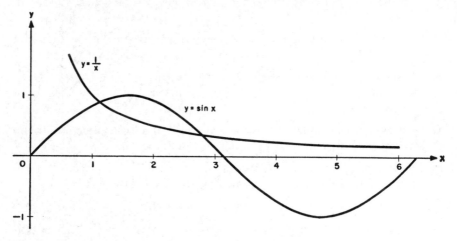

Figure 86-3

need only look for positive solutions.   We write the given equation as $\sin x = 1/x$, and then graph the equations $y = \sin x$ and $y = 1/x$ for $x > 0$ (see Fig. 86-3).   We then see that the original equation has infinitely many solutions, two of which are the numbers 1.1 and 2.8. It is clear from Fig. 86-3 that those solutions whose absolute value is large are approximately integral multiples of π.   This fact was to be expected, since $1/x$ is small when x is large, and the solutions to our equation are almost solutions to the equation $\sin x = 0$.

Problems 86

Use graphical methods to find some of the solutions to each of the following equations.

1. $\sin 2x - \tan x = 0$.   **2.** $\tan \pi x = x + 1$.

3. $\pi x - 3 \sin \pi x = 0.$

4. $\sin 2\pi x + \cos 2\pi x = \pi x.$

5. $\sin (3x - 1) = x.$

6. $x \tan \pi x = 1.$

7. $x^2 = \cos 2\pi x.$

8. $x - \text{Arcsin } x = 0.$

9. $x - \text{Arccos } x = 0.$

10. $x + \text{Tan}^{-1} x = 1.$

11. $2^x = \sin \pi x.$

12. $\log x = \sin \pi x.$

13. $|\sin \pi x| = x - [x].$

Review Problems, Chapter Ten

You should be able to answer the following questions without referring back to the text.

1. Can the graph of F be symmetric with respect to the y-axis if F has an inverse?

2. If a function F has an inverse, show that F^{-1} has an inverse and that $(F^{-1})^{-1} = F.$

3. What can you say about the signs of the following?
    (a) $\sin (\text{Cos}^{-1} y)$ (c) $\tan (\text{Arcsin } y)$
    (b) $\cos (\text{Sin}^{-1} y)$ (d) $\sin (\text{Arctan } y)$

4. Does every linear function have an inverse? If a linear function has an inverse, show that the inverse function is a linear function.

5. The greatest integer function does not have an inverse. Can you restrict its domain to get a function that does have an inverse?

6. The domain of a function f is the set of all numbers $x > \frac{1}{3}$, and its rule of correspondence is expressed by the equation $y = \dfrac{x + 2}{3x - 1}.$ Show that f^{-1} exists and that $f^{-1} = f.$

7. Let a and b be positive numbers. Show that $\text{Sin}^{-1} a = \text{Cos}^{-1} b$ if, and only if, $a^2 + b^2 = 1.$

8. Solve for x:
    (a) $\text{Sin}^{-1} (\text{Cos}^{-1} x) = 0$ (c) $\text{Tan}^{-1} (\text{Arccos } x) = \pi/3$
    (b) $\text{Sin}^{-1} (\text{Cos}^{-1} x) = \pi/4$ (d) $\text{Tan}^{-1} (\text{Arccot } x) = 1$

9. For what values of x is $|\sin x| = |\cos x|$? For what values of x is $\sin x < \cos x$?

10. Graph the equation $\sin (y - x) = 0.$

11. Solve the following equations, graphically if necessary.
    (a) $\text{Arcsin } x = \text{Arccos } x$ (c) $\text{Arctan } x = \text{Arccos } x$
    (b) $\text{Arctan } x = \text{Arccot } x$ (d) $\text{Sin } x = \text{Sin}^{-1} x$

Miscellaneous Problems, Chapter Ten

These problems are designed to test your ability to apply your knowledge of inverse functions to somewhat more difficult problems.

1. An A.P. is a linear function whose domain is the set of positive integers. Do all A.P.'s have inverses? Is there an A.P. whose inverse is also an A.P.?

2. A function f is **strictly increasing** if whenever $x_1 < x_2$, then $f(x_1) < f(x_2)$. A function f is **strictly decreasing** if whenever $x_1 < x_2$, then $f(x_1) > f(x_2)$. Show that strictly increasing functions and strictly decreasing functions have inverses. Can you construct a function that is neither strictly increasing nor strictly decreasing yet has an inverse?

3. Let the function f be determined by the equation $f(x) = x + \dfrac{1}{x}$. Show that f does not have an inverse. Can you restrict the domain of f to obtain a function F that does have an inverse?

4. Let F be a function with an inverse, and suppose that the addition formula for F is $F(u + v) = F(u) + F(v)$. Show that the addition formula for F^{-1} is $F^{-1}(u + v) = F^{-1}(u) + F^{-1}(v)$.

5. Let F be the function that is defined by the equation $F(x) = [x] + x$. Does F have an inverse? If so, define F^{-1} by giving its domain and its rule of correspondence.

6. Suppose the positive solutions $x_1, x_2, x_3, \ldots$ of the equation $\tan x = 2$ are arranged so that $0 < x_1 < x_2 < x_3 \ldots$. Show that $\{x_n\}$ is an A.P. If $y_n = 10^{x_n} \sin x_n$, show that $\{y_n\}$ is a G.P.

7. Let m be a positive integer and let N be the number of solutions to the equation $\sin x = \frac{1}{2}$ such that $0 < x < m\pi$. Express N in terms of m.

8. Draw the graph of the function F that is defined by the equation $F(x) = (x - [x])^2 + [x]$. Does F have an inverse? If so, draw the graph of F^{-1}.

9. Find graphically two solutions to the system of equations
$$y = \tan x$$
$$x = \tan y.$$

10. The smaller area between a unit circle and a chord d units from the center of the circle is $\frac{1}{4}$ the area of the whole circle. Use Problem 83-10 and graphs to find d.

11. Let $\{u_n\}$ be the sequence that is defined by the equation
$$u_n = (-1)^{n-1} \frac{x^{2n-1}}{2n - 1} \quad \text{for } n \geq 1.$$

In calculus it is shown that the limit of the sequence of partial sums $\{S_n\}$ of the sequence $\{u_n\}$ is $\operatorname{Tan}^{-1} x$, if $|x| \leq 1$.   Thus,

$$\operatorname{Tan}^{-1} x = x - \frac{x^3}{3} + \frac{x^5}{5} - \ldots + (-1)^{n-1} \frac{x^{2n-1}}{2n-1} + \ldots$$

for $|x| \leq 1$.   Let $x = 1$ and calculate the partial sum S_5 to find the approximate value of π.

12. Prove that $\pi/4 = \operatorname{Tan}^{-1} \frac{1}{2} + \operatorname{Tan}^{-1} \frac{1}{3}$.   Evaluate the right-hand side of this equation by using the equation of $\operatorname{Tan}^{-1} x$ in the preceding problem to obtain an approximate value of $\pi/4$.

13. Let x be the solution to the equation $\sin x = 1/x$ that lies between 10π and $21\pi/2$.   Show that $x - 10\pi < \frac{1}{20}$.

TABLES

AND

ANSWERS

TABLE I

n	0	1	2	3	4	5	6	7	8	9
1.0	.0000	.0043	.0086	.0128	.0170	.0212	.0253	.0294	.0334	.0374
1.1	.0414	.0453	.0492	.0531	.0569	.0607	.0645	.0682	.0719	.0755
1.2	.0792	.0828	.0864	.0899	.0934	.0969	.1004	.1038	.1072	.1106
1.3	.1139	.1173	.1206	.1239	.1271	.1303	.1335	.1367	.1399	.1430
1.4	.1461	.1492	.1523	.1553	.1584	.1614	.1644	.1673	.1703	.1732
1.5	.1761	.1790	.1818	.1847	.1875	.1903	.1931	.1959	.1987	.2014
1.6	.2041	.2068	.2095	.2122	.2148	.2175	.2201	.2227	.2253	.2279
1.7	.2304	.2330	.2355	.2380	.2405	.2430	.2455	.2480	.2504	.2529
1.8	.2553	.2577	.2601	.2625	.2648	.2672	.2695	.2718	.2742	.2765
1.9	.2788	.2810	.2833	.2856	.2878	.2900	.2923	.2945	.2967	.2989
2.0	.3010	.3032	.3054	.3075	.3096	.3118	.3139	.3160	.3181	.3201
2.1	.3222	.3243	.3263	.3284	.3304	.3324	.3345	.3365	.3385	.3404
2.2	.3424	.3444	.3464	.3483	.3502	.3522	.3541	.3560	.3579	.3598
2.3	.3617	.3636	.3655	.3674	.3692	.3711	.3729	.3747	.3766	.3784
2.4	.3802	.3820	.3838	.3856	.3874	.3892	.3909	.3927	.3945	.3962
2.5	.3979	.3997	.4014	.4031	.4048	.4065	.4082	.4099	.4116	.4133
2.6	.4150	.4166	.4183	.4200	.4216	.4232	.4249	.4265	.4281	.4298
2.7	.4314	.4330	.4346	.4362	.4378	.4393	.4409	.4425	.4440	.4456
2.8	.4472	.4487	.4502	.4518	.4533	.4548	.4564	.4579	.4594	.4609
2.9	.4624	.4639	.4654	.4669	.4683	.4698	.4713	.4728	.4742	.4757
3.0	.4771	.4786	.4800	.4814	.4829	.4843	.4857	.4871	.4886	.4900
3.1	.4914	.4928	.4942	.4955	.4969	.4983	.4997	.5011	.5024	.5038
3.2	.5051	.5065	.5079	.5092	.5105	.5119	.5132	.5145	.5159	.5172
3.3	.5185	.5198	.5211	.5224	.5237	.5250	.5263	.5276	.5289	.5302
3.4	.5315	.5328	.5340	.5353	.5366	.5378	.5391	.5403	.5416	.5428
3.5	.5441	.5453	.5465	.5478	.5490	.5502	.5514	.5527	.5539	.5551
3.6	.5563	.5575	.5587	.5599	.5611	.5623	.5635	.5647	.5658	.5670
3.7	.5682	.5694	.5705	.5717	.5729	.5740	.5752	.5763	.5775	.5786
3.8	.5798	.5809	.5821	.5832	.5843	.5855	.5866	.5877	.5888	.5899
3.9	.5911	.5922	.5933	.5944	.5955	.5966	.5977	.5988	.5999	.6010
4.0	.6021	.6031	.6042	.6053	.6064	.6075	.6085	.6096	.6107	.6117
4.1	.6128	.6138	.6149	.6160	.6170	.6180	.6191	.6201	.6212	.6222
4.2	.6232	.6243	.6253	.6263	.6274	.6284	.6294	.6304	.6314	.6325
4.3	.6335	.6345	.6355	.6365	.6375	.6385	.6395	.6405	.6415	.6425
4.4	.6435	.6444	.6454	.6464	.6474	.6484	.6493	.6503	.6513	.6522
4.5	.6532	.6542	.6551	.6561	.6571	.6580	.6590	.6599	.6609	.6618
4.6	.6628	.6637	.6646	.6656	.6665	.6675	.6684	.6693	.6702	.6712
4.7	.6721	.6730	.6739	.6749	.6758	.6767	.6776	.6785	.6794	.6803
4.8	.6812	.6821	.6830	.6839	.6848	.6857	.6866	.6875	.6884	.6893
4.9	.6902	.6911	.6920	.6928	.6937	.6946	.6955	.6964	.6972	.6981
5.0	.6990	.6998	.7007	.7016	.7024	.7033	.7042	.7050	.7059	.7067
5.1	.7076	.7084	.7093	.7101	.7110	.7118	.7126	.7135	.7143	.7152
5.2	.7160	.7168	.7177	.7185	.7193	.7202	.7210	.7218	.7226	.7235
5.3	.7243	.7251	.7259	.7267	.7275	.7284	.7292	.7300	.7308	.7316
5.4	.7324	.7332	.7340	.7348	.7356	.7364	.7372	.7380	.7388	.7396

TABLE I—Cont.

n	0	1	2	3	4	5	6	7	8	9
5.5	.7404	.7412	.7419	.7427	.7435	.7443	.7451	.7459	.7466	.7474
5.6	.7482	.7490	.7497	.7505	.7513	.7520	.7528	.7536	.7543	.7551
5.7	.7559	.7566	.7574	.7582	.7589	.7597	.7604	.7612	.7619	.7627
5.8	.7634	.7642	.7649	.7657	.7664	.7672	.7679	.7686	.7694	.7701
5.9	.7709	.7716	.7723	.7731	.7738	.7745	.7752	.7760	.7767	.7774
6.0	.7782	.7789	.7796	.7803	.7810	.7818	.7825	.7832	.7839	.7846
6.1	.7853	.7860	.7868	.7875	.7882	.7889	.7896	.7903	.7910	.7917
6.2	.7924	.7931	.7938	.7945	.7952	.7959	.7966	.7973	.7980	.7987
6.3	.7993	.8000	.8007	.8014	.8021	.8028	.8035	.8041	.8048	.8055
6.4	.8062	.8069	.8075	.8082	.8089	.8096	.8102	.8109	.8116	.8122
6.5	.8129	.8136	.8142	.8149	.8156	.8162	.8169	.8176	.8182	.8189
6.6	.8195	.8202	.8209	.8215	.8222	.8228	.8235	.8241	.8248	.8254
6.7	.8261	.8267	.8274	.8280	.8287	.8293	.8299	.8306	.8312	.8319
6.8	.8325	.8331	.8338	.8344	.8351	.8357	.8363	.8370	.8376	.8382
6.9	.8388	.8395	.8401	.8407	.8414	.8420	.8426	.8432	.8439	.8445
7.0	.8451	.8457	.8463	.8470	.8476	.8482	.8488	.8494	.8500	.8506
7.1	.8513	.8519	.8525	.8531	.8537	.8543	.8549	.8555	.8561	.8567
7.2	.8573	.8579	.8585	.8591	.8597	.8603	.8609	.8615	.8621	.8627
7.3	.8633	.8639	.8645	.8651	.8657	.8663	.8669	.8675	.8681	.8686
7.4	.8692	.8698	.8704	.8710	.8716	.8722	.8727	.8733	.8739	.8745
7.5	.8751	.8756	.8762	.8768	.8774	.8779	.8785	.8791	.8797	.8802
7.6	.8808	.8814	.8820	.8825	.8831	.8837	.8842	.8848	.8854	.8859
7.7	.8865	.8871	.8876	.8882	.8887	.8893	.8899	.8904	.8910	.8915
7.8	.8921	.8927	.8932	.8938	.8943	.8949	.8954	.8960	.8965	.8971
7.9	.8976	.8982	.8987	.8993	.8998	.9004	.9009	.9015	.9020	.9025
8.0	.9031	.9036	.9042	.9047	.9053	.9058	.9063	.9069	.9074	.9079
8.1	.9085	.9090	.9096	.9101	.9106	.9112	.9117	.9122	.9128	.9133
8.2	.9138	.9143	.9149	.9154	.9159	.9165	.9170	.9175	.9180	.9186
8.3	.9191	.9196	.9201	.9206	.9212	.9217	.9222	.9227	.9232	.9238
8.4	.9243	.9248	.9253	.9258	.9263	.9269	.9274	.9279	.9284	.9289
8.5	.9294	.9299	.9304	.9309	.9315	.9320	.9325	.9330	.9335	.9340
8.6	.9345	9350	.9355	.9360	.9365	.9370	.9375	.9380	.9385	.9390
8.7	.9395	.9400	.9405	.9410	.9415	.9420	.9425	.9430	.9435	.9440
8.8	.9445	.9450	.9455	.9460	.9465	.9469	.9474	.9479	.9484	.9489
8.9	.9494	.9499	.9504	.9509	.9513	.9518	.9523	.9528	.9533	.9538
9.0	.9542	.9547	.9552	.9557	.9562	.9566	.9571	.9576	.9581	.9586
9.1	.9590	.9595	.9600	.9605	.9609	.9614	.9619	.9624	.9628	.9633
9.2	.9638	.9643	.9647	.9652	.9657	.9661	.9666	.9671	.9675	.9680
9.3	.9685	.9689	.9694	.9699	.9703	.9708	.9713	.9717	.9722	.9727
9.4	.9731	.9736	.9741	.9745	.9750	.9754	.9759	.9763	.9768	.9773
9.5	.9777	.9782	.9786	.9791	.9795	.9800	.9805	.9809	.9814	.9818
9.6	.9823	.9827	.9832	.9836	.9841	.9845	.9850	.9854	.9859	.9863
9.7	.9868	.9872	.9877	.9881	.9886	.9890	.9894	.9899	.9903	.9908
9.8	.9912	.9917	.9921	.9926	.9930	.9934	.9939	.9943	.9948	.9952
9.9	.9956	.9961	.9965	.9969	.9974	.9978	.9983	.9987	.9991	.9996

TABLE II

t	sin t	cos t	tan t	cot t	sec t	csc t
.00	.0000	1.0000	.0000	. . . . .	1.000	. . . . .
.01	.0100	1.0000	.0100	99.997	1.000	100.00
.02	.0200	.9998	.0200	49.993	1.000	50.00
.03	.0300	.9996	.0300	33.323	1.000	33.34
.04	.0400	.9992	.0400	24.987	1.001	25.01
.05	.0500	.9988	.0500	19.983	1.001	20.01
.06	.0600	.9982	.0601	16.647	1.002	16.68
.07	.0699	.9976	.0701	14.262	1.002	14.30
.08	.0799	.9968	.0802	12.473	1.003	12.51
.09	.0899	.9960	.0902	11.081	1.004	11.13
.10	.0998	.9950	.1003	9.967	1.005	10.02
.11	.1098	.9940	.1104	9.054	1.006	9.109
.12	.1197	.9928	.1206	8.293	1.007	8.353
.13	.1296	.9916	.1307	7.649	1.009	7.714
.14	.1395	.9902	.1409	7.096	1.010	7.166
.15	.1494	.9888	.1511	6.617	1.011	6.692
.16	.1593	.9872	.1614	6.197	1.013	6.277
.17	.1692	.9856	.1717	5.826	1.015	5.911
.18	.1790	.9838	.1820	5.495	1.016	5.586
.19	.1889	.9820	.1923	5.200	1.018	5.295
.20	.1987	.9801	.2027	4.933	1.020	5.033
.21	.2085	.9780	.2131	4.692	1.022	4.797
.22	.2182	.9759	.2236	4.472	1.025	4.582
.23	.2280	.9737	.2341	4.271	1.027	4.386
.24	.2377	.9713	.2447	4.086	1.030	4.207
.25	.2474	.9689	.2553	3.916	1.032	4.042
.26	.2571	.9664	.2660	3.759	1.035	3.890
.27	.2667	.9638	.2768	3.613	1.038	3.749
.28	.2764	.9611	.2876	3.478	1.041	3.619
.29	.2860	.9582	.2984	3.351	1.044	3.497
.30	.2955	.9553	.3093	3.233	1.047	3.384
.31	.3051	.9523	.3203	3.122	1.050	3.278
.32	.3146	.9492	.3314	3.018	1.053	3.179
.33	.3240	.9460	.3425	2.920	1.057	3.086
.34	.3335	.9428	.3537	2.827	1.061	2.999
.35	.3429	.9394	.3650	2.740	1.065	2.916
.36	.3523	.9359	.3764	2.657	1.068	2.839
.37	.3616	.9323	.3879	2.578	1.073	2.765
.38	.3709	.9287	.3994	2.504	1.077	2.696
.39	.3802	.9249	.4111	2.433	1.081	2.630

TABLE II—Cont.

t	sin t	cos t	tan t	cot t	sec t	csc t
.40	.3894	.9211	.4228	2.365	1.086	2.568
.41	.3986	.9171	.4346	2.301	1.090	2.509
.42	.4078	.9131	.4466	2.239	1.095	2.452
.43	.4169	.9090	.4586	2.180	1.100	2.399
.44	.4259	.9048	.4708	2.124	1.105	2.348
.45	.4350	.9004	.4831	2.070	1.111	2.299
.46	.4439	.8961	.4954	2.018	1.116	2.253
.47	.4529	.8916	.5080	1.969	1.122	2.208
.48	.4618	.8870	.5206	1.921	1.127	2.166
.49	.4706	.8823	.5334	1.875	1.133	2.125
.50	.4794	.8776	.5463	1.830	1.139	2.086
.51	.4882	.8727	.5594	1.788	1.146	2.048
.52	.4969	.8678	.5726	1.747	1.152	2.013
.53	.5055	.8628	.5859	1.707	1.159	1.978
.54	.5141	.8577	.5994	1.668	1.166	1.945
.55	.5227	.8525	.6131	1.631	1.173	1.913
.56	.5312	.8473	.6269	1.595	1.180	1.883
.57	.5396	.8419	.6410	1.560	1.188	1.853
.58	.5480	.8365	.6552	1.526	1.196	1.825
.59	.5564	.8309	.6696	1.494	1.203	1.797
.60	.5646	.8253	.6841	1.462	1.212	1.771
.61	.5729	.8196	.6989	1.431	1.220	1.746
.62	.5810	.8139	.7139	1.401	1.229	1.721
.63	.5891	.8080	.7291	1.372	1.238	1.697
.64	.5972	.8021	.7445	1.343	1.247	1.674
.65	.6052	.7961	.7602	1.315	1.256	1.652
.66	.6131	.7900	.7761	1.288	1.266	1.631
.67	.6210	.7838	.7923	1.262	1.276	1.610
.68	.6288	.7776	.8087	1.237	1.286	1.590
.69	.6365	.7712	.8253	1.212	1.297	1.571
.70	.6442	.7648	.8423	1.187	1.307	1.552
.71	.6518	.7584	.8595	1.163	1.319	1.534
.72	.6594	.7518	.8771	1.140	1.330	1.517
.73	.6669	.7452	.8949	1.117	1.342	1.500
.74	.6743	.7385	.9131	1.095	1.354	1.483
.75	.6816	.7317	.9316	1.073	1.367	1.467
.76	.6889	.7248	.9505	1.052	1.380	1.452
.77	.6961	.7179	.9697	1.031	1.393	1.437
.78	.7033	.7109	.9893	1.011	1.407	1.422
.79	.7104	.7038	1.009	.9908	1.421	1.408

TABLE II—Cont.

t	$\sin t$	$\cos t$	$\tan t$	$\cot t$	$\sec t$	$\csc t$
.80	.7174	.6967	1.030	.9712	1.435	1.394
.81	.7243	.6895	1.050	.9520	1.450	1.381
.82	.7311	.6822	1.072	.9331	1.466	1.368
.83	.7379	.6749	1.093	.9146	1.482	1.355
.84	.7446	.6675	1.116	.8964	1.498	1.343
.85	.7513	.6600	1.138	.8785	1.515	1.331
.86	.7578	.6524	1.162	.8609	1.533	1.320
.87	.7643	.6448	1.185	.8437	1.551	1.308
.88	.7707	.6372	1.210	.8267	1.569	1.297
.89	.7771	.6294	1.235	.8100	1.589	1.287
.90	.7833	.6216	1.260	.7936	1.609	1.277
.91	.7895	.6137	1.286	.7774	1.629	1.267
.92	.7956	.6058	1.313	.7615	1.651	1.257
.93	.8016	.5978	1.341	.7458	1.673	1.247
.94	.8076	.5898	1.369	.7303	1.696	1.238
.95	.8134	.5817	1.398	.7151	1.719	1.229
.96	.8192	.5735	1.428	.7001	1.744	1.221
.97	.8249	.5653	1.459	.6853	1.769	1.212
.98	.8305	.5570	1.491	.6707	1.795	1.204
.99	.8360	.5487	1.524	.6563	1.823	1.196
1.00	.8415	.5403	1.557	.6421	1.851	1.188
1.01	.8468	.5319	1.592	.6281	1.880	1.181
1.02	.8521	.5234	1.628	.6142	1.911	1.174
1.03	.8573	.5148	1.665	.6005	1.942	1.166
1.04	.8624	.5062	1.704	.5870	1.975	1.160
1.05	.8674	.4976	1.743	.5736	2.010	1.153
1.06	.8724	.4889	1.784	.5604	2.046	1.146
1.07	.8772	.4801	1.827	.5473	2.083	1.140
1.08	.8820	.4713	1.871	.5344	2.122	1.134
1.09	.8866	.4625	1.917	.5216	2.162	1.128
1.10	.8912	.4536	1.965	.5090	2.205	1.122
1.11	.8957	.4447	2.014	.4964	2.249	1.116
1.12	.9001	.4357	2.066	.4840	2.295	1.111
1.13	.9044	.4267	2.120	.4718	2.344	1.106
1.14	.9086	.4176	2.176	.4596	2.395	1.101
1.15	.9128	.4085	2.234	.4475	2.448	1.096
1.16	.9168	.3993	2.296	.4356	2.504	1.091
1.17	.9208	.3902	2.360	.4237	2.563	1.086
1.18	.9246	.3809	2.427	.4120	2.625	1.082
1.19	.9284	.3717	2.498	.4003	2.691	1.077

TABLE II—Cont.

t	sin t	cos t	tan t	cot t	sec t	csc t
1.20	.9320	.3624	2.572	.3888	2.760	1.073
1.21	.9356	.3530	2.650	.3773	2.833	1.069
1.22	.9391	.3436	2.733	.3659	2.910	1.065
1.23	.9425	.3342	2.820	.3546	2.992	1.061
1.24	.9458	.3248	2.912	.3434	3.079	1.057
1.25	.9490	.3153	3.010	.3323	3.171	1.054
1.26	.9521	.3058	3.113	.3212	3.270	1.050
1.27	.9551	.2963	3.224	.3102	3.375	1.047
1.28	.9580	.2867	3.341	.2993	3.488	1.044
1.29	.9608	.2771	3.467	.2884	3.609	1.041
1.30	.9636	.2675	3.602	.2776	3.738	1.038
1.31	.9662	.2579	3.747	.2669	3.878	1.035
1.32	.9687	.2482	3.903	.2562	4.029	1.032
1.33	.9711	.2385	4.072	.2456	4.193	1.030
1.34	.9735	.2288	4.256	.2350	4.372	1.027
1.35	.9757	.2190	4.455	.2245	4.566	1.025
1.36	.9779	.2092	4.673	.2140	4.779	1.023
1.37	.9799	.1994	4.913	.2035	5.014	1.021
1.38	.9819	.1896	5.177	.1931	5.273	1.018
1.39	.9837	.1798	5.471	.1828	5.561	1.017
1.40	.9854	.1700	5.798	.1725	5.883	1.015
1.41	.9871	.1601	6.165	.1622	6.246	1.013
1.42	.9887	.1502	6.581	.1519	6.657	1.011
1.43	.9901	.1403	7.055	.1417	7.126	1.010
1.44	.9915	.1304	7.602	.1315	7.667	1.009
1.45	.9927	.1205	8.238	.1214	8.299	1.007
1.46	.9939	.1106	8.989	.1113	9.044	1.006
1.47	.9949	.1006	9.887	.1011	9.938	1.005
1.48	.9959	.0907	10.983	.0910	11.029	1.004
1.49	.9967	.0807	12.350	.0810	12.390	1.003
1.50	.9975	.0707	14.101	.0709	14.137	1.003
1.51	.9982	.0608	16.428	.0609	16.458	1.002
1.52	.9987	.0508	19.670	.0508	19.695	1.001
1.53	.9992	.0408	24.498	.0408	24.519	1.001
1.54	.9995	.0308	32.461	.0308	32.476	1.000
1.55	.9998	.0208	48.078	.0208	48.089	1.000
1.56	.9999	.0108	92.620	.0108	92.626	1.000
1.57	1.0000	.0008	1255.8	.0008	1255.8	1.000
1.58	1.0000	−.0092	−108.65	−.0092	−108.65	1.000
1.59	.9998	−.0192	−52.067	−.0192	−52.08	1.000
1.60	.9996	−.0292	−34.233	−.0292	−34.25	1.000

TABLE III

θ	sin θ	tan θ	cot θ	cos θ	
0°	.0000	.0000	. . . . .	1.0000	90°
1°	.0175	.0175	57.290	.9998	89°
2°	.0349	.0349	28.636	.9994	88°
3°	.0523	.0524	19.081	.9986	87°
4°	.0698	.0699	14.301	.9976	86°
5°	.0872	.0875	11.430	.9962	85°
6°	.1045	.1051	9.5144	.9945	84°
7°	.1219	.1228	8.1443	.9925	83°
8°	.1392	.1405	7.1154	.9903	82°
9°	.1564	.1584	6.3138	.9877	81°
10°	.1736	.1763	5.6713	.9848	80°
11°	.1908	.1944	5.1446	.9816	79°
12°	.2079	.2126	4.7046	.9781	78°
13°	.2250	.2309	4.3315	.9744	77°
14°	.2419	.2493	4.0108	.9703	76°
15°	.2588	.2679	3.7321	.9659	75°
16°	.2756	.2867	3.4874	.9613	74°
17°	.2924	.3057	3.2709	.9563	73°
18°	.3090	.3249	3.0777	.9511	72°
19°	.3256	.3443	2.9042	.9455	71°
20°	.3420	.3640	2.7475	.9397	70°
21°	.3584	.3839	2.6051	.9336	69°
22°	.3746	.4040	2.4751	.9272	68°
23°	.3907	.4245	2.3559	.9205	67°
24°	.4067	.4452	2.2460	.9135	66°
25°	.4226	.4663	2.1445	.9063	65°
26°	.4384	.4877	2.0503	.8988	64°
27°	.4540	.5095	1.9626	.8910	63°
28°	.4695	.5317	1.8807	.8829	62°
29°	.4848	.5543	1.8040	.8746	61°
30°	.5000	.5774	1.7321	.8660	60°
31°	.5150	.6009	1.6643	.8572	59°
32°	.5299	.6249	1.6003	.8480	58°
33°	.5446	.6494	1.5399	.8387	57°
34°	.5592	.6745	1.4826	.8290	56°
35°	.5736	.7002	1.4281	.8192	55°
36°	.5878	.7265	1.3764	.8090	54°
37°	.6018	.7536	1.3270	.7986	53°
38°	.6157	.7813	1.2799	.7880	52°
39°	.6293	.8098	1.2349	.7771	51°
40°	.6428	.8391	1.1918	.7660	50°
41°	.6561	.8693	1.1504	.7547	49°
42°	.6691	.9004	1.1106	.7431	48°
43°	.6820	.9325	1.0724	.7314	47°
44°	.6947	.9657	1.0355	.7193	46°
45°	.7071	1.0000	1.0000	.7071	45°
	cos θ	cot θ	tan θ	sin θ	θ

TABLE IV

n	$\log n!$	n	$\log n!$	n	$\log n!$
1	0.0000	35	40.0142	69	98.2333
2	0.3010	36	41.5705		
3	0.7782	37	43.1387	70	100.0784
4	1.3802	38	44.7185	71	101.9297
		39	46.3096	72	103.7870
5	2.0792			73	105.6503
6	2.8573	40	47.9116	74	107.5196
7	3.7024	41	49.5244		
8	4.6055	42	51.1477	75	109.3946
9	5.5598	43	52.7812	76	111.2754
		44	54.4246	77	113.1619
10	6.5598			78	115.0540
11	7.6012	45	56.0778	79	116.9516
12	8.6803	46	57.7406		
13	9.7943	47	59.4127	80	118.8547
14	10.9404	48	61.0939	81	120.7632
		49	62.7841	82	122.6770
15	12.1165			83	124.5961
16	13.3206	50	64.4831	84	126.5204
17	14.5511	51	66.1906		
18	15.8063	52	67.9066	85	128.4498
19	17.0851	53	69.6309	86	130.3843
		54	71.3633	87	132.3238
20	18.3861			88	134.2683
21	19.7083	55	73.1037	89	136.2177
22	21.0508	56	74.8519		
23	22.4125	57	76.6077	90	138.1719
24	23.7927	58	78.3712	91	140.1310
		59	80.1420	92	142.0948
25	25.1906			93	144.0632
26	26.6056	60	81.9202	94	146.0364
27	28.0370	61	83.7055		
28	29.4841	62	85.4979	95	148.0141
29	30.9465	63	87.2972	96	149.9964
		64	89.1034	97	151.9831
30	32.4237			98	153.9744
31	33.9150	65	90.9163	99	155.9700
32	35.4202	66	92.7359	100	157.9700
33	36.9387	67	94.5620		
34	38.4702	68	96.3945		

ANSWERS

Problems 1. *Page 4.*

1. (a) -3; (c) 4400. **2.** (a) $1 - 3x$; (c) $x - 6$. **3.** (a) $x^3 + y^3$; (c) $x^3 - 6x^2y + 12xy^2 - 8y^3$; (e) $6x^2 + 5xy - 6y^2$. **4.** (a) $(x + y)(x^2 - xy + y^2)$; (c) $(2x - 3/y)(4x^2 + 6x/y + 9/y^2)$; (e) $(.1x - 3)(.1x + 3)$; (g) $(x - 2)(x + 2)(x^2 + 2x + 4)(x^2 - 2x + 4)$; (i) $(2x - y - 3z)(2x - y + 3z)$; (k) $2z(z - 3x)(x + 3y)$. **5.** (a) *Positive* integer if $x = 1$ or $x = 2$, integer for all integral values of x; (c) Positive integer if x is odd positive integer other than 1, integer if x is odd.

Problems 2. *Page 8.*

1. (a) $\frac{17}{1}$; (c) $\frac{14}{3}$; (e) $\frac{1}{3}$.   **2.** $\frac{21}{11}$.   **4.** (a) $(x + y/z - w)$; (c) $1/bc$; (e) $3/(x - y)$; (g) $1/(1 - x)$. **5.** (a) $1/(x + y)$; (c) $xy/(x + y)$; (e) $\frac{3}{4}$. **6.** (a) $\dfrac{x}{x^2 + xy + y^2}$; (c) $\dfrac{14x + 9}{6x(1 - 2x)(1 + 2x)}$; (e) $\dfrac{5(1 - x)}{3(x - 4)}$; (g) 0.   **7.** Not true for $x = 1$.

Problems 3. *Page 12.*

1. (a) $\frac{7}{3}$; (c) $(a + b)/2$. **5.** $b = \frac{142}{999}$, $c = 3$. **7.** Yes, no, irrational unless the rational factor is 0. **10.** (a) Irrational; (c) Irrational.

Problems 4. *Page 16.*

5. (a) False; (c) True; (e) True; (g) True. **6.** (a) $x > 3$; (c) $x > \frac{15}{17}$; (e) $x > 1$; (g) $x < 1$ or $x > 4$; (i) $x < -4$ or $x > 1$. **9.** (a) $x = 3.141$, $y = 3.142$, for example; (c) $x = 6.1$, $y = 6.9$, for example. **11.** $\frac{50}{9} < R_2 < \frac{50}{4}$.

Problems 5. *Page 19.*

1. (a) 0; (c) $x \geq 1$; (e) $x \leq 0$; (g) $x > -1$ or $x \leq -3$; (i) $x < 0$ or $x > 4$. **3.** $21.743 \leq$ perimeter ≤ 21.765. **5.** Less than 3.2 miles.

Problems 6. *Page 22.*

1. (a) $x = 6$ or $x = -6$; (c) No numbers; (e) $x = 5$ or $x = -5$. **2.** (a) $x \geq 0$; (c) $x = 2$ or $x = -1$; (e) $x \geq 0$. **3.** x is either 3 units from 0 or 7 units from 0. **4.** (a) 5 or 3; (c) 1 or 7. **5.** No. **7.** Yes.

Problems 7. *Page 25.*

1. (a) $-\frac{2}{3} < x < \frac{2}{3}$; (c) $-2 < x < 4$; (e) $-\frac{1}{6} \leq x \leq \frac{7}{6}$. **2.** (a) $x > \frac{3}{2}$ or $x < -\frac{3}{2}$; (c) $x > 9$ or $x < -7$; (e) $x \geq 2$ or $x \leq -1$. **3.** (a) True for all x; (c) $x \geq \frac{5}{2}$; (e) $x > \frac{1}{2}$. **5.** (a) $|x - 2| < 1$; (c) $|x - \frac{5}{4}| < \frac{5}{4}$; (e) $|8x + 1| < 7$.

Problems 8. *Page 29.*

1. (a) $-\frac{1}{9}$; (c) -12; (e) $\frac{4}{9}$; (g) x; (i) $\frac{2}{3}x^2y^{-5}$; (k) x^6. **2.** (a) $\frac{7}{12}$; (c) $1/(1 + x)$; (e) $x + y$; (g) $\frac{13}{72}$; (i) $(x + 1)/x^3$. **3.** (a) $(1/x^{-2}) - (1/y^{-2})$; (c) $(1/x^{-2}) + y^{-3}$; (e) $(x/3)^{-2}$. **5.** (a) $\frac{2}{3} < x < \frac{4}{3}$; (c) $x > 2$ or $x < -2$; (e) $x \geq 3$.

Problems 9. *Page 33.*

1. (a) 4; (c) -27; (e) 81; (g) -1024. **3.** (a) $\sqrt[4]{x^3}/x$; (c) $|x + y|$; (e) $(\sqrt{x} - y)/(x - y^2)$. **4.** (a) $x^{1/3}y^{-1/3}$; (c) $x^{5/6}y^{-1/3}$; (e) $-x^{-1/3}$; (g) $x^{1/4}$.

Review Problems. *Page 34.*

1. (a) 0, 1, 2, 3, 4. **2.** (a) $2(x - 2)(x + 2)$; (b) $3(x - 2)(x - 3)$. **3.** Yes, if $a \neq 0$. **8.** (a) $-2 < x < 5$. **9.** $|x - \frac{5}{2}| < \frac{3}{2}$. **11.** No. **13.** No. **15.** No. **17.** (a) $\sqrt[3]{x^2 y}/xy$.

Miscellaneous Problems. *Page 35.*

1. (a) True; (c) May be true or false; (e) May be true or false. **3.** $x = 2$, $y = 2$. **7.** Copper is cheaper on cost-per-year basis. If cost-per-year is the same, then the iron pipe costs less than \$100. **9.** $10 \pm \frac{5}{90}$. **11.** $(25 + 5 \cdot 2^{1/3} + 2^{2/3})/123$.

Problems 10. *Page 41.*

1. (a) $f(n) = n + 1$; (c) $h(n) = 1$. **2.** (a) All positive numbers; (c) $x \geq 1$ or $x \leq -2$; (e) $t > 1$ or $t \leq 0$. **3.** (a) $\{2,5,8\}$; (c) $\{0,1\}$; (e) $\{1\}$. **4.** (a) 5; (c) $3\sqrt{y} - 1$; (e) $3|a| - 1$; (g) 3; (i) $3y - \frac{1}{3}$. **5.** (a) 1; (c) 12; (e) $a^2 + 2ah + h^2$; (g) $2a + h$; (i) y.

Problems 11. *Page 44.*

1. (a) 4; (c) 3; (e) $2\sqrt{2}$. **2.** (a), (c), and (d) are true. **3.** All true. **5.** $C = 80x + 180,000/x$. **7.** $d = 50\sqrt{41t^2 - 50t + 25}$ for $t \geq 1$. **9.** $V = 4x(4 - x)(5 - x)$.

Problems 12. *Page 50.*

1. (a) $\sqrt{29}$; (c) 5; (e) $\sqrt{16 + 2\sqrt{10}}$. **2.** (a) $2\sqrt{a^2 + b^2}$; (c) $2\sqrt{a + b}$. **3.** Not right triangle. **5.** One set consists of the points $(4,2)$ and $(4,-5)$. **7.** 8. **9.** $(4,0)$. **11.** (a) Not collinear; (c) Collinear.

Problems 13. *Page 55.*

3. $(-3,2)$. **5.** (a) 1.2; (c) 1.2. **9.** The point $(-a,b)$ is on the graph.

Problems 14. *Page 59.*

1. $(3,2)$. **3.** $(\frac{1}{2}, \frac{2}{5})$. **8.** (b,a), $(-a,-b)$, and $(-b,-a)$. **9.** $a = 2$ or $a = 0$.

Problems 15. *Page 62.*

1. $f(x) = 3x/2$. **3.** (a) 129 miles, (b) 4 hr., 38 min. **5.** Not unless $a = 0$. **7.** Constant represents his hourly wage. 250/3 hr.

Problems 16. *Page 66.*

1. $f(x) = 3x - 2$. **2.** (a) $f(x) = mx$; (c) $f(x) = mx + m - 1$; (e) $f(x) = (x/4) + \frac{5}{4}$. **3.** (a) Yes. **5.** (a) $\frac{1}{4}$; (c) $-\frac{3}{2}$. **7.** $V = -32t + 100$. $\frac{25}{8}$ sec. after firing. **11.** 80 cal.

Problems 17. *Page 70.*

1. $f(x) = 5/x$. **3.** $f(x) = 24/x^3$. **4.** 8 amp. $R > 240$ ohms. **5.** $5\sqrt{10}$ cm. **9.** $h = 2$ ft.

Review Problems. *Page 71.*

1. (b) and (d) are true. **3.** It must lie in a rectangle 2 units wide and 4 units high with center at the origin. **4.** $f(x) = 2x + 1$. **9.** Yes. **10.** 3, −1. **13.** $f(i) = i/12$.

Miscellaneous Problems. *Page 72.*

2. $R = \dfrac{10x}{3x + 10}$. **3.** $L = L_0(mt + 1)$. **4.** $t = \dfrac{12 - x}{5} + \dfrac{\sqrt{x^2 + 36}}{4}$. **5.** $x = 3$. **8.** (a) $p = 1$; (c) $p = -\frac{1}{3}$. **10.** True if $x \geq 0$ or if x is a negative integer.

Problems 18. *Page 78.*

3. (a) 2.7; (c) 2.97; (e) 3.3. **8.** $3000(.6)^t$, 233 cu ft. **9.** $N = N_0(.8)^t$.

Problems 19. *Page 81.*

1. (a) $\log_3 81 = 4$; (c) $\log_M 5 = k$. **2.** (a) 125; (c) 2; (e) 2. **3.** (a) $x = 1$; (c) x is any positive number except 1. **4.** (a) 1.6; (c) −.4. **7.** −2. **9.** (a) 5; (c) 5. **10.** (a) 3; (c) 5.

Problems 20. *Page 85.*

2. (a) −.41; (c) 1.38; (e) 2.20; (g) 3.17; (i) 4.50; (k) −1.10; (m) .08. **3.** (a) $\frac{5}{2} \log_b x$; (c) $\log_b 3x^{5/4}$. **4.** (a) $\frac{100}{69}$. **5.** $\sqrt[3]{5}$. **6.** (a) 14; (c) a^2. **9.** $\log_{10} 4 = .6020$, $\log_{10} 5 = .6990$, $\log_{10} 6 = .7781$, $\log_{10} 8 = .9030$, $\log_{10} 9 = .9542$.

Problems 21. *Page 89.*

1. (a) 1.58; (c) −.58. **3.** .65. **9.** (a) 2; (c) $\frac{2}{3}$. **11.** 7.

Problems 22. *Page 93.*

1. (a) 4.8627; (c) .9600 − 5.   **2.** (a) .9499; (c) .2330 − 2; (e) 3.6031.
3. (a) 155,000; (c) 2.52.   **4.** (a) 61.1; (c) 6.31.   **5.** (a) .00455; (c) .0753;
(e) 6.84; (g) 4130.   **8.** (a) 1.43; (c) .356.   **9.** (a) .3633.

Problems 23. *Page 97.*

1. (a) .9550; (c) .3938 + 3; (e) .5712 − 6.   **2.** (a) 3.565; (c) .5226.
3. (a) −.4005; (c) 1.3644.   **4.** (a) 2.483; (c) 1.585; (e) .001913.
5. 3.25, too small.   **7.** $\frac{38}{9}$.

Problems 24. *Page 100.*

1. (a) 107.6; (c) 17.41; (e) .183.   **2.** (a) −.1692.   **3.** (a) $25^{7/6}$; (c) 3^{21}.
5. $A = p(1.03)^n$, \$25.16.   **7.** 2.108 sec.

Problems 25. *Page 104.*

1. (a) .63; (c) 1.76.   **2.** (a) .37; (c) .836.   **3.** (a) .46.   **5.** 6 hr 20 min.
7. $N = 7$, $k = 10$g2.   **9.** 6% (approx.).

Review Problems. *Page 104.*

2. (a) True; (c) False; (e) True; (g) True.   **3.** $(\log_e 10)^2$.   **5.** 12,630.
7. $x = 1$ or $x = 100$.   **10.** $x \geq 1$.   **14.** $\frac{5}{3}$.
15. $n = \dfrac{\log(a - S + rS) - \log a}{\log r}$; (c) $n = \sqrt{\dfrac{\log y}{\log x}}$.

Miscellaneous Problems. *Page 105.*

1. $N^{\log_b a}$.   **3.** No.   **8.** No.   **9.** $A = p\left(1 + \dfrac{i}{2}\right)^n$, 23 yr., 7%.

Problems 26. *Page 113.*

1. (a) (1,0); (c) (0,1); (e) (0,−1).   **2.** (a) $(-\sqrt{2}/2, -\sqrt{2}/2)$; (c) $(\sqrt{2}/2,$
$-\sqrt{2}/2)$.   **3.** (a) $(-\frac{1}{2}, \sqrt{3}/2)$; (c) $(-\frac{1}{2}, -\sqrt{3}/2)$.   **4.** (a) $(\sqrt{3}/2, -\frac{1}{2})$;
(c) $(\sqrt{3}/2, -\frac{1}{2})$; (e) $(\sqrt{3}/2, \frac{1}{2})$.   **5.** (.54, .84).   **6.** (a) II; (c) I; (e) IV.

Problems 27. *Page 117.*

1. (a) $\sin t = 2/\sqrt{5}$; (c) $\sec t = -3$.   **2.** (a) .84; (c) .07.   **3.** (a) $-3\pi/2$,
$-\pi/2$, $\pi/2$, $3\pi/2$; (c) -2π, $-\pi$, 0, π, 2π.   **4.** (a) Positive; (c) Positive;
(e) Negative.

Problems 28. *Page 121.*

1. (a) .8985; (c) 1.038; (e) .3662. 2. cos .333. 3. To 4 decimal places the numbers are equal. 6. (a) $\pi/6$; (c) .17; (e) .92. 7. $\sqrt{15}/4$. 10. (a) .5312; (c) $-.02976$.

Problems 29. *Page 125.*

1. (a) $-.4078$; (c) 1.185; (e) -1.450. 2. (a) $\frac{1}{2}$; (c) $1/\sqrt{3}$; (e) $\sqrt{2}$; (g) -2; (i) $-1/\sqrt{3}$. 3. (a) $(-.4158, .9094)$, (c) $(-.6539, -.7565)$; (e) $(.9602, -.2794)$; (g) $(.8776, -.4794)$; (i) $(-.4536, -.8912)$. 4. (a) .8718; (c) .1343; (e) 1.908; (g) $-.3071$. 5. (a) cos 6; (c) tan 10.

Problems 30. *Page 130.*

5. $f(x) = f(-x)$. 6. $f(-x) = -f(x)$. 7. (a) Increasing; (c) Decreasing; (e) Decreasing. 8. (a) True; (c) True. 13. $x = .74$.

Problems 31. *Page 135.*

4. $-\sin u$. 6. $\dfrac{\sqrt{2}}{4}(\sqrt{3} - 1)$. 9. $\dfrac{\sqrt{2}}{4}(1 + \sqrt{3})$. 15. (a) 0. 16. (a) $\pi/3$; (c) $\pi/12$. 17. (b), (c), and (f) are even. 18. (a), (b), (c), (d), and (e) are odd.

Problems 32. *Page 139.*

1. $\dfrac{\cot u - \tan v}{1 + \cot u \tan v}$. 4. (a) $\dfrac{\sqrt{2}}{4}(\sqrt{3} - 1)$; (c) $-\sqrt{2}(\sqrt{3} + 1)/4$. 5. (a) .9975; (c) .8415. 6. (a) 1; (c) 0. 7. (a) cos u; (c) cos y. 8. $\sin x \cos y \cos z + \cos x \sin y \cos z + \cos x \cos y \sin z - \sin x \sin y \sin z$.

Problems 33. *Page 141.*

1. $\dfrac{2 \tan t}{1 - \tan^2 t}$. 3. $\dfrac{1 - \cos 2t}{1 + \cos 2t}$. 4. (a) $\dfrac{\sqrt{2 + \sqrt{2}}}{2}$; (c) $\sqrt{2} - 1$.

6. $3 \sin t \cos^2 t - \sin^3 t$. 7. $\dfrac{\sqrt{2 - \sqrt{2 + \sqrt{2}}}}{2}$. 8. (a) 1; (c) $-\cos 4t$.

9. (a) $\frac{24}{25}$; (c) $\frac{117}{125}$. 11. (a) .4208; (c) .6967. 12. (a) $\dfrac{2z}{a^2}\sqrt{a^2 - z^2}$;

(c) $\dfrac{\sqrt{a - \sqrt{a^2 - z^2}}}{2a}$.

Section 34. *Page 145.*

1. (a) $\sin t$; (c) $\cos u$. **2.** (a) $1/\sqrt{1 - \sin^2 t}$; (c) $\sqrt{1 - \sin^2 t}/\sin t$.

3. (a) $-\cot 2t$; (c) 1. **5.** $\pi/4$. **6.** (a) $1 + \dfrac{\sin 2t}{2}$; (c) $\sec 2t$.

7. $\tan \tfrac{1}{2}x = \dfrac{\sin x}{1 + \cos x}$. **10.** $2\pi/3$.

Problems 35. *Page 150.*

1. (c) and (d) are periodic. **3.** (a) 1; (c) 1; (e) 2π. **5.** $F(3.5) = -1$,
$F(-\tfrac{16}{3}) = -1$, $F(201.7) = -1$. **6.** (a) π; (c) $\pi/2$. **7.** $f(7) = \tfrac{1}{2}$.
9. (a) Not necessarily; (c) Not necessarily.

Problems 36. *Page 154.*

2. (a) Unbounded; (c) Greatest lower bound is 0; (e) Unbounded.
3. (a) 5, (c) $\tfrac{1}{2}$; (e) $\tfrac{1}{2}$. **5.** Amplitude $\tfrac{3}{4}$; period 2π. **6.** (a) 3; (c) .4.
7. Amplitude is 1.

Problems 37. *Page 158.*

2. (a) Frequency is 1, phase shift is $-\tfrac{1}{2}$; (c) Frequency is 1, phase shift is $\tfrac{1}{2}$.
3. (a) Frequency is $3/2\pi$, phase shift is $\pi/6$, and amplitude is 4; (c) Frequency is 1, phase shift is 2, and amplitude is 3. **5.** $A = B$, $a = c$, and
$b = d + \pi/2$. **7.** $B = A$, $c = -a$, and $d = \pi - b$. **9.** $B = -A$,
$c = a$, and $d = b + \pi/2$. **11.** $\sqrt{10^5/2\pi}$.

Problems 38. *Page 163.*

4. (a) Infinitely many solutions. **10.** $\tfrac{1}{720}$.

Problems 39. *Page 167.*

2. (a) $5\pi/4$; (c) $11\pi/6$; (e) 1.836. **3.** (a) $15°$; (c) $172°$; (e) $40.8°$.
4. (a) $27° \, 12'$; (c) $57° \, 17' \, 45''$; (e) $177° \, 36' \, 1''$. **5.** (a) .017; (c) .0000048;
(e) 2.6. **8.** $51° \, 25' \, 43''$. **9.** (a) $78°$; (c) 58^2 degrees. **11.** (.3907,
.9205).

Problems 40. *Page 171.*

3. $5\pi/12$. **5.** $45/4\pi$ in. **9.** $42\pi/5$. **11.** $x = r \cos \omega T + \sqrt{L^2 - r^2 \sin^2 \omega T}$.

Problems 41. *Page 176.*

1. (a) .6508; (c) −11.430; (e) .0584; (g) 1.07; (i) 3.86. 2. (a) cos 3°;
(c) sin 7. 3. (a) $\sin\theta = \dfrac{3}{\sqrt{13}}$; (c) $\tan\theta = -\tfrac{5}{3}$; (e) $\sec\theta = \dfrac{\sqrt{313}}{12}$.
4. (a) 53°; (c) 162°; (d) 294°. 7. (a) (4.096,2.868); (c) (−4.890,−1.040).
9. (−.8090 cos θ + .5878 sin θ, −.5878 cos θ − .8090 sin θ).

Problems 42. *Page 182.*

1. ($\sqrt{2}$, $\sqrt{2}$). 3. (a) 53°; (c) 16°. 4. (a) $b = 4.2$, $r = 6.5$; (c) $a = 4.1$,
$r = 9.17$. 5. 89 ft. 7. $\alpha = 45°$. 9. 14 ft. 11. $16\pi + 24\sqrt{3}$.

Problems 43. *Page 187.*

2. (a) $\alpha = 75°$, $c = 5$, $b = 2.6$; (c) $\gamma = 95°\,42'$, $a = 6.9$, $b = 9.7$.
3. (a) $\beta = 38°\,41'$, $\gamma = 111°\,19'$, $c = 7.4$ or $\beta = 141°\,19'$, $\gamma = 8°\,41'$,
$c = 1.2$; (c) No triangle. 5. 270 miles. 7. 6.4 in. and 5 in. 9. 4.3
miles.

Problems 44. *Page 190.*

1. (a) $c = \sqrt{7}$, $\alpha = 79°$, $\beta = 41°$; (c) $\sqrt{65}$; (e) $c = 2\sqrt{26}$. 3. 7.9 ft.
6. Approximately 5500 ft. 10. (a) 34°, 56°, 90°; (c) 27°, 63°, 90°;
(e) 57°, 59°, 64°.

Problems 45. *Page 194.*

1. (a) $\tfrac{35}{2}$; (c) 17.   2. (a) 3.3; (c) 30.   3. (a) $\tfrac{3}{4}\sqrt{15}$;
(c) $\dfrac{\sqrt{\log 30\ \log (15/2)\ \log (10/3)\ \log (6/5)}}{4}$. 5. No. 7. $4\sqrt{66}$ rd.

Review Problems. *Page 195.*

1. No. 3. (a), (b), (d), (e), and ·(f) are true. 5. (a) .7456; (c) 1.8.
7. (a) $(-\tfrac{4}{5},\tfrac{3}{5})$. 11. (a) $0 < x < \pi$, $2\pi < x < 3\pi$, etc. 13. (a) $x = 0$.
16. (a) 0; (c) $(-1)^n$. 17. 22π miles.

Miscellaneous Problems. *Page 196.*

1. (a) Origin; (c) Not symmetric if $bm \neq 0$; (c) y-axis.   4. $\pi/2 - 1$.
11. (a) $2r^2\left(\dfrac{\pi}{3} - \dfrac{\sqrt{3}}{4}\right)$.   13. 32 miles, 216 ft.   14. $5r^2 \tan 18°$
$(1 - \sin 18°)$.

Problems 46. *Page 203.*

1. (a) $9 + 2i$; (c) $8 - 3i$. **2.** (a) $8 + 4i$; (c) $17i$. **3.** $-i, 1, -1, i, -1$.
4. (a) $-1 + 12i$; (c) 11; (e) $-2i$; (g) 8. **6.** $x = -\sqrt{\frac{3}{2}} + \sqrt{\frac{3}{2}}\,i$ or
$x = \sqrt{\frac{3}{2}} - \sqrt{\frac{3}{2}}\,i$. **7.** (a) $2i - 1, 1 + 2i$. **9.** $(a,b)(c,d) = (ac - bd, ad + bc)$.

Problems 47. *Page 206.*

7. $-i, -1, i, 1, -i, i$. **9.** (a) $\frac{7}{2} - \frac{5}{2}i$; (c) $-\frac{8}{25} - \frac{6}{25}i$. **11.** (a) $\frac{3}{2}$,
(c) $\frac{2}{5} - \frac{1}{5}i$.

Problems 48. *Page 210.*

1. (a) $2, 30°$; (c) $1, 180°$; (e) $2, 240°$. **2.** (a) $-\sqrt{3} + i$; (c) $\sqrt{2} + \sqrt{2}\,i$;
(e) $-6.58 - 2.39i$.   **8.** (a) $uv = 48\left(\cos\dfrac{7\pi}{12} + i\sin\dfrac{7\pi}{12}\right)$,
$\dfrac{u}{v} = 3\left(\cos\dfrac{\pi}{12} + i\sin\dfrac{\pi}{12}\right)$;   (c) $uv = 6\,(\cos 80° + i\sin 80°)$,
$\dfrac{u}{v} = 24\,(\cos 40° + i\sin 40°)$. **9.** (a) $-12 + 12i$; (c) 2. **11.** (a) Circle
of radius 1, center at origin; (c) Region bounded by circle of radius 2,
center at origin.

Problems 49. *Page 215.*

1. (a) 1; (c) 2^{12}; (e) Practically 1. **3.** (a) $1, \dfrac{-1 + \sqrt{3}\,i}{2}, \dfrac{-1 - \sqrt{3}\,i}{2}$;
(c) $-1, \dfrac{1 - \sqrt{3}\,i}{2}, \dfrac{1 + \sqrt{3}\,i}{2}$. **5.** (a) $4i$; (c) $\sqrt{\sqrt{2} + 1} - \sqrt{\sqrt{2} - 1}\,i$;
(e) $(1 - i)/\sqrt{2}$. **7.** $\cos^3\theta - 3\cos\theta\sin^2\theta$. **9.** (a) $1 - i, i - 1$; (c) i,
$(-\sqrt{3} + i)/2, (\sqrt{3} - i)/2$.

Review Problems. *Page 216.*

1. $-\frac{5}{97}(5 - 13i)$. **3.** The set of all real numbers. **5.** (a), (c), and (d).
6. (a) 3, (c) Not for *all* complex numbers. **7.** $3 - i$, yes, yes.

Miscellaneous Problems. *Page 217.*

1. (a) Circle of radius 3, center at point $(2,0)$; (c) Area between circles cen-
tered at origin of radii 1 and 2; includes latter circle, too. **2.** (a) If the
line joining z and the origin is rotated through an angle of α radians, it

becomes the line joining the point $f(z)$ and the origin. **4.** $1 + 2i$, $-1 - 2i$. **5.** $u = 0 + bi, v = 0 + ci$ $(c \neq 0)$. **6.** (a) Circle of radius 2 with center at origin.

Problems 50. *Page 222.*

1. (a) $x^4 + x^2 + x - 24$; (c) $x^6 + 4x^5 - 2x^4 - 7x^3 + 4x^2 - 2x - 8$.
2. (a) $6x^5 - 8x^4 + 5x^3 - 10x^2 + 9x - 2$; (c) $13x^3 - 4x^2 - 4x - 65$.
3. (a) $m + n$; (c) nk. **4.** (a) 25; (c) $2x^2 + 2$; (c) $9hx^2 + h(9h + 2)x + 3h^3 + h^2 - 2h$. **6.** (a) $q = 4, r = 1$; (c) $q = 17, r = 8$. **7.** (a) $Q(x) = x^2 - x + 1, R(x) = -x$; (c) $Q(x) = 1, R(x) = 2x^2 + 2$. **8.** (a) $Q(x) = x^2 + 1$, $R = 0$; (c) $Q(x) = x^4 - x^3 + x^2 - x + 1$, $R = 0$; (e) $Q(x) = 3x^3 + x^2 - 2x + 11$, $R = 0$.

Problems 51. *Page 226.*

1. (a) $\frac{17}{10}$; (c) If $b \neq 0$, $x = (3 + d)/2$; (e) If y is neither 0 nor 2, $x = (-3y - 1)/(y^2 - 2y)$; (g) If $y \neq i$, $x = (1 + y)/(i + y)$. **3.** 4000 min. **5.** $\frac{35}{6}$. **7.** (a) 464; (c) 3310.

Problems 52. *Page 232.*

1. (a) $0, -\frac{3}{2}$; (c) $3, 0$. **2.** (a) $-1 + \sqrt{2}, -1 - \sqrt{2}$. **3.** (a) $(7 + \sqrt{77})/2$, $(7 - \sqrt{77})/2$; (c) $(-2 + \sqrt{6})/4, (-2 - \sqrt{6})/4$; (e) $-\sqrt{3} + 2$, $-\sqrt{3} - 2$. **4.** (a) $(-b + \sqrt{b^2 - ac})/a, (-b - \sqrt{b^2 - ac})/a$; (c) $(v_0 + \sqrt{v_0^2 - 2gs})/g, (v_0 - \sqrt{v_0^2 - 2gs})/g$. **5.** (a) Positive; (c) Negative. **6.** (a) $\dfrac{-i + \sqrt{7}}{4}, \dfrac{-i - \sqrt{7}}{4}$; (c) $-1, 1 + 2i$. **7.** (a) Twice. **8.** (a) $(1 + i\sqrt{3})y/2, (1 - i\sqrt{3})y/2$. **10.** (a) $1 - \sqrt{2} < x < 1 + \sqrt{2}$; (c) $x < -1$ or $x > 4$. **11.** (a) $|k| > 2\sqrt{5}$; (c) $k \leq \frac{1}{7}$. **13.** 420 mph.

Problems 53. *Page 235.*

1. (a) $i, -i, \sqrt{2}, -\sqrt{2}$; (c) $\sqrt{1 + i}, -\sqrt{1 + i}, \sqrt{1 - i}, -\sqrt{1 - i}$.
2. (a) $-1, 32$; (c) $8, -\frac{8}{27}$. **3.** (a) $\pi/2$; (c) $\pi/3$. **4.** (a) 3; (c) No solution. **7.** $2, -1 + i\sqrt{3}, -1 - i\sqrt{3}, -1, (1 - i\sqrt{3})/2, (1 + i\sqrt{3})/2$.
9. $\dfrac{3 + \sqrt{5}}{2}, \dfrac{1 + \sqrt{5}}{2}$.

Problems 54. *Page 238.*

1. (a) $x^2 - 5x - 1$; (c) $\left(x - \dfrac{5 + \sqrt{29}}{2}\right)\left(x - \dfrac{5 - \sqrt{29}}{2}\right)$.

2. (a) -1; (c) 9.

5. $\left(x - \dfrac{7 + \sqrt{53}}{2}\right)\left(x - \dfrac{7 - \sqrt{53}}{2}\right)$;

(c) $\left(x - \dfrac{-1 + i\sqrt{3}}{2}\right)\left(x - \dfrac{-1 - i\sqrt{3}}{2}\right)$;

(e) $\dfrac{2}{3}\left(x - \dfrac{3 + 3i\sqrt{255}}{16}\right)\left(x - \dfrac{3 - 3i\sqrt{255}}{16}\right)$.

6. (a) $x^2 + (4x/3) + \frac{1}{3}$; (c) $x^2 - 4x + 5$; (e) $x^2 - 1 + 2\sqrt{2}\,i$; (g) $x^2 + b^2$.

7. (a) $\left(x - \dfrac{1 + i\sqrt{3}}{2}\,y\right)\left(x - \dfrac{1 - i\sqrt{3}}{2}\,y\right)$; (c) $(x - k)(kx + 1)$.

Problems 55. *Page 241.*

1. (a) $x^4 - 3x^3 + 9x^2 - 27x + 82$, $R = -245$; (c) $x^2 + \sqrt{5}\,x + 5$, $R = 5 + 5\sqrt{5}$. **2.** (a) 2; (c) 485. **3.** (a) 100,000,003. **4.** (a) $x^3 - x^2 + x - 1$; (c) $x^3 - 3ix^2 - 4x + 2i$. **5.** $P(0) = 4$.

7. (a) $(x + 2)(x - 2)(x + 2i)(x - 2i)$;

(c) $12\left(x - \dfrac{2}{3}\right)\left(x - \dfrac{3 + \sqrt{73}}{8}\right)\left(x - \dfrac{3 - \sqrt{73}}{8}\right)$.

8. (a) 2; (c) $\dfrac{3 + \sqrt{133}}{4}, \dfrac{3 - \sqrt{133}}{4}$.

Problems 56. *Page 244.*

1. No. No. **3.** $a = 3, b = -2$.

6. (a) $(x - 1)\left(x - \dfrac{-1 + \sqrt{5}}{2}\right)\left(x - \dfrac{-1 - \sqrt{5}}{2}\right)$;

(c) $(x - 1)(x + 2)\left(x - \dfrac{-1 + i\sqrt{3}}{2}\right)\left(x - \dfrac{1 - i\sqrt{3}}{2}\right)$;

(e) $(x - 1)^3\left(x - \dfrac{-3 + i\sqrt{15}}{2}\right)\left(x - \dfrac{-3 - i\sqrt{15}}{2}\right)$.

8. $\dfrac{3}{2}x^2 + \dfrac{x}{2} + 1$. **9.** $\dfrac{-5}{2}x^2 + \dfrac{11}{2}x$.

Problems 57. *Page 249.*

1. (a) $x^3 + x^2 + x + 1$; (c) $x^4 - 4x^3 + 11x^2 - 14x + 10$. **2.** (a) $i, -i, \frac{1}{2}$; (c) $3 - 2i, (-1 + \sqrt{10})/3, (-1 - \sqrt{10})/3$; (e) $-1 + \sqrt{6}, -1 - \sqrt{6}$.

6. (a) $(x - 1)(x^2 + x + 1)$; (c) $(x^2 - 2x + 2)(x^2 - x - 1)$.

Problems 58.   *Page 252.*

2. (a) None; (c) $0, -\frac{1}{2}, \frac{1}{2}, -\frac{1}{3}$.   **3.** (a) $-1, 2$; (c) $7, -1, 2i, -2i$; (e) $\frac{1}{2}, \frac{1}{3}$, $-\frac{1}{2}, \frac{3}{4}$.   **6.** (a) None.

Problems 59.   *Page 256.*

. (a) A zero at 1 and a zero between 1 and 2; (c) A zero between 5 and 6 and another between -3 and -4.   **3.** (a) 1.9.   **4.** (a) .62.   **5.** (a) 2.65; (c) 1.91.   **7.** 2.69.   **9.** About 6 in.

Review Problems.   *Page 257.*

1. $A(x) = a_0 \neq 0$ and $B(x) = 1/a_0$ for some number a_0.   **2.** (a) k is odd.   **3.** $c = -1$.   **4.** (a) $(1 - c^2r)/(3c^2r + 1)$; (c) No solution.   **5.** 3150 miles.   **7.** 5.   **9.** $x^2 + 2x + 4 + a = 0$.   **11.** $b = -2, c = -1$.   **13.** $nb^2 = ac\ (n + 1)^2$.   **15.** (a) $-b/c$; (c) $(3abc - b^3)/a^3$.

Miscellaneous Problems.   *Page 258.*

1 0.   **3.** 1.   **5.** $\frac{3}{5}, -\frac{12}{5}$.   **7.** (a) $\dfrac{19 + i7\sqrt{11}}{2}, \dfrac{19 - i7\sqrt{11}}{2}$;

(c) $\dfrac{-1 + \sqrt{3 + 2\sqrt{5}}}{2}, \dfrac{-1 - \sqrt{3 + 2\sqrt{5}}}{2}, \dfrac{-1 + \sqrt{3 - 2\sqrt{5}}}{2}$,

$\dfrac{-1 - \sqrt{3 - 2\sqrt{5}}}{2}$.   **9.** $x^2 + (b^3 - 3bc)x + c^3$.

Problems 60.   *Page 264.*

1. (a) Yes; (c) Yes; (e) No.   **2.** (a) $(1,1), (2,\frac{1}{2})$; (c) $(10,1)$; (e) $\dfrac{7 + i\sqrt{11}}{6}$,

$\dfrac{-5 + i\sqrt{11}}{6}$.   **3.** All.   **5.** $6 + \sqrt{6}$ ft and $6 - \sqrt{6}$ ft.

Problems 61.   *Page 269.*

1. (a) $(2,-1)$; (c) $(-\frac{6}{13}, \frac{28}{13})$.   **2.** (a) $\left(\dfrac{4 + 3i}{2}, \dfrac{-9 + 4i}{4}\right)$; (c) $\left(0, -\dfrac{i}{2}\right)$.
3. (a) $x = 2, y = -\frac{1}{2}, z = -\frac{3}{2}$; (c) $x = -1, y = 2, z = 3, w = 6$.
4. (a) $(\frac{19}{34}, \frac{19}{3})$; (c) $(10,100)$.   **5.** 75% cheap, 25% expensive.

Problems 62. *Page 274.*

2. (a) $(-13,9)$; (c) $t = 6$, $v = 5$.   **3.** $x = \frac{2}{15}$, $y = -\frac{10}{3}$, $z = -\frac{76}{15}$.
4. (a) $r = \frac{1}{5}$, $s = \frac{7}{10}$, $t = -\frac{1}{2}$; (c) $x = 2$, $y = 0$, $z = -1$, $w = 3$.
5. $80°$, $85°$, $15°$.   **7.** $a = -3$, $b = 2$, $c = 4$.

Problems 63. *Page 277.*

1. (a) $x = -1$, $y = 7$, $z = 10$; (c) $x = 1 + i$, $y = 1 - 3i$, $z = -5i$.
3. (a) Dependent; (c) Dependent.   **4.** (a) Inconsistent.   **5.** (a) $(0, -\frac{1}{3})$;
(c) Do not intersect.   **7.** 374, no.

Problems 64. *Page 282.*

1. (a) $(-1,1)$, $(-8,-13)$; (c) $(1,-2)$, $(\frac{169}{9}, \frac{26}{3})$.   **2.** (a) $(3,2i)$, $(-3,-2i)$,
$(3,-2i)$, $(-3,2i)$.   **3.** (a) $(6,3)$, $(-6,-3)$, $(3i,-6i)$, $(-3i,6i)$; (c) $(0,0)$.
5. 9 in. by 12 in.   **7.** $\sqrt{abc}$.

Problems 65. *Page 287.*

1. (a) 5; (c) $1 - 3i$.   **2.** (a) $-\frac{1}{2}$; (c) 2, $-1 + i\sqrt{3}$, $-1 - i\sqrt{3}$.   **3.** $x < 3$.
6. $(0,0)$, $(2,1)$, $(4,2)$, etc.

Problems 66. *Page 291.*

1. (a) 3; (c) 1.   **2.** (a) 12; (c) -1.   **3.** (a) -24; (c) 4.   **4.** (a) 32.

Review Problems. *Page 292.*

1. $x = r \cos t + s \sin t$, $y = s \cos t - r \sin t$.   **3.** $a = 2$, $b = -1$, $c = 3$.
5. $k = 2$ or $k = 7$.   **9.** 120 6's and 230 8's.

Miscellaneous Problems. *Page 293.*

1. $(2,2)$, $(i,-4i)$, $(-i,4i)$.   **3.** $(-5,-1)$, $(\frac{15}{13}, \frac{3}{13})$.   **5.** 4 nickels, 3 dimes,
and 3 quarters; or 1 nickel, 7 dimes, and 2 quarters.   **7.** $x_1 = 3$, $x_2 = 7$,
$x_3 = 2$, $x_4 = 6$, $x_5 = 1$, $x_6 = 5$, $x_7 = 0$, $x_8 = 4$, $x_9 = -1$.   **9.** -1, $3 +$
$2\sqrt{3}$, $3 - 2\sqrt{3}$.

Problems 67. *Page 299.*

1. (a) $\frac{1}{990}$; (c) $(n + 1)/n$.   **2.** (a) 1.014×10^{16}; (c) 2.24×10^{-84}.   **3.** 9000.
5. 36.   **7.** 216, 112.   **9.** 18.

Problems 68. *Page 304.*

2. (a) 7.89×10^6; (c) 1.29×10^{58}. **3.** (a) P_9^{15}; (c) 5,005. **5.** $12 \times 56 \times P_7^{20}$. **7.** $9!$, $9!/(4!3!2!)$. **9.** $8!$, 12, $(n-1)!$.

Problems 69. *Page 308.*

1. (a) 21; (c) n; (e) 1. **3.** (a) 5; (c) 5. **5.** 6.35×10^{11}. **7.** (a) C_2^7. **9.** 2500.

Problems 70. *Page 311.*

1. (a) $35x^3y^4$; (c) $840x^{12}y^4$. **5.** (a) $15a^2x^2$. **6.** (a) $-1920x^4$; (c) $-56/x^{7/2}$. **7.** (a) 1.219; (c) 1.05×10^{10}. **8.** (a) $-4 - 4i$; (c) $1 + 6\tan x + 15\tan^2 x + 20\tan^3 x + 15\tan^4 x + 6\tan^5 x + \tan^6 x$.

Problems 71. *Page 315.*

1. (a) $3960a^8b^4$; (c) $70x^4$. **2.** (a) $x^{30} + 30x^{29}y + 435x^{28}y^2 + 4060x^{27}y^3$;

(c) $a^{19} - 38a^{18}b + 684a^{17}b^2 - 7752a^{16}b^3$. **5.** $nx^{n-1} + \dfrac{n(n-1)}{2!}x^{n-2}h +$

$\ldots + h^{n-1}$. **7.** (a) $\sin 1 + \dfrac{\sin 2}{2} + \dfrac{\sin 3}{3} + \dfrac{\sin 4}{4}$; (c) $2^3 - 2^2 + 2 - 1$

$+ \frac{1}{2} - (\frac{1}{2})^2 + (\frac{1}{2})^3 - (\frac{1}{2})^4$. **9.** 25. **10.** (a) -3.

Problems 72. *Page 319.*

1. $\frac{1}{18}$. **3.** $C_2^{13}C_2^7/C_4^{20} = \frac{546}{1615}$. **5.** $\frac{3}{26}$. **7.** $\frac{1}{6}$, 1.17. **8.** 1.90. **9.** $\frac{2}{13}$, $\frac{11}{13}$. **11.** $\frac{5}{12}$, 0. **12.** (a) $4/C_5^{52}$; (c) $4(C_5^{13} - 10)/C_5^{52}$.

Problems 73. *Page 324.*

1. (a) $\frac{1}{4}$; (c) $\frac{1}{2}$. **2.** (a) $(\frac{5}{36})^2$; (c) $(\frac{5}{36})^2 + (\frac{3}{36})^2$. **3.** (a) $\frac{1}{19}$; (c) $\frac{27}{38}$. **4.** (a) $\frac{2}{5}$. **5.** 25. **7.** (a) 6.38; (c) 5.25. **9.** $\frac{37}{75}$. **10.** (a) $\frac{9}{24}$; (c) 0.

Problems 74. *Page 33l.*

1. No. **2.** (a) $\frac{63}{256}$; (c) 5. **3.** 2, .296. **5.** (a) 6; (c) 6. **7.** (a) 4. **9.** $\frac{35}{18}(\frac{5}{6})^4$.

Problems 75. *Page 333.*

1. 1, $\frac{1}{2}$, $\frac{1}{1024}$. **2.** (a) $\frac{1}{128}$; (c) $\frac{1}{2}$. **3.** (a) $(\frac{4}{5})^{10}$; (c) .0027.

5. $\sum\limits_{r=0}^{7} C_r^{30}(\frac{2}{5})^{30-r}(\frac{3}{5})^r$; .0002.

Review Problems. *Page 333.*

1. 15.   **2.** (a) $n + 2$; (c) $(\tfrac{1}{2})/1!$, $(\tfrac{1}{2})^2/2!$, $(\tfrac{1}{2})^3/3!$, $(\tfrac{1}{2})^4/4!$, $(\tfrac{1}{2})^5/5!$.   **3.** 5, $n(n - 3)/2$.   **5.** $10!/(3!2!2!)$, $9!/(3!2!)$, $7!/2!$.   **7.** $(\tfrac{7}{8})^5$.   **9.** 72.
11. 5, .017.

Miscellaneous Problems. *Page 334.*

1. $k = 6$, $n = 2$; or $k = 5$, $n = 3$.   **4.** No.   **6.** 1.   **7.** $\tfrac{41}{180}$.   **11.** $10\cancel{c}$.

Problems 76. *Page 341.*

1. Yes, no.   **2.** (a) 1, $\tfrac{5}{2}$, 4, $\tfrac{11}{2}$, 7; (c) $(\tfrac{1}{2})/1!$, $(\tfrac{1}{2})^2/2!$, $(\tfrac{1}{2})^3/3!$, $(\tfrac{1}{2})^4/4!$, $(\tfrac{1}{2})^5/5!$; (e) 1, 0, -1, 0, 1.   **3.** (a) 3, 7, 15, 31, 63; (c) 1, 1, $\tfrac{3}{2}$, 3, $\tfrac{15}{2}$; (e) 3, 2, $\tfrac{5}{2}$, $\tfrac{9}{4}$, $\tfrac{19}{8}$.   **4.** (a) $\tfrac{3}{2}n-1$; (c) $2^n - 1$.   **5.** (a) -1, 0, -1, 0; (c) 1, $\tfrac{1}{2}$, $\tfrac{7}{12}$, $\tfrac{83}{144}$.   **6.** (a) $\tfrac{1}{2}$, $\tfrac{3}{4}$, $\tfrac{7}{8}$, $\tfrac{15}{16}$, $\tfrac{31}{32}$; (c) 3, 9, 18, 30, 45.   **7.** 33.

Problems 77. *Page 345.*

2. (a), (c), (d).   **5.** (a) $(\tfrac{5}{4})^{n-1}$; (c) $(-1)^{n+1}10/(n + 1)$.

Problems 78. *Page 350.*

1. (a) $y_7 = -9$, $S_7 = -21$;   (c) $y_7 = 9$, $d = 1$;   (e) $y_1 = \tfrac{1}{2}$, $y_{12} = \tfrac{23}{2}$.
3. $n(n + 1)$.   **5.** 1955.   **7.** (a) 5, 8, 11, 14; (c) $\tfrac{3}{4}$, $\tfrac{5}{4}$, $\tfrac{7}{4}$, $\tfrac{9}{4}$.   **8.** (a) $f(x) = -x + 3$; (c) $f(x) = 3x - 8$.   **9.** (a) 234; (c) -3157.   **11.** 195 ft.

Problems 79. *Page 354.*

1. $S_n = ny_1$.   **2.** (a) $y_5 = 405$, $S_5 = 605$.   **3.** (a) $r = 2$, -2, $2i$, or $-2i$, $S_5 = 155$, 55, $65 - 30i$, or $65 + 30i$.   **5.** $(\tfrac{2}{3})^5$, 12.   **7.** (a) 6138, (c) 107.
9. (a) 2, 4, 8, 16; (c) 2, $\tfrac{1}{2}$, $\tfrac{1}{4}$, $\tfrac{1}{8}$.   **10.** (a) $f(x) = \tfrac{9}{2}(\tfrac{2}{3})^x$.

Problems 80. *Page 358.*

1. (a) 6, 8; (c), $\tfrac{1}{3}$, $\tfrac{11}{3}$.   **3.** 24, 36, 54.   **5.** $a = 5$, $b = 8$, $c = 12$.   **7.** $\tfrac{1}{3}$, 1.
8. (a) $(\tfrac{1}{2})^9$; (c) $2 - (\tfrac{1}{2})^9$.   **9.** (a) $\tfrac{2}{3}$; (c) 32.

Problems 81. *Page 362.*

1. Yes.

Review Problems. *Page 363.*

2. (a) Yes, no, no.   **3.** No, 64.4831.   **5.** (a) 1.   **7.** "100%."

Miscellaneous Problems. *Page 363.*

1. $1140.   **3.** No.   **5.** (a) $y_{2n} - (n-1)y_{n-1} - (n-2)y_1$.   **7. 35,**
$n(n+1)(2n+4)/12$.   **9.** (a) $1, \frac{1}{2}, \frac{1}{3}, \frac{1}{4}$; (c) $2ab/(a+b)$.

Problems 82. *Page 371.*

1. Yes, $f^{-1}(y) = \log_2 y$.   **2.** (a) $f^{-1}(y) = (y-2)/3$; (c) No inverse; (e) No inverse; (g) No inverse.   **7.** Let F be the function whose domain is the set of positive numbers and whose rule of correspondence is given by the equation $y = 1/x$.   **9.** $F^{-1}(y) = f^{-1}[g^{-1}(y)]$.

Problems 83. *Page 376.*

1. (a) $\pi/3$; (c) 1.03; (e) $\pi/2$; (g) $\pi/2$.   **2.** (a) x; (c) $\text{Sin}^{-1}(\sin x)$.   **3.** (a) $.6$; (c) $.96$.   **4.** (a) $\sqrt{3}/2$; (c) 0.   **7.** (a) 1.   **9.** (a) $\text{Sin}^{-1} v$; (c) $\text{Sin}^{-1}(v-u)$.

Problems 84. *Page 382.*

1. (a) $\pi/3$; (c) $3\pi/4$; (e) $.2$; (g) 1.5.   **2.** (a) x; (c) $\text{Tan}^{-1}(\tan x)$; (e) $1/\sqrt{1+x^2}$; (g) $x/\sqrt{1+x^2}$.   **3.** (a) $.6$; (c) $\frac{7}{25}$.   **4.** (a) $2x/(1-x^2)$; (c) $2x/(1+x^2)$.   **5.** (a) 0; (c) None.   **9.** $\text{Arccot}(1/x) = \pi + \text{Arctan } x$. **10.** (a) $\sqrt{2}/2$.

Problems 85. *Page 385.*

1. (a) No solution; (c) $\{5\pi/6 + k\pi\}$.   **2.** (a) $\{\pi/6 + k\pi, -\pi/6 + k\pi\}$; (c) $\{.46 + k\pi, 2.03 + k\pi\}$.   **3.** (a) $\{k\pi, \pi/6 + 2k\pi, 5\pi/6 + 2k\pi\}$; (c) $\{k\pi\}$.   **4.** (a) $\{k\pi, 2\pi/3 + 2k\pi, -2\pi/3 + 2k\pi\}$; (c) $\{(k-\frac{1}{2})\pi, \pi/6 + k\pi, -\pi/6 + k\pi\}$.   **5.** (a) $\{\pi/6 + 2k\pi, 3\pi/2 + 2k\pi\}$. **6.** (a) $x = k\pi, y = 2h\pi$, where h and k are integers.   **7.** (a) $\frac{1}{2}$; (c) $2 + \sqrt{2}$, $2 - \sqrt{2}$.   **9.** 0.

Problems 86. *Page 388.*

1. $-\pi, -\pi/4, 0, \pi/4, \pi$.   **3.** $0, .7, -.7$.   **5.** $.5, .95$.   **7.** $.24, -.24, 1, -1$. **9.** $.74$.   **11.** $-1.2, -1.9$.   **13.** $\{k, .74 + k\}$.

Review Problems. *Page 389.*

1. No.   **3.** (a) Positive; (c) Same as sign of y.   **8.** (a) $\pi/2$; (c) $-.16$. **9.** $\{\pi/4 + k\pi/2\}$; $-3\pi/4 < x < \pi/4$, for example.   **11.** (a) $\sqrt{2}/2$; (c) $.67$.

Miscellaneous Problems. *Page 390.*

1. All A.P.'s with different terms have inverses.   **3.** Let the domain of F be the set of numbers x for which $x \geq 1$.   **5.** Domain of F^{-1} consists of all numbers y such that $2k \leq y < 2k + 1$, where k is an integer.   **7.** $N = m + 1$ if m is odd, $N = m$ if m is even.   **9.** $(0,0)$, $(4.07.1.33)$.   **11.** 3.36.

INDEX

C